C000063531

Colin Clegg is the author of the successful, prizewinning Advanced level textbook *Biology for Schools and Colleges*, and two practical laboratory teaching guides as well as *Pan Study Aids Revision Cards: Biology*.

Still fully involved in teaching, he is currently Lecturer in Biology at Bournemouth and Poole College of Further Education.

He has been an examiner for the London and Cambridge Boards and has had considerable teaching experience in schools and colleges both in England and abroad.

Pan Study Aids for A level include:

Advanced Biology
Advanced Chemistry
Advanced Computing Science
Advanced Economics
Advanced Mathematics
Advanced Physics
Advanced Sociology

ADVANCED BIOLOGY

Colin Clegg

Pan Books London and Sydney

First published in 1982 by Pan Books Ltd
in association with Heinemann Educational Books Ltd.
This edition published 1987 by Pan Books Ltd,
Cavaye Place, London SW10 9PG
9 8 7 6 5 4 3 2 1
© Colin Clegg 1987
ISBN 0 330 29432 6

Text design by Peter Ward
Text illustrations by ML Design
Photoset by Parker Typesetting Service, Leicester
Printed and bound in Spain by
Mateu Cromo S.A., Madrid

This book is sold subject to the condition that it shall not, by
way of trade or otherwise, be lent, re-sold, hired out or
otherwise circulated without the publisher's prior consent in
any form of binding or cover other than that in which it is
published and without a similar condition including this
condition being imposed on the subsequent purchaser

CONTENTS

ACKNOWLEDGEMENTS

The publishers are grateful to the following Examination Boards, whose addresses are listed below, for permission to reproduce questions from examination papers:

Associated Examination Board, University of Cambridge Local Examinations Syndicate, Joint Matriculation Board, University of London Schools Examination Board, Northern Ireland Schools Examinations Council, Oxford Delegacy of Local Examinations, Oxford and Cambridge Schools Examination Board, Southern Universities Joint Board, Welsh Joint Education Committee.

THE EXAMINATION BOARDS

The addresses given below are those from which copies of syllabuses and past examination papers may be ordered. The abbreviations (AEB etc.) are those used in the text to identify actual questions.

Associated Examining Board
(AEB),
Stag Hill House, Guildford,
Surrey GU2 5XJ

University of Cambridge Local
Examinations Syndicate (CAM),
Syndicate Buildings,
1 Hills Road,
Cambridge CB1 2EU

Joint Matriculation Board (JMB),
Manchester MI5 6EU

University of London School
Examinations Department
(publications office), (L),
52 Gordon Square,
London WC1H 0PJ

Northern Ireland Schools
Examinations Council,
Examinations Office (NI),
Beechill House, Beechill Road,
Belfast BT8 4RS

Oxford Delegacy of Local
Examinations (OX),
Ewert Place, Summertown,
Oxford OX2 7BZ

Oxford and Cambridge Schools
Examination Board (O & C),
10 Trumpington Street,
Cambridge CB2 1QB

Welsh Joint Education
Committee (WEL),
245 Western Avenue,
Cardiff CF5 2YX

TO THE READER

1 The aim of this book is to act as an aid to your studies in A level biology. The text is selective – it is designed to cover the fundamental topics of biology which are most frequently examined in as straightforward a way as possible.

2 Special attention is paid to key points that experience shows often cause students the most problems.

3 The diagrams are so designed that they may be learned and reproduced under exam conditions.

4 **In-text exercises** are designed to test understanding, reinforce learning, and to give pause for thought. They are an integral part of the text. Where they are of the multiple choice type, the answers are given at the end of the book.

5 There is a collection of recent **past examination questions** at the end of each chapter, which have been carefully selected to illustrate the topics emphasized in examinations (an emphasis that is not always obvious from a study of the syllabuses).

6 An **outline answer** is given to a specimen type of question at the end of each chapter, to illustrate the general structure and content of typical Advanced level answers, and sometimes to incorporate extra material.

7 Biology is essentially a practical subject. Although a book such as this cannot possibly include a description of all the necessary practical work, some of the **main experimental work** at this level is referred to at the end of certain chapters. Only a minority of Exam Boards have a practical exam, but all of them set questions based on a knowledge of practical work, and on the interpretation of experimental data.

8 Advice on tried and tested revision techniques is included in the *Guide to revision* (p. 9). Revision is a highly personal affair, but much can be gained from following the advice given.

9 The *Guide to examinations* (p. 12) includes vital information on the technique of answering exam questions, which can at times be an important factor in determining your grade.

10 To develop your knowledge of the necessary vocabulary of the subject, all key words are printed in **bold type** and explained on their first occurrence; the *Glossary* (p. 369) includes some of the more general terminology of the subject not necessarily explained elsewhere.

11 The list of *Biological synonyms* (p. 389) should help to clarify problems that often arise with the use of alternative forms of certain terms.

GUIDE TO REVISION

Ideally you should start your revision as soon as you start your course of study. You should read your notes (assuming you have a decent set) as soon after the lesson as possible. The sooner you do this the more strongly is your ability to recall the details reinforced. But if you have not done this (as most will not have) a list of points to guide your revision is set out below.

1   Get organized. Tidy up your notes, and if possible get a copy of the syllabus and copies of recent past examination papers (for Exam Board addresses see page 7).

2   Whilst rereading your notes and reading the relevant part of this book, you should underline or write down any points about which you are not sure and ask your teacher questions as soon as possible to clarify the situation.

3   Much learning for examinations is done 'parrot fashion', but needless to say, if you understand the subject then you will remember it the better. If your teacher is not readily accessible or approachable (as is sometimes the case!), then try to find somebody who can help. Also try to explain your ideas to a classmate, as attempting to explain to others is a good way to find out if you understand a topic.

4   One of the main draw-backs about much revision is that it is a solitary pursuit; whilst solitude is sometimes necessary, there is much to be said for working together with friends in a study group from time to time. Discussion of problems, worries or anxieties can serve to alleviate them.

5   Try to cultivate the questioning approach. Even in the absence of somebody to help you, there is still much to be said for formulating questions, as thinking about specific points in a questioning manner often brings understanding.

6   Avoid long sessions of revision. It is simply not possible to maintain a high level of concentration over a period of hours. The key to successful revision is 'little and often'. Do some every day of the week, and keep the sessions short (under an hour).

7   Fit short sessions into 'unusual' parts of the day; do not always leave it to the evening.

8   Vary the activity; for example read, rewrite passages in a different form, and draw sketches and flow diagrams. There is much to be said for writing and drawing diagrams as revision activities. Reading is a rather 'detached' activity, and can frequently deteriorate into a rapid skimming over the words. Writing and drawing, act to concentrate

the attention, and to slow the rate of mental activity to a realistic level. Furthermore, by involving more parts of the body and of the brain, the learning process is reinforced.

9 The best way to learn a diagram is to keep redrawing it until it becomes familiar. Also drawing should not only be restricted to the learning of diagrams. A well established effective revision technique is the construction of a **flow diagram** of a particular topic. In constructing the diagram from the written word, many faculties are involved, and the end-product serves as a useful summary for revision. In the example taken here the various stages in the build up are shown as separate diagrams, whereas when making your own you will build up a single diagram. The example is provided (with all its imperfections) as a model only; the essential point about these flow diagrams is that they involve **you** in their construction.

Fig A

Fig B

Remember that such a flow diagram is a useful revision technique, and answer planning guide in the examination, but it is *not* an acceptable alternative to a fully explained answer to an examination question. In essay questions avoid taking short cuts as has been done above with the use of the word 'opposite'. Always write out the full explanation of the 'opposite' sequence of events.

10 Something that has to be remembered can be more easily learnt if it is associated mentally with something else at the time of learning. Although this would seem to involve more learning than just learning the particular information required, in fact the memory thrives on such associations – the more vivid the better.

Fig C

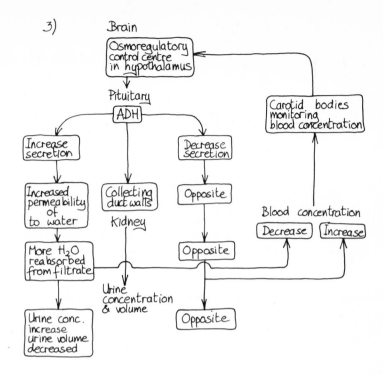

3) Brain

Mnemonics in which the first letters of a sequence of things to be remembered are arranged to form a word or phrase are a form of *associative learning*. For example, the seven characteristics of living things can be arranged so that their first letters spell 'MR GREEN' (Movement, Reproduction, Growth, Respiration, Excretion, Excitability, Nutrition).

11 Try to avoid intensive memorization by recitation, which generates much stress and anxiety. Frequent readings, without attempting to commit facts to memory, soon lead to a much less stressful acquisition of knowledge. Also, rather surprisingly perhaps, it has been shown that it is easier to remember a long sequence, rather than its separate component parts; apparently the continuous flow of ideas aids the memory process.

12 Keep a record of the time spent revising. This can be a great aid to revision. For example it provides you with a permanent record of what you have done, which can be a great reassurance in moments of anxiety, when feeling that you cannot remember anything and that you have achieved very little. Also the weekly total soon becomes a target to be surpassed.

13 Try to think positively about your progress – do not be over critical of your efforts as this can be self-defeating.

14 Be selective. It is impossible to cover all the material with equal emphasis.

15 Do not stop your other activities completely; alternatives to studies help to maintain a balanced approach and to decrease anxiety.

GUIDE TO EXAMINATIONS

The following list contains some of the main points relating to the examination system and exam technique. Some insight into the system by which you are examined will help to improve your grade, no matter what the state of your knowledge is.

1 It is essential that you familiarize yourself with recent past examination papers so that you know the form of each paper and the style of the question set. Also, if possible, read the *Examiners Reports* published by the Exam Boards, which identify the commonest errors in exams.

2 Timing is of the utmost importance in all examinations. Do not, no matter how tempting, spend more than the allocated time on a question, if it means rushing your answer to another. In a sense it is easier to gain the first marks on a question than the last (for example it is easier to gain 50% of the available marks than it is to gain the remaining 50%), therefore an extra twenty minutes spent on an early question will not be as productive as if it were spent as the first twenty minutes on a later question.

It is impossible to finish an examination early – there are always some improvements to be made and some extra marks to be gained.

3 Read the question very carefully, as more marks are lost by not answering the question than in any other way. For example, the word "NOT" overlooked somewhere in a question could dramatically alter your answer. It is a good idea to read a question two or three times and to underline key words, so that careless mistakes of interpretation are avoided.

4 Where a choice of questions is available, choose with care. Given an equal choice between questions, choose the one on the subject containing the most facts, not the one you think is an easy option because there is less to say. The less there is to say on a subject, the harder it is to score the available marks.

5 Marking schemes (which are fairly rigid) are used by examiners to ensure as close a correlation as possible between the different examiners marking all the scripts. Thus any material not relevant to the question simply cannot score any marks, even if it is perfectly correct.

6 Ambiguous questions present particular problems in examinations.

Often students will get caught in the trap of staring at the wording of a question amidst a rising tide of anxiety, convinced that it is they who are lacking in understanding. This of course undermines their confidence and plays havoc with their time allocation for other questions. It must be realized that questions are set from time to time that *are* ambiguous, and no amount of concentration will reveal any clearer meaning. Obviously it is best to avoid these if possible, but in the absence of a choice, the only course open to you is to spread your answer as widely as possible, and not to commit yourself too closely to one particular approach.

For example, with reference to the factors influencing the loss of water vapour from a leaf, (temperature, light, humidity, air flow), a question asking: '. . . *which of these factors would you expect to have the greatest influence over a twenty-four hour period in hot summer weather*', is very ambiguous.

A majority would interpret this as meaning which *one* of these factors was having the greatest influence over a twenty-four hour period, whereas others would describe which factors were having the greatest influence at particular times of the day.

7 Diagrams score marks for the information they convey, therefore an overelaborate diagram or drawing with no or very few labels or annotations, will not score nearly as highly as an adequate sketch with many labels or annotations. This applies even to questions that centre around diagrams, such as 'illustrated accounts', 'explain by means of diagrams', and even to drawings in practical examinations.

8 If you have an equal choice of describing something either in words or diagrams, give priority to the written description, as marks are often only allocated if the particular points are developed, i.e. explained fully, and this can be difficult when only using a diagram.

9 Questions based on experimental data are often rather long and difficult to concentrate on when feeling anxious, but they are usually worth persevering with, as in many ways the answer is on the paper in front of you. When attempting such questions use the given data to illustrate your answer at every opportunity.

10 When answering questions in the examination, it is very important to develop or explain each point fully (unless, of course, you are instructed otherwise; as for example when the question says 'state' or 'list', etc.) This does not necessarily require any extra knowledge, but can gain many marks which would otherwise not be awarded.

For example, in a question asking how excess water is expelled by a freshwater amoeba, a response stating that: '. . . *excess water is expelled by a contractile vacuole*', would not score nearly as highly as one along the following lines: '. . .*excess water is expelled by means of the contractions of a contractile vacuole, which is an active process utilizing energy from respiration*'.

Try to get into the habit of asking yourself: 'How?' or 'Why?' after each point that you make, which will help you to check whether you have developed a point enough.

Even if not specifically asked for, always give named examples if possible; for example in describing feeding in amoeba it would be better to say that: '... *in this way small food particles e.g. diatoms, are engulfed*': than to say that '... *in this way small food particles are engulfed*'.

Although only a relatively minor point, this attention to small detail throughout all the questions can significantly affect your overall grade. Do not be afraid to state the obvious; many marks are lost by students thinking certain things are too simple to put down in an A level examination. For example, in describing the pathway by which carbon dioxide passes from the air to the site of photosynthesis, all the following points would be relevant: The pathway starts with carbon dioxide present in the air close to the leaf surface; through the stomatal pore between the guard cells into the sub-stomatal cavity; into the intercellular spaces of the spongy and palisade mesophyll; dissolves in the film of water on the cellulose cell wall of the mesophyll cells; passes through the cell wall; passes through the cell membrane; into the cytoplasm; into the chloroplastid; into the stroma of the chloroplastid.

11 Always take great care with the organization and general presentation of your answers, and with your writing and spelling.

TYPES OF EXAMINATION QUESTIONS

The examination papers of all Examination Boards contain a variety of types of question. Examples of the commonest types are set out below together with some guidelines as to how to answer them. The factual content of these answers is important of course, but it is the technique of answering that we are more concerned with here, so that whatever the question the best attempt may be made at it.

OBJECTIVE QUESTIONS

In these questions, one of a given number of alternatives must be chosen. With such multiple choice questions, read all the alternatives offered even if you think you have got the right one early on, as the alternatives are designed to be temptingly similar. Also, even if you are not sure of the answer, an educated guess based on a process of elimination is better than no attempt at all.

Example *In aerobic respiration by mammals, pyruvic acid is*
A   *one of the products of the Krebs' cycle*
B   *used to synthesize lactic acid*
C   *used in the Krebs' cycle*
D   *used to synthesize glycogen*

(CAM)

SHORT ANSWER QUESTIONS

Short answer questions usually provide a space for the answer to be written in, and although this is a guide to how much information is required, do not worry overmuch if you cannot fill the space exactly, as the space available is not always a precise guide to the length of what should be written.

Remember objective question and short answer question papers are designed to give a wide coverage to the syllabus content, and with little or no choice of questions available, there can be no avoidance of certain topics.

Example

(*a*)   *In the table below, name* (i) *a hormone which in a mammal raises the blood sugar level and* (ii) *another hormone which lowers the blood sugar level. For each hormone specify the site at which it is produced.*

	Name	Site of production
(i)	....	
(ii)	....	

(*b*)   *In the table below, name* (i) *a hormone which in a mammal is responsible for the onset of the oestrous cycle and* (ii) *another hormone which in a mammal is responsible for the suspension of the oestrous cycle. For each hormone, specify the site at which it is produced.*

	Name	Site of production
(i)	....	
(ii)	....	

(*c*)   *Describe briefly the inter-relationships of the activities of the pairs of hormones in each event.*

Blood sugar level:

....

Oestrous cycle:

....

(LON)

STRUCTURED QUESTIONS

These are questions which are divided up into sections. The marks awarded for each section are usually shown, and you should use these to help you estimate the amount of time to spend on each section. With structured questions stick as closely to the sequence of the question as possible, give the information required for each section in the appropriate place. Marking schemes are often quite 'compartmentalized', so that information given in the wrong section may not score marks even though it is correct.

In the case of ambiguous questions, where you are not sure in which section you should include some information, include it in both.

Also, do not refer back to a section, for example do not say '. . . as described in a previous section'; if reference is needed to the same information then repeat it (if time allows).

Example

(a)   *Give a definition of an enzyme (3).*

(b)   *List the factors which influence the rate of enzyme controlled reactions (3).*

(c)   *Draw an annotated graph to illustrate the effect of one of these on the rate of enzyme controlled reactions (4).*

(d)   *Describe how you would demonstrate the presence of an enzyme in a solution, if you were provided with a dilute (1%) starch solution and a sample of an enzyme solution (10).*

ANALYSIS OF THE QUESTION

Note the words used in each section; 'give', 'list', 'draw', and 'describe'; and the mark allocation which gives an indication of the required length. Remember, when describing an experimental procedure, the experiment must be able to work as described.

Answers (a) An enzyme is a complex organic catalyst composed of protein, produced in living cells, which speeds up the rate of chemical reactions in the body.

(b)   Temperature
         pH (acidity/alkalinity)
         Enzyme inhibitors (heavy metals, cyanide)
         Substrate concentration.
         End-product concentration
         Enzyme concentration

(c)   Graph to show effect of temperature on enzyme activity (Fig D).

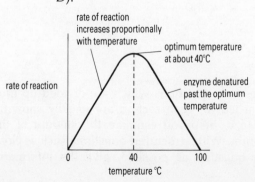

Fig D

COMMENT ▶

Two accounts are presented here to illustrate further the point that care in explaining simple points fully can greatly improve the standard of an answer. Note in particular how little extra factual knowledge as such is required to turn a poor answer into a good one.

(d)   1 *Original version*

Fig E

Add some enzyme solution to the starch solution in a test-tube labelled A, and leave it a while. At the same time add some enzyme solution to another sample of starch in test-tube B and boil it, and again leave it for a time. This acts as the boiled control.

At the end of the experiment the two mixtures are tested with iodine for the absence of starch, and with Benedicts solution for the presence of glucose.

The iodine test should be negative in test-tube A and positive in the boiled control in test-tube B.

The Benedicts test should be positive in test-tube A, and negative in test-tube B.

This experiment proves that there is an enzyme in the solution that converts starch to glucose.

COMMENT ▶

Somebody writing the above might think that they have covered all the main points and done quite well on this question.

Before reading the second version, try to see what in fact is wrong with the above account.

2 *Improved version* Test the starch solution and the enzyme solution sample separately for the presence of reducing sugars, by adding a sample to some Benedicts solution and boiling for a few minutes. The result should be negative. (A positive result would show a yellow, green, orange, or red precipitate.) Set up three test-tubes labelled A, B, C.

To tube A add 5 cm^3 of starch and 5 cm^3 of distilled water.

To tube B add 5 cm^3 of starch and 5 cm^3 of enzyme solution.

To tube C add 5 cm^3 of starch and 5 cm^3 of boiled and cooled enzyme solution.

Incubate all three tubes at 30–40°C for about 15 minutes. After this period test all three tubes for the presence of starch by adding a sample from each tube to iodine in KI solution on a white tile (a positive result is shown by a blue/black coloration, and a negative result by no change in colour of the iodine in KI solution). Also test a sample from each tube for the presence of reducing sugars by boiling with Benedict's solution. Expected results would be:

	I_2 test	Benedict's
A	Positive	Negative
B	Negative	Positive
C	Positive	Negative

Tube A acts as a 'blank' control, showing that starch does not break down spontaneously into reducing sugars.

Tube B shows that starch has been broken down into reducing sugars.

Tube C acts as a boiled control, showing that it is in fact an **enzyme** that is catalyzing the reaction in B, and not some inorganic catalyst, as only enzymes are **denatured** by heat. The initial tests of the starch and enzyme solution for the presence of reducing sugars, are necessary to show that the reducing sugars appeared during the experiment and were not there to begin with (at least as far as tube B is concerned).

ESSAY QUESTIONS

With unstructured essay questions, quickly plan out your answer before you begin, as it is very easy to forget key points once immersed in your answer.

Also it must be remembered that introductions, conclusions, and diagrams will not gain marks unless they contain additional relevant information not found in the main account.

EXAMPLE

Describe the roles of water in the lives of living organisms.

ANALYSIS OF THE QUESTION

This is an extremely wide-ranging question, which presents problems of organization. One approach would be to divide the answer into two, one section considering external roles, and the other internal roles. Another difficulty is the problem of how far to go in describing the properties of water, which in fact determines its roles. Strictly speaking the question is about 'the roles of water', so the properties should only be described in so much as they illustrate the roles. Points that could be included are:

1   **External roles** – in providing support, allowing large size, and delicate structures with large surface areas e.g. gills: in providing an environment safe from the dangers of dessication by evaporation, optimum medium for early stages of development; in providing a medium without dramatic fluctuations in temperature (due to its high specific heat); as an external transport medium, in transporting gametes, dispersal of offspring, transport of suspended food particles.

2   **Internal roles** – as an essential component of cytoplasm, both as free water and combined chemically; as an internal transport medium, (low viscosity for ease of flow, high cohesion in transpiration stream); as a 'universal solvent' and medium for the dissociation of electrolytes in the body; as a reactant in chemical processes, e.g. hydrolysis (in digestion), and in photosynthesis; in providing support as a hydrostatic skeleton; in reproduction as a transport medium for gametes; in excretion as a transport medium for excretory products; as secretions, e.g. saliva, tears; as a lubricant, e.g. pleural fluid, synovial fluid; in providing protection against mechanical shock; in activating dormant structures, e.g. the hydration phase of germination; in temperature control in terrestrial organisms, especially mammals (due to its high latent heat of evaporation).

COMMENT ▶

Each point would need to be properly developed, but not all of them would be needed for an 'A' grade answer.

Although this is just one specific example, the lessons to be drawn from this which would be applicable to all essay answers are:
1 Organize your answer into manageable sections.
2 Stick closely to the question.
3 Provide straightforward factual information.
4 Avoid repetition.

SOME TERMS COMMONLY USED IN EXAMINATIONS

The following is an explanatory list of certain key terms and phrases which frequently occur in the wording of examination questions, an understanding of which is necessary for the correct interpretation of the questions.

1   **Annotated diagrams** Annotations are brief notes relating to certain features on the diagram which must be linked by a line to the actual feature. Many marks have been lost by not joining notes to the diagram by a line, even though all the information given was perfectly correct.

2   **Comment on (discuss)** This term is frequently used in relation to experimental results, and requires certain observations and explanations to be made.

3   **Compare, contrast, compare and contrast** The use of these words in questions can cause problems of interpretation. Compare can be taken as mean-

ing to describe the similarities and differences between two or more things, whereas contrast can be taken as meaning to emphasize the differences. However, if this is so there should be no need to use the words together as in '. . . compare and contrast', which implies that 'compare' refers to similarities, and 'contrast' refers to differences.

4   **Define** State or describe precisely what is meant by.

5   **Discuss** This requires a critical approach to a topic, involving some reference to the significance and relative importance of various points.

6   **Distinguish between** Emphasize the differences between things.

7   **Exemplify** Give examples of.

8   **Illustrated account** An account where the diagrams are of central importance; but even here remember that far more marks will be awarded for labels and annotations than for the diagrams.

9   **List (enumerate)** Write down the required information in a clearly numbered or lettered list.

10 **Survey** Make a general account of, or describe the main points of a broad field of knowledge.

PRACTICAL EXAMINATIONS

Not all boards have a practical examination as such, but the following points will also be of use in the general practical work performed throughout the course, and in those examination questions based on practical work.

1   If you are provided with a description of an experimental method, no marks will be gained by repeating that information in your account, unless some extra detail or comment is asked for.

2   For clarity of presentation, always tabulate any results.

3   When drawing diagrams the following points should be kept in mind:
    (*a*)   Diagrams should be large, clear and as simple as possible; avoid colouring and shading except in exceptional circumstances.
    (*b*)   Use a sharp H or HB pencil and keep your lines 'clean'.
    (*c*)   Label as much as you can, ensuring that the labelling lines actually touch the structure involved and that they do not cross.
    (*d*)   Always have a title, and indicate the magnification used.
    (*e*)   With drawings of plant tissues, a lower power (LP) plan should not show any details of cells; these should be reserved for high power (HP) drawings, where about 50 cells could be drawn, with the smallest no less than 0.5 cm across, and where meticulous attention to detail should be paid.

(f)   With dissection drawings always draw the outline of the animal or part of the animal so that the anatomy can be seen in context.

AFTER THE EXAMINATION

Try to avoid post-mortems after the examination, as they usually only serve to reveal even more mistakes that you might have made. The percentage marks required for the various grades at A level vary from year to year according to the relative standard of difficulty of the examination papers. Therefore do not worry unduly if the examination papers are considered by common consent to be more difficult than those of preceding years, as this will not necessarily affect your grade.

If illness, bereavement, or personal problems impair your performance on the day, then you should inform the exam supervisor, as there are procedures by which allowances can be made in genuine cases. Should you fail the examination, or not attain anywhere near the grade you confidently expected, then it is possible for your performance to be reassessed. For example it is possible with most Exam Boards to obtain one or more of the following: a clerical recheck of the marks awarded; a complete remark of the paper(s) concerned; a complete remark accompanied by a brief report; a special group report (where most candidates from a particular centre appear to have under-achieved).

However, all such appeals must be initiated through the particular school or college involved, as obviously abuse of the system by ill-founded appeals would work against the best interests of the genuine cases. Should you decide to resit the examination, as do about 15% of A level candidates in one year, then try to identify what went wrong as honestly as you can, and take the appropriate course of action to ensure success.

The Universities Central Council on Admissions (UCCA PO Box 28, Cheltenham, Gloucestershire) issue an annual report which can be a useful source of information about national trends in A level results and University admissions, which may help you better assess your aspirations.

CELLS AND TISSUES

CONTENTS

CELLS

All animals and plants are composed of microscopically small discrete units known as cells. A cell typically consists of a nucleus within a mass of cytoplasm which is bounded by a cell membrane or plasmalemma. Some cells, for example the bacteria, do not have a distinct nucleus and are referred to as **akaryotic** or prokaryotic, whereas those with a nucleus are known as **eukaryotic.**

The relevant units of size with respect to cells are:

The **micrometre:** $1\mu m = 10^{-6}m = \frac{1}{1\,000\,000}m$

The **nanometre:** $1nm = 10^{-9}m = \frac{1}{1\,000\,000\,000}m$

In unicellular organisms such as the Protozoa, simple algae, and bacteria, the cell constitutes the entire organism. In multicellular organisms there are many such cells, and much inter-cellular material secreted by them. There is a wide variety of cell structure and function as different cells are adapted to different functions, in a process of division of labour within the body. This prevents the description of a typical cell, but there are sufficient common features in most animal and plant cells to enable a 'generalized' cell to be described.

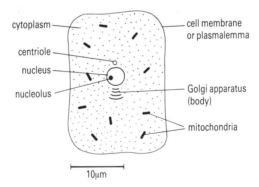

Fig 1.1. Generalized animal cell as seen under the light microscope.

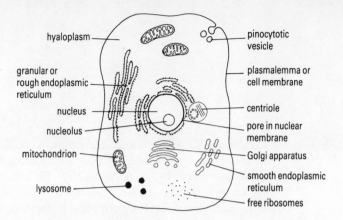

hyaloplasm

pinocytotic
vesicle

granular or
rough endoplasmic
reticulum

plasmalemma or
cell membrane

nucleus

centriole

nucleolus

pore in nuclear
membrane

mitochondrion

Golgi apparatus

lysosome

smooth endoplasmic
reticulum

free ribosomes

Fig 1.2. Generalized animal cell as seen under the electron microscope.

Only samples of the different types of organelles are shown, and these are not drawn to scale either in relation to each other or to the overall size of the cell.

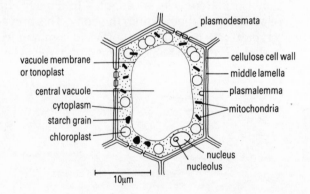

plasmodesmata

vacuole membrane
or tonoplast

cellulose cell wall

middle lamella

central vacuole

plasmalemma

cytoplasm

mitochondria

starch grain

chloroplast

nucleus
nucleolus

10µm

Fig 1.3. Generalized plant cell (chlorenchyma) as seen under the light microscope.

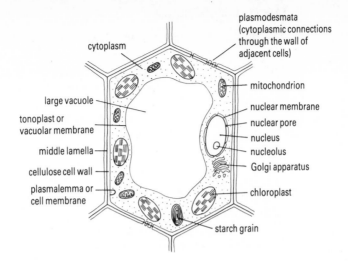

Fig 1.4. Generalized plant cell (chlorenchyma) as seen under the electron microscope.

Table 1.1. Differences between plant and animal cells

Plant cells	Animal cells
1 Cell membrane and cellulose cell wall	1 Cell membrane only
2 Features associated with the cell wall: middle lamella, pits, plasmodesmata	2 None
3 Chloroplasts with chlorophyll in photosynthetic cells	3 None
4 Large central vacuole	4 Small, scattered vacuoles
5 Tonoplast membrane surrounds vacuole	5 None
6 Cytoplasm, organelles and nucleus usually peripheral due to central vacuole	6 Not
7 Centrioles absent	7 Centrioles present
8 Cilia absent in higher plants	8 Cilia often present

HYALOPLASM

This is the apparently structureless mass of cytoplasm found between the organelles. It is a complex organic colloid, with a disperse phase of suspended matter (mainly protein) and a continuous phase of various organic and inorganic substances in solution. It is capable of changing from a gel to a sol and streaming around the cell, using energy from respiration, but above about 60°C it coagulates irreversibly and the cell dies.

CELL ORGANELLES

These are specialized regions of the cytoplasm which are centres of specific cell activities. The description given here is the conventional one, in which most appear to be membranous in nature.

ENDOPLASMIC RETICULUM

The endoplasmic reticulum appears in electronmicrographs to be a network of internal membranes. Granular or **rough endoplasmic reticulum** has protein-synthesizing ribosomes attached to the membranes, and its function is assumed to be the storage and transport of the protein products of the ribosomes. It is in fact best seen in glandular cells secreting protein-rich products such as enzymes.

Agranular or **smooth endoplasmic reticulum** lacks the associated ribosomes and in electronmicrographs appears as ill-defined vesicles which are interpreted as being tubules seen in section. A wide variety of functions are attributed to the smooth endoplasmic reticulum in various tissues, for example it forms a network throughout striated muscle fibres, known as the sarcoplasmic reticulum, which transmits the nerve impulse from the surface of the muscle to all fibres; and it is involved in hormone synthesis in the gonads.

RIBOSOMES

These are dense structures about 15 nm in diameter and appear as small black dots in electromicrographs of the whole cell. They occur attached to the granular endoplasmic reticulum, and free in the hyaloplasm. They are involved in protein synthesis (see p. 62).

THE GOLGI COMPLEX

This appears as a collection of membranous sacs and vesicles, particularly in nerve cells and secretory cells of animals. It is suggested that it somehow processes protein products prior to their secretion, and may be involved in membrane maintenance and repair.

LYSOSOMES

These are membrane-bound vesicles containing hydrolytic enzymes which are capable of digesting the cell constituents. Their identification depends mainly on biochemical tests determining the presence of these enzymes, but relatively large (0.2–0.8 micrometres (μm)), darkly staining sacs are identified as lysosomes in electronmicrographs.

MITOCHONDRIA

These appear as spherical or elliptical bodies from 0.2 μm to 2.0μm in diameter in electronmicrographs. They are found in all cells except bacteria, blue-green algae, and mature red blood corpuscles. They are the centres of cellular aerobic respiration, and provide the cell with energy-rich ATP. They are often found close to other cell structures that use energy, such as the myofibrils of muscle cells.

Mitochondria contain some DNA, and they arise by division of existing mitochondria.

CHLOROPLASTIDS

These have a wide variety of shapes, but in higher plants they appear spherical or disc shaped, about 4–6 μm in diameter. Under the electron microscope they appear to contain membranes which are concentrated at intervals to form discrete grana. The grana contain the chlorophyll and are considered to be the centres of the light stage of photosynthesis, and the matrix or stroma between the grana is considered to be the site of the dark stage.

Chloroplastids contain some DNA, and arise from pre-existing proplastids, which are small self-replicating bodies in the cytoplasm. The development of proplastids into chloroplastids requires light and the presence of iron.

EXERCISE ▶

Exercise 1.1

All the cell organelles (except the ribosomes) appear to be membranous in nature. What could the significance of this common feature be?

Answer It is suggested that membranes provide large internal surface areas for the ordered attachment of enzymes and other factors involved in the many sequential reactions that occur in organelles.

CELL MEMBRANE

The cell membrane or **plasmalemma** is thought to have a fairly uniform structure throughout the animal and plant kingdoms.

Neither the light microscope or the electron microscope reveals much of the structure of the cell membrane, but models of membrane structure are constructed on the basis of its behaviour under certain experimental conditions. It is considered as a protein/lipid mosaic about 7 nm thick.

The cell membrane is perceived as a double layer of lipid molecules, with its outer surface more or less covered with protein molecules, some of which penetrate right through the membrane. This lipid bilayer is strong but at the same time fluid. The fluid nature of the lipids allows the proteins to move within and across the

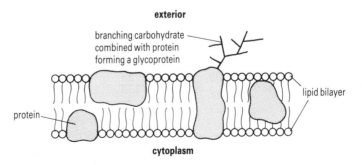

Fig 1.5. Fluid mosaic model of cell membrane structure.

membrane. Also by binding with specific substances these proteins can act as carriers of substances into the cell.

In cells requiring a large surface area for the absorption or exchange of materials, it is thrown into folds known as **microvilli.**

Where cells need to be tightly joined, regions are specialized for attachment such as the **desmosomes** and **tight junctions.**

The membrane acts as a differentially permeable selective barrier in regulating the entry and exit of substances in and out of the cell. Some substances do pass through it by simple diffusion (and water by osmosis) but the passage of many others is controlled by various energy-dependent active processes, for example the sodium pump of nerve cells which actively expels sodium ions.

EXERCISE ▶

Exercise 1.2

Which type of cell organelle would you expect to be prominent in those cells with much active transfer across their membranes?

Answer Mitochondria, the centres of cellular aerobic respiration which provide the necessary energy in the form of ATP.

CELL WALL

Plant cells are surrounded by a cell wall which is external to the plasmalemma. In the formation of a new cell wall after cell division, a layer of pectic substances is laid down which forms the middle lamella; onto this the primary cell wall of cellulose is laid.

The first layers of cellulose microfibrils are laid down whilst the cell is still enlarging and the microfibrils form a loose meshwork which allows extension. The wall that is formed whilst the cell is still enlarging is known as the **primary cell wall.**

When the cell stops expanding the microfibrils are laid down in bundles known as **macrofibrils** which are visible under the light microscope. The wall that is laid down after the cell has stopped expanding is known as the **secondary cell wall**. Throughout the cell wall, small areas are left unthickened to form pits through which stands of cytoplasm or plasmodesmata pass to adjacent cells.

In the cells of sclerenchyma and xylem tissue the secondary cell wall is impregnated with **lignin**, a waterproof impermeable substance which in conjunction with the cellulose fibres confers great tensile strength. Because lignin is waterpoof the original cytoplasmic contents die, leaving empty elements.

EXERCISE ▶

Exercise 1.3

The cellulose cell wall is completely permeable to the passage of dissolved substances. At what point can substances be said to enter the plant cell?

Answer When they pass through the cell membrane, which is closely applied to the inner surface of the cell wall. Much of the so-called uptake of substances by the plant cell, studied in simple experiments, is in fact only absorption into the spaces of the cell wall. Thus the disappearance of a substance from a solution surrounding plant cells, is not sufficient proof of the uptake of that substance into the cell.

ENZYMES

Much of the protein of cytoplasm, both of the hyaloplasm and the organelles, is in the form of enzymes; and many types of cell (especially gland cells) synthesize and secrete enzymes for extra-cellular processes (especially digestion).

CHARACTERISTICS OF ENZYMES

1 All enzymes are proteins.
2 Some consist solely of protein e.g. amylase, trypsin, pepsin.
3 Others require the presence of a non-protein **organic** compound.
   If the non-protein organic compound is an integral part of the enzyme structure it is termed a **prosthetic group** e.g. iron porphyrin of catalase, and the enzyme is known as a conjugated protein.
   If it is more loosely associated the non-protein organic compound is known as a **co-enzyme** e.g. nicotinamide adenine dinucleotide (NAD) with dehydrogenases.
4 Others require the presence of a non-protein inorganic compound or **co-factor** e.g. calcium activates thrombokinase in blood clotting.
5 Each enzyme has a particular 3-dimensional tertiary structure, with a specific area known as the **active site** which combines with a specific substrate.
6 Enzymes act as **catalysts**, that is they speed up the rate of reactions that would otherwise proceed very slowly, if at all, under the conditions existing in living organisms; without themselves being used up in the reaction. Relatively small amounts of enzyme catalyse large amounts of reactants.
7 Enzymes are **specific**, that is each enzyme will only catalyse a specific reaction. This is explained by means of the 'lock and key' mechanism (Fig 1.6), by which the active site will only 'fit' a correspondingly

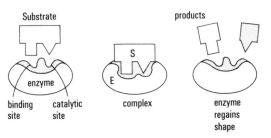

Fig 1.6. Enzyme-substrate complex formation.

Enzyme-substrate complex formation

shaped substrate to form the enzyme-substrate complex, which then forms the reaction products. As the enzyme and substrate molecules fit together slight changes occur in the shape of the molecules. So that the active site has a shape exactly complimentary to that of the substrate *only* after the substrate is bound. It is thought that these slight distortions of the molecular shape of the enzyme and substrate account for the rapid reaction. After the reaction, the enzyme regains its original shape and is available for the next reaction.

In a spontaneous reaction the energy level of the initial substrate is higher than the energy level of the products. Before reaction can occur however, an initial activation energy is required. The presence of an enzyme and the formation of an enzyme-substrate complex lowers the activation energy and the reaction can proceed more rapidly.

8   The rate of enzyme-catalysed reactions is fastest under certain optimum conditions of temperature and pH (acidity/alkalinity) as shown in Fig 1.4. Too high a temperature and extremes of pH disturb the 3-dimensional shape, and the enzyme is rendered inactive or denatured.

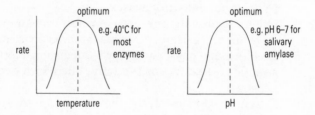

Fig 1.7

9   Enzymes may also be inhibited by a variety of substances.

Competitive inhibition (reversible) The inhibitor has a similarity of shape to the substrate and competes with the substrate for the reversible combination with the enzyme active site. The degree of inhibition is determined by the relative concentrations of the inhibitor and of the substrate; e.g. malonic acid competes with succinic acid for succinic dehydrogenase.

Non-competitive inhibition (non-reversible) The inhibitor forms a permanent combination with the enzyme and thus prevents the substrate from combining with the enzyme. The degree of inhibition depends on the concentration of the inhibitor only; e.g. cyanide inhibits cytochrome oxidase.

THE NUCLEUS

All eukaryotic cells have at least one nucleus at some stage in their development. It is the control centre of the cell, controlling the development and function of the cell via the DNA/RNA mechanism.

In the non-dividing cell there is little apparent structure within the nucleus apart from the small spherical nucleolus, which appears to be the centre of nuclear RNA.

When stained, the scattered 'chromatin' of DNA and nucleoproteins can be seen, and it is these that condense to form the chromosomes just prior to nuclear and cell division. (See p. 47)

TISSUES

Collections of similar cells performing a particular function are known as **tissues.** A collection of different tissues coordinated towards a common function constitutes an **organ.** The study of such tissues (histology) involves the study of all organ systems of the body, but there are some basic types of tissue that can be described in general terms.

ANIMAL TISSUES

There are four basic types of tissue, namely epithelial, connective, muscular and nervous.

EPITHELIAL TISSUES

These cover internal and external surfaces, and the cells are held tightly together by a thin layer of intercellular cement.

(i) **Simple epithelia** are one cell thick, and typically form sheets of large surface area and thin cross-section, across which exchanges by diffusion and osmosis can occur.

The cells (which are often secretory) are fixed to a basement membrane, and have a free surface which can be highly specialized, with, for example, microvilli or cilia.

Examples include the following.

Pavement or **squamous** epithelium found in the alveoli of the lung and in the Bowman's capsule of the kidney;

simple cuboidal epithelium of the kidney tubules and thyroid gland;

simple columnar epithelium of the gall bladder; and

ciliated epithelium of the trachea and bronchi.

(ii) **Stratified epithelia** are more than one cell thick, so that the cells of the basal layer are the only ones attached to the basement membrane, and the cells of the upper layer are the only ones with a free surface. Examples include the following.

Stratified squamous epithelium of the skin (keratinised), and of the oesophagus (unkeratinised);

stratified columnar epithelium of the duct of the mammary glands; and the stretchable stratified **transitional** epithelium of the bladder.

(iii) **Glandular** epithelia are specialized to form secretory glands, either with a duct (exocrine), or without a duct (endocrine).

CONNECTIVE TISSUES

These are characterized by having a few relatively small cells, but large amounts of intercellular ground substance (matrix) and fibres which are secreted by those cells.

White collagen fibres are non-elastic and have a high tensile strength. They form tendons, and also contribute to mixed connective tissues.

Yellow elastic fibres are elastic. They form ligaments, and contribute to mixed connective tissues.

Areolar tissue has an amorphous matrix and a scattering of collagen and elastic fibres. It forms connecting sheets (mesenteries) and sheaths around organs. It also contains phagocytic macrophage cells which engulf micro-organisms and thus plays a role in the defence of the body against infection.

Adipose tissue has similarities with areolar tissue, but fat-storing cells predominate. In forming insulating layers of subcutaneous fat beneath the skin of mammals, it prevents heat loss, as well as acting as a food storage depot.

Cartilage consists of scattered chondroblasts which secrete an intercellular matrix of clear chondrin.

Hyaline cartilage found forming the embryonic skeleton, the articular cartilages of the adult skeleton, and the rings of cartilage in the trachea, has few fibres in the chondrin.

White fibrous cartilage found in the intervertebral discs has many white collagen fibres.

Yellow elastic cartilage found in the external ear and at the end of the nose has many yellow elastic fibres.

BONE

Bone consists of concentric rings of osteocytes which secrete the intercellular matrix of collagen fibres, and hard calcium phosphate. The rings or lamellae are arranged around longitudinally running Haversian canals which contain the blood and lymph vessels which supply the osteocytes. In compact or dense bone these Haversian systems are closely packed, but in so-called 'spongy' bone, sponge-like irregular spaces or lacunae occur (Fig 1.8).

EXERCISE ▶

Exercise 1.4
What do you think could be one of the main factors limiting the maximum number of bone lamellae around each Haversian canal?

Answer One of the main factors could be the maximum diffusion distance over which the osteocytes could be kept supplied with oxygen and nutrients from the blood vessels in the Haversian canal.

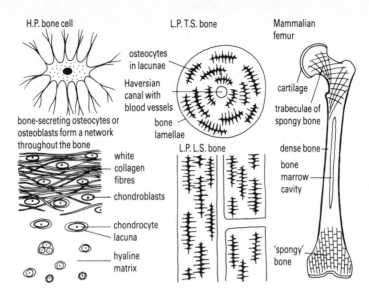

Fig 1.8. *Structure of cartilage and bone.* So-called 'spongy' bone has the same hard composition as 'dense' or 'compact' bone, but it has sponge-like irregular spaces or lacunae.

PLANT TISSUES

Plant tissues can be broadly divided into **meristematic tissues**, which consist of undifferentiated cells which are capable of repeated mitotic cell division; and **permanent tissues**, which consist of fully differentiated cells which are usually incapable of any further cell division.

MERISTEMATIC TISSUES

Primary meristems

These are derived directly from the original embryonic meristems, without ever having lost the power of continual mitotic cell division.

(*a*)   **Apical meristems** occur at the tips of shoots and roots; and consist of small, many sided cells, with dense granular cytoplasm, small scattered vacuoles, and with no intercellular spaces between them. Their divisions result in growth in length of stems and roots.

(*b*)   **Lateral meristems** or **cambium tissues** occur along the length of roots and stems of Dicotyledons, and consist of long thin cells which give rise to long tubular elements of xylem and phloem during secondary thickening.

(*c*)   **Intercalary meristems** occur as isolated bands between regions of permanent tissues, for example at the base of leaves in many Monocotyledons.

Secondary meristems

These are derived from a differentiated permanent tissue, (usually parenchyma) which regains the ability to divide.

Interfascicular cambium arises from parenchyma tissue between vascular bundles in dicotyledons undergoing secondary thickening.

Phellogen or **cork cambium** arises in the epidermis or cortex of Dicotyledons undergoing secondary thickening and gives rise to the bark.

PERMANENT TISSUES

These can be classified into supporting tissues, vascular tissues, dermal tissues and photosynthetic tissues.

Supporting tissue

All tissues have some functions as supporting tissue, due either to their turgidity or to their specially thickened walls, but so-called 'supporting tissues' have support as their main function.

(*a*)   **Parenchyma** consists of rounded cells with thin cellulose cell walls and many intercellular spaces. They form the bulk of the primary structure of a plant, and their turgidity is important in the support of non-woody parts. They act as storage tissue in storage organs such as swollen roots, stems and leaves; they can develop chloroplastids and become photosynthetic and they can become secondarily meristematic (as in the inter-fascicular cambium).

(*b*)   **Collenchyma** consists of elongated cells with cellulose cell walls thickened at the angles of the cells. It is the only specialized support tissue present in actively growing regions, where it is often found just beneath the epidermis.

(*c*)   **Sclerenchyma** consists of fibres and sclereids.

Fibres are elongated (1 mm−50 cm) with thick lignified walls and no living contents. They provide great mechanical strength and are usually found associated with vascular bundles.

Sclereids or stone cells are not elongated, and typically they form the hard shells of nuts and stones of fruit (they can also occur scattered as in the flesh of pear fruit).

Vascular tissues

(*a*)   **Xylem** consists of elongated tubular elements with lignified cell walls and no living contents; they are either **tracheids** which are separated by cross walls, or **vessels** which have long stretches (up to several feet) uninterrupted by cross walls. Xylem tissue transports water and dissolved substances in the transpiration stream. The lignified walls confer great strength, so that xylem also serves as a supporting tissue, especially in plants with secondary thickening.

(*b*)   **Phloem** consists of elongated tubular sieve tube elements with cellulose walls and living contents, which are separated from each other by perforated end walls known as **sieve plates.** Young sieve tubes show active cytoplasmic streaming, and cytoplasmic con-

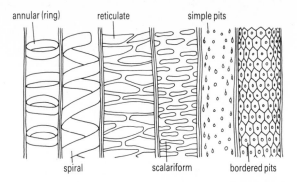

Fig 1.9. *Patterns of lignification in xylem tissue.* Annular and spiral thickening is found in protoxylem which is laid down in the zone of elongation. They allow for stretching. The early metaxylem often has scalariform thickening, and the later metaxylem reticulate thickening. Pitted vessels or tracheids are typically found in the last of the metaxylem and in the secondary xylem. The pits of adjacent elements coincide and allow for the lateral transfer of water, they can be either simple or bordered.

nections exist between elements through the sieve plates. As the phloem ages the streaming stops, the sieve plates become blocked with callose deposits, and it becomes non-functional.

Next to the sieve tubes are the companion cells which contribute to the function and maintenance of the sieve tubes.

Phloem tissue transports soluble organic substances, for example sucrose around the plant.

Fig 1.10. Phloem tissue.

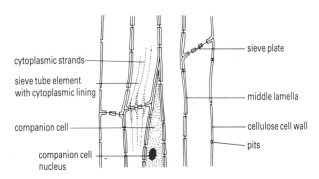

Photosynthetic tissues
Many tissues, for example parenchyma and collenchyma can be photosynthetic, but the mesophyll cells of the leaf are particularly adapted for this function.

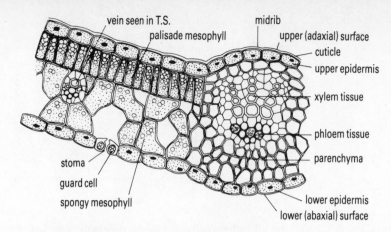

Fig 1.11. *Leaf of dicotyledonous plant T. S.* Palisade mesophyll cells are elongated with many chloroplastids at the edge for rapid CO_2 uptake from the extensive vertical intercellular spaces. Also light can penetrate without having to pass through many cross walls and air spaces. The spongy mesophyll has large air spaces for rapid diffusion of CO_2 to the palisade mesophyll, and their regular horizontal arrangement possibly aids in supporting the thin lamina due to the turgidity of cells acting against the non-elastic epidermis. The leaf has a large surface area to volume ratio which allows for rapid exchanges by diffusion.

Dermal tissues

These are protective tissues usually found in continuous 'cylinders', which are penetrated at intervals by specialized openings or passage cells.

(*a*)   The **epidermis** has no intercellular spaces and forms a continuous layer over the surface of the plant. On the aerial parts of plants the epidermal cells are covered with a waterproof cuticle of a waxy substance known as **cutin.**

The epidermis is penetrated by pores or **stomata**, especially on the lower surface of the leaves of Dicotyledons. The opening and closing of the stomata is controlled by specialized guard cells, which are usually the only epidermal cells to contain chloroplasts. Epidermal cells are also often modified to form hairs and secretory glands.

(*b*)   The **endodermis** forms a continuous protective cylinder around the vascular tissue of the root. The mature cell walls are thickened with waterproof suberin, except for the thin-walled passage cells which control the passage of water and dissolved salts from the root hairs to the xylem in the centre of the root.

(*c*)   The **periderm** is an outer protective tissue found in stems and roots undergoing secondary thickening. It consists of the **cork cambium** or **phellogen** and the tissues derived from it, namely the **cork** or **phellem** (comprising waterproof suberized dead cells) to the outside, and the secondary cortex or **phelloderm** to the inside.

EXPERIMENTAL WORK

The **examination of slides** of stained cells and tissues is an important part of all practical examinations, and it is a test not only of memory but also of correct microscope technique.

Increasingly, examinations contain photographs of microscopic preparations: both photomicrographs taken with the light microscope and electron micrographs taken with the electron microscope.

If you are given a photograph and the magnification is not stated, you should look for clues such as the size of some well-known structure, for example the nuceus in light micrographs and mitochondria in electron micrographs, and use this as a point of reference.

With electron micrographs where the magnification is given you may be asked to calculate the actual size of an organelle such as a mitochondrion. In these cases the actual measured size of the organelle in the electron micrograph is divided by the magnification and the result expressed in micrometres (10^{-6} metre). For example:

$$\text{Size of mitochondria on electronmicrograph} = 5\,\text{mm}$$
$$\text{Magnification} = \times 1000$$
$$\text{Actual size} = \frac{5\,\text{mm}}{1000}$$
$$= 5\,\mu\text{m}$$

If the magnification is not given, a good 'rule of thumb' is that at a magnification of 25,000 $\times$ an average sized mitochondrion is about the size of a thumbprint.

Table 1.2. Comparison of light and electron microscopes

Light microscope	Electron microscope
1 Utilizes light focused by lenses on to the retina of the eye	1 Utilizes a beam of electrons, focused by electromagnets on to a fluorescent screen
2 Light travels through air	2 Electrons pass through the specimen in a vacuum.
3 Sections can be one cell thick	3 Sections must be about 0.05 μm (50 nm) to allow electrons through.
4 Resolving power (resolution) limited by wavelength of light to about 0.25 μm	4 Resolving power much greater of about 0.001 μm (1 nm)
5 Magnification up to 1500 $\times$	5 Magnification up to 500,000 $\times$
6 Differential staining gives coloured image	6 No colour

Enzyme experiments are of great importance. Although there is a great variety of enzyme-catalysed reactions used to illustrate enzyme activity, all enzyme experiments involve the same basic principles.

In all enzyme experiments close attention should be paid to the volumes used, the times involved and the temperature range. It is also essential to have a **control experiment**, the use of which allows more valid conclusions to be reached.

The commonest form of control for an enzyme experiment is the so-called boiled control. In this method a sample of the enzyme solution is boiled and cooled before being used in the same way as the normal sample. Boiling **denatures** enzymes and renders them inactive, and the use of a boiled control shows that whatever changes occur in the experiment with the normal sample are due to enzyme activity, and not some inorganic reaction.

The rate of enzyme reaction under different conditions can be studied by varying the temperature, pH, enzyme concentration, substrate concentration, or anion concentration (e.g. chloride ions, Cl^-).

COMMENT ▶

In those experiments using prepared enzyme solutions, it sometimes happens that the pure enzyme sample will give a slightly positive Benedict's test (yellow/green/red precipitate after boiling with Benedict's solution or Fehlings solutions A and B). Enzymes are protein and this result would be most unexpected. In fact the pure protein powder of the enzyme which is used to make the solution is sometimes mixed with some inert powder to give it more volume, and at times this powder can be contaminated with reducing sugars.

In those experiments using living material as the source of the enzyme, a variety of techniques is used.

Plant material such as soaked seeds and the 'eyes' of potatoes (and boiled controls) can be placed in circular wells cut into 1% **starch agar** in a Petri dish. After incubation (usually for 2–3 days at 25–35°C) the extent of any breakdown of the starch by enzymes diffusing from the plant material will be revealed by flooding the plate with iodine solution, when the areas of digested starch will not stain blue-black.

Another interesting technique is to use black developed **photographic film** as the substrate for protein-digesting enzymes. The silver grains which make the black colour of exposed and developed film are held to the film by gelatin – a protein. As this is digested, the black coloured grains are washed off revealing transparent areas.

Respiratory enzymes can be investigated in a variety of ways.

Catalase catalyses the breakdown of hydrogen peroxide into water and oxygen, and the rate of reaction can be studied by estimating the amount of effervescence produced.

Methylene blue can act as an artificial hydrogen acceptor, and in doing so is decolourized as the particular substrate is oxidized.

Digestive enzymes of animals can be obtained as extracts of macerated guts, usually of invertebrates (these are referred to in the chapter on nutrition).

QUESTION ▶

Q. What is meant by a cell? (5)
Describe the structure of proteins (7)
Outline the main role of proteins in the cell (6)
Why does specialization of a cell often result in the loss of its ability to divide? (2)

COMMENT ▶

OUTLINE ▶
ANSWER

This question requires care in restricting discussion of a broad subject (the role of proteins) to a selective area (the cell).

Cell definition (5)
Basic structural and functional unit of living organisms;
consists of cytoplasm and genetic material;
cytoplasm bounded by a selectively permeable cell membrane;
eukaryotes have complex membranous organelles e.g. mitochondria, endoplasmic reticulum, chloroplasts in photosynthetic cells, and membrane bound nucleus;
can be taken to include any substances it forms within or around itself e.g. cellulose cell wall in plants.

Protein structure (7)
Large macro molecules of several hundred amino acids;
about twenty different types of amino acids with a very large number of possible combinations;
amino acids are linked by peptide bonds (CO–NH) to form long polypeptide chains;
as a result of internal molecular forces chain becomes coiled to give a secondary structure;
and folded again to give a specific 3–D tertiary structure;
are amphoteric having both acidic and basic properties;
many are conjugated proteins in combination with a non-protein part.

Role of proteins in the cell (6)
As enzymes i.e. specific catalysts, tertiary structure gives active site;
as components of membranes e.g. fluid-protein-lipid-mosaic structure;
as contractile fibrils e.g. cilia, muscle fibres;
as structural fibres of high tensile strength e.g. keratin;
as buffers e.g. help maintain constant pH of cytoplasm;
as a source of energy i.e. may be used as a respiratory substrate.

Loss of ability to divide (2)
Organelles may be lost e.g. no nucleus in mammalian erythrocytes, no living contents in xylem vessels;
range of metabolic activities may be restricted i.e. no longer able to synthesize new cell material.

QUESTIONS

1 Briefly describe the structure of the mitochondrion. Give an account of the way in which this organelle is involved in the release of energy from food. (SCE)

2 Write concise notes on the structure and functions of **four** of the

following: cell membrane; chloroplast; cytoplasm; lysosome; microtubule; nucleolus; vacuole. (O)

3 An important difference between the rough ER (endoplasmic reticulum) and the smooth ER lies in the presence or absence of **A** plastids, **B** centrosomes, **C** mitochondria, **D** ribosomes;

(CAM)

4 Compare the ultrastructure of plant and animal cells, emphasizing their similarities and differences. (W)

5 Read the following passage, which describes methods for studying cell chemistry, and then answer the questions that follow.

'Cell fractionation is an important technique for studying cell chemistry. The different subcellar structures are separated by centrifugation of homogenates. In the preparation of homogenates, solutions of sucrose or other sugars are generally used because they can be readily adjusted to maintain the integrity of organelles and to counteract the tendency of organelles freed from the cell to clump together. Some organelles, such as mitochondria and plastids, remain essentially intact whereas endoplasmic reticulum and plasma membrane are fragmented into pieces of variable size.

The most widely used method for separating cell organelles is called differential centrifugation. It is based on differences in the speed with which structures sediment to the bottom of a centrifuge tube. Thus, using comparatively low forces (slow speed of centrifuge), large cell organelles and fragments would be sedimented as a pellet. If the suspension remaining is then subjected to a higher centrifugal force, different cellular structures are sedimented as a second fraction.

Isolated fractions are subsequently examined by electron microscopy and are subjected to biochemical analysis. With the use of radioactive precursors and by isolating fractions at different time intervals, knowledge of metabolic events may be gained. If cells are exposed, for example, to radioactive amino acids and fractions are isolated early after exposure, radioactive proteins are found in some fractions but not in others.'

(a)   What are *homogenates* (line 2)?

(b)   In relation to the use of sugar solutions in homogenization techniques, explain what is meant by the phrase 'to maintain the integrity of organelles' (line 4).

(c)   What are *plastids*? (line 6)?

(d)   (i) Explain what is meant by *radioactive amino acids* (line 18).
(ii) If the liver cells of an animal were treated in the manner described in lines 18 to 20 of the passage, in which structures would you expect to detect radioactive proteins? Give reasons for your answer. (CAM)

6 How would you measure the rate of a reaction catalysed by a **named** enzyme?

Explain what is meant by

(a)   denaturation of an enzyme,

(b)   enzyme inhibition.

One of the most distinctive features of enzyme activity is its specificity. Explain this specificity by reference to the structure and mode of action of an enzyme.   (O&C)

7

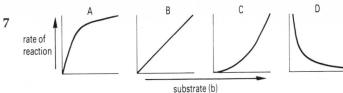

Which of the above graphs best describes the way in which the rate of an enzyme-catalysed reaction depends on the substrate concentration?   (CAM)

8 Complete the following table relating to **four different** tissues.

Name of tissue	Special property	Location
cardiac muscle		heart
	controlled by involuntary part of nervous system	
		attached to bones
	elastic and tough	at joints

(AEB)

9 The following epithelial cells are found in various parts of the lung and associated structures. Which list represents the correct combination of these?

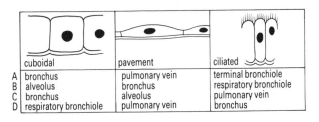

	cuboidal	pavement	ciliated
A	bronchus	pulmonary vein	terminal bronchiole
B	alveolus	bronchus	respiratory bronchiole
C	bronchus	alveolus	pulmonary vein
D	respiratory bronchiole	pulmonary vein	bronchus

(JMB)

10 (*a*)   Give an illustrated account of the structure of the various types of mechanical tissue in a *named* herbaceous angiosperm.
(*b*)   Briefly describe the distribution of these tissues in this plant.
(*c*)   What other roles may be played by these tissues?
(LOND)

11 Illustrate the range of cell structure found in the supporting tissues of angiosperms.   (SUJB)

CELL DIVISION AND GENETICS

CONTENTS

CELL DIVISION

Prior to cell division there is no visible activity in the nucleus, but in fact it is during this so-called 'resting-phase' or **interphase** that most nuclear activity occurs, as the relevant genetic information in the DNA is being expressed via the DNA/RNA mechanism.

Also the amount of DNA present is doubled, in preparation for the division of the nucleus into two, in the process of mitosis.

NUCLEAR DIVISION

MITOSIS

The division of the nucleus by mitosis produces genetically identical daughter nuclei, with each one receiving a diploid set of chromosomes from the diploid parent nucleus (Fig 2.1).

For convenience it can be considered as occurring in a number of stages.

1 PROPHASE

Prior to the onset of mitosis the amount of DNA present in the nucleus is doubled, and in prophase each chromosome forms from the chromatin as a double structure of two chromatids joined at a single centromere. Each chromatid contains the same amount of genetic information as the original chromosome, but they are called chromatids whilst they are both attached by a single centromere. Once the centromere divides and they separate each becomes known as a chromosome.

The nuclear membrane disappears, and is replaced by the nuclear spindle apparatus consisting of several fibres joined at the poles by small structures known as centrioles, which somehow control the later separation of the chromatids.

2 METAPHASE

The chromosomes move to the equator of the spindle and attach to the spindle fibres by their centromeres.

3 ANAPHASE

The chromatids separate to each pole, thus forming two new diploid sets of chromosomes.

4 TELOPHASE

Two new diploid nuclei are formed and the chromosomes spread out through the nuclei as chromatin.

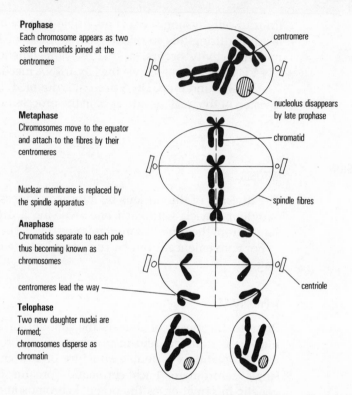

Prophase
Each chromosome appears as two sister chromatids joined at the centromere

centromere

nucleolus disappears by late prophase

Metaphase
Chromosomes move to the equator and attach to the fibres by their centromeres

chromatid

Nuclear membrane is replaced by the spindle apparatus

spindle fibres

Anaphase
Chromatids separate to each pole thus becoming known as chromosomes

centromeres lead the way

centriole

Telophase
Two new daughter nuclei are formed; chromosomes disperse as chromatin

Fig 2.1. *Mitosis.* The chromosomes are not visible during interphase when the nucleus is not dividing, and the DNA is active in expressing the genetic code. Also during interphase the DNA replicates so that the DNA content is twice the normal diploid content, in readiness for the nuclear division. The centrioles also replicate during interphase and migrate to both poles of the dividing nucleus.

EXERCISE ➡

Exercise 2.1

Mitosis occurs in all dividing body cells. What tissues in adult animals and plants are sites of active mitosis?

Answer Sites of active mitosis in higher plants are the apical and lateral meristems; and in mammals, the Malpighian layer of the skin, the lining of the gut, and the bone marrow. Mitosis is also involved in all forms of asexual reproduction.

In animals the new cells are formed by constriction or cleavage of the cytoplasm between the two new daughter nuclei.

In plants the new cells are formed by the laying down of a middle lamella upon which the new cellulose cell walls are formed.

GENETICS

Genetics is concerned with the study of inheritance. The expression of the genetic message depends on an interaction between the genetic information or **genotype** and the environment; and produces the actual organism or **phenotype.**

The results of various breeding experiments can be understood in terms of the behaviour of chromosomes during gamete production and fertilization, as it is the chromosomes in the nuclei of cells which carry the genetic message or information in the form of **genes.**

Gregor Mendel (1822–84), the founder of modern genetics, had no knowledge of chromosome behaviour and their importance in carrying the genetic message, but his deductions foreshadowed their discovery and the understanding of their role in the transmission of the genetic information from generation to generation.

An understanding of chromosome behaviour, particularly the process of **meiosis** or 'reduction division' in the formation of haploid sex cells; and the process of **fertilization** by which a diploid zygote (fertilized egg) is formed, is of central importance to an understanding of genetics.

MEIOSIS

As a result of fertilization each diploid zygote receives one set of chromosomes from the female gamete and one set from the male gamete. Each set contains information for all the characters of the organism, therefore a diploid zygote contains two complete sets of information (Fig 2.2).

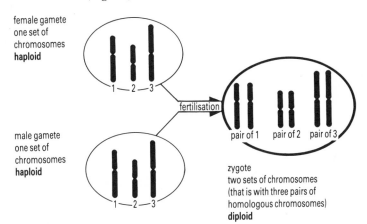

Fig 2.2. Formation of diploid cells in fertilization.

This means that each chromosome has a partner in the other set; in other words there are pairs of similar or **homologous chromosomes.**

The zygote undergoes cell division to produce the multicellular adult, and each cell receives an exact copy of each chromosome via **mitosis.**

When the individual produced in this way in turn produces its gametes, the chromosome number must be halved, so that each gamete only contains one set of chromosomes. This is achieved by means of the process of reduction division or **meiosis** (Fig 2.3), which occurs in the gonads of animals. (In plants meiosis occurs during spore formation.)

Main points involved in meiosis include the following.

1 The homologous chromosomes become attracted to each other to form pairs of homologous chromosomes or bivalents.
2 Each chromosome doubles into two **chromatids**, and then the homologous chromosomes repel each other, thus **halving the chromosome number.**
3 The chromatids then separate to form double the number of haploid gametes.

Meiosis results in a mixing or genetic recombination of the original maternal and paternal sets of chromosomes. This is brought about in the following ways:

1 By the crossing over that always occurs between homologous chromosomes.
2 The independent assortment of maternal and paternal chromosomes to each new gametic nucleus.

It is this meiotic genetic recombination and the subsequent random fusion of different gametes that produce variation in the offspring of sexual reproduction.

EXERCISE ▶

Exercise 2.2
Match each chromosome event with the appropriate stage of meiosis: 1 Crossing-over occurs, 2 Chiasmata align on the equators, 3 Homologous chromosomes shorten, thicken, and coil around each other, 4 Sister chromatids separate, 5 Homologous chromosomes pair to form bivalents.

A First prophase – zygotene, B First Prophase – pachytene, C First prophase – diplotene, D First metaphase, E Second anaphase.

COMMENT ▶

An understanding of meiosis is essential for an understanding of genetics, and many examination questions are based on relating the two.

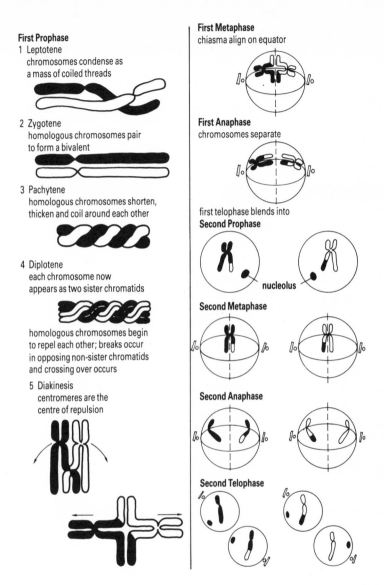

First Prophase

1 Leptotene
chromosomes condense as
a mass of coiled threads

2 Zygotene
homologous chromosomes pair
to form a bivalent

3 Pachytene
homologous chromosomes shorten,
thicken and coil around each other

4 Diplotene
each chromosome now
appears as two sister chromatids

homologous chromosomes begin
to repel each other; breaks occur
in opposing non-sister chromatids
and crossing over occurs

5 Diakinesis
centromeres are the
centre of repulsion

First Metaphase
chiasma align on equator

First Anaphase
chromosomes separate

first telophase blends into
Second Prophase

nucleolus

Second Metaphase

Second Anaphase

Second Telophase

Fig 2.3. *Meiosis.* Four haploid daughter nuclei are formed with chromosomes containing a mixture of paternal and maternal alleles (due to crossing over) and with mixtures of maternal and paternal chromosomes (due to independent assortment).

Mitosis and meiosis contrasted

Mitosis	**Meiosis**
1 Chromosome number remains the same	1 Chromosome number is halved
2 One division of nucleus	2 Two divisions of nucleus
3 Two daughter nuclei (and cells) produced	3 Four daughter nuclei (and cells) produced
4 No variation in daughter cells unless mutation occurs	4 Variation in daughter cells due to genetic mixing events
5 Homologous chromosomes do not pair	5 Homologous chromosomes pair
6 Centromeres align on the equator of the spindle	6 Chiasmata align on the equator of the spindle

MENDELIAN GENETICS

Gregor Mendel (1822–84) carried out a series of breeding experiments with the garden pea, which led him to formulate two laws of inheritance.

This work laid the foundations for the scientific study of inheritance, which became known as genetics.

Mendel avoided earlier confusions by choosing simple, easily identified features to study and by treating the results statistically.

The garden pea is habitually self-pollinating in the flower bud stage, and thus has **pure lines** of unchanging inherited traits.

Mendel artificially crossed different pure lines – the **parentals** – to produce seeds which grew into the first filial or **F1 generation.**

These were then allowed to self-fertilize to produce seeds which grew into the second filial or **F2 generation.**

> Parentals: tall × dwarf
> F1: all tall
> F2: 3 tall : 1 dwarf

From these results he deduced that each individual carries two 'doses' of each character, only one of which is carried in each gamete; and that tall was dominant to dwarf, as illustrated in Fig 2.4.

Fig 2.4

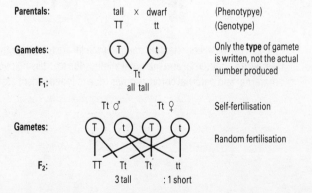

From the **3:1 monohybrid ratios** obtained, he derived his first law of the **segregation** of germinal units. This states that, of a pair of characters, only one can be carried in a single gamete (Fig 2.5)

Fig 2.5

Tt   pair of characters

(T) (t)   only one can be carried in each gamete i.e. they segregate

Random fusion at fertilization subsequently results in the production of the 3:1 monohybrid ratio (so-called as it involves only one pair of contrasting characters).

This segregation of characters is now understood in terms of the halving of the chromosome number by homologous chromosomes repelling each other during meiosis.

EXERCISE ▶

Exercise 2.3

In genetic diagrams such as Fig 2.5, the segregation of a pair of characters is shown as:

T t

(T) (t)

How does this format relate to meiosis in which each diploid cell gives rise to four haploid daughter nuclei?

Answer If the format of genetic diagrams was to exactly match or reflect the mechanism of meiosis, it would be presented as follows:

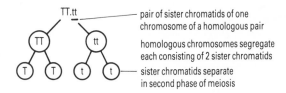

TT.tt ———— pair of sister chromatids of one chromosome of a homologous pair

homologous chromosomes segregate each consisting of 2 sister chromatids

sister chromatids separate in second phase of meiosis

However, the doubling of each chromosome into two chromatids is not genetically significant in itself, and tends to detract from the key point – which is that each gamete only contains one of a pair of characters.

Mendel also studied the inheritance of two pairs of characters, and on obtaining a **9:3:3:1 dihybrid Mendelian ratio** in the F2 generation, formulated his second law of **independent assortment.** This states that any one of a pair of characters can go into a gamete with any one of another pair (Fig 2.6).

Fig 2.6

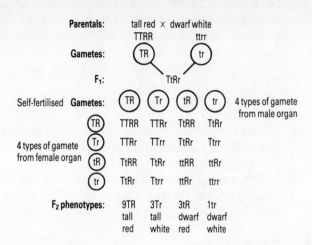

Parentals: tall red × dwarf white
            TTRR   ttrr

In terms of chromosome behaviour in meiosis this means that either of a pair of homologous chromosomes can go with either of another pair into a gamete (Fig 2.7).

Fig 2.7

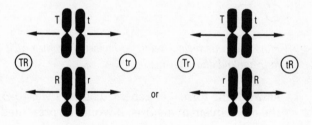

or

EXERCISE ▶

Exercise 2.4
Which of the following shows the types of gamete produced by an individual with the genotype Aabb?

1 Aa bb	2 Aa Ab
3 Ab Ab	4 Ab ab

BACK CROSS OR TEST CROSS

This is a way of determining the genotype of an organism by crossing it with a homozygous recessive. The genes from the homozygous recessive do not mask any genes from the organism under test (Fig 2.8).

Fig 2.8

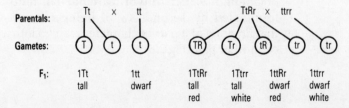

INCOMPLETE DOMINANCE

In some cases the different versions or alleles of the same gene carried on homologous chromosomes do not bear a simple dominant/recessive relationship to each other.

Sometimes they exhibit incomplete dominance, or co-dominance, as shown in Fig 2.9.

Fig 2.9

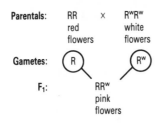

GENETIC INTERACTION

In some cases more than one gene affects a single phenotypic character. In these cases genetic interaction occurs, as shown in Fig 2.10.

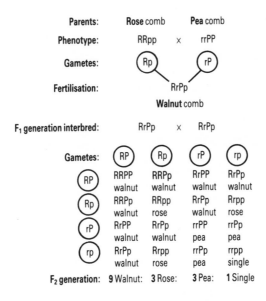

Fig 2.10 Genetic interaction in the control of comb shape in chickens.

LINKAGE

Genes that are found on the same chromosome are said to be linked. Such genes cannot assort independently in the normal way. When considering the inheritance of two pairs of contrasting characters we would expect a 9:3:3:1 dihybrid ratio. However, when the two pairs of contrasting characters are carried on one pair of chromosomes, a 3:1 monohybrid ratio is obtained (Fig 2.11).

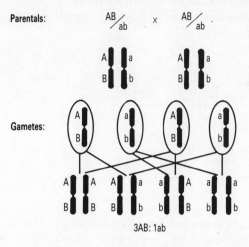

Fig 2.11

Mendel's second law depends upon the two pairs of contrasting characters under study being on two pairs of chromosomes.

CROSSING-OVER

Crossing-over occurs in meiosis when two non-sister chromatids break and rejoin with each other (Fig 2.12 (*a*)).

Crossing-over allows a degree of independent assortment of linked genes, as in those chromosomes where it occurs there is an exchange of genetic material (Fig 2.12 (*b*)).

Fig 2.12

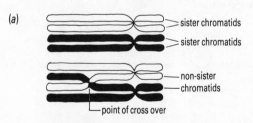

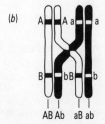

The closer together genes are on a chromosome, the less chance there is of a cross-over occurring between them.

By carrying out breeding experiments and calculating the percentage crossing over occurring between two linked genes, chromosome maps can be constructed, with genes in the correct linear order and with the correct relative distance between them.

$$\% \text{ cross over} = \frac{\text{number of offspring showing character combinations arising as a result of crossing over}}{\text{total number of offspring}} \times 100$$

Crossing over thus leads to increased variation in the offspring as a result of the exchange of genetic material between maternal and paternal chromosomes. It also ensures that each pair of chromosomes remains a single unit until the end of the first metaphase of meiosis, as shown in Fig 2.13.

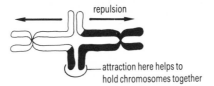

Fig 2.13

Without this attraction the homologous chromosomes could tend to lose contact too quickly before lining up on the equator of the nuclear spindle at first metaphase of meiosis, with little chance of the exact halving of the chromosome number into two haploid sets occurring.

EXERCISE ▶

Exercise 2.5

In a breeding experiment, in which a heterozygous tall red organism (TtRr) was crossed with a homozygous recessive dwarf white organism (ttrr), the following offspring were obtained: 352 tall red, 51 tall white, 49 dwarf red, 353 dwarf white. Do these results indicate that these genes are linked?

Answer Yes. If they were not linked, a 1:1:1:1 ratio would be expected. The 51 tall white (Ttrr) and the 49 dwarf red (ttRr) offspring are the result of crossing-over between linked genes, in gamete formation.

SEX LINKAGE

In many organisms the differences between the sexes is mainly determined by special sex chromosomes (Fig 2.14).

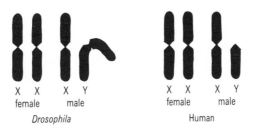

Fig 2.14

The sex with the pair of identical sex chromosomes is known as the **homogametic sex** and is usually the female; the sex with the unequal pair of sex chromosomes is known as the **heterogametic sex** and is usually the male. (This situation is reversed in birds.)

These sex chromosomes also carry genes not involved in sex determination, and these genes are said to be **sex-linked.** In most cases sex-linked genes are recessive and are carried on the X chromosome. A well known example in humans is the disease haemophilia, shown in Fig 2.15. An example in *Drosophila* is one type of eye colour (Fig 2.16).

Sex-linked genes give different results in reciprocal crosses, for example the results of a cross between a red-eyed female *Drosophila* and a white-eyed male would be different from the results of a cross between a white-eyed female and a red-eyed male. With non-sex linked or **autosomal** genes the results would be the same.

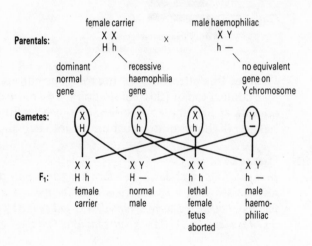

Fig 2.15

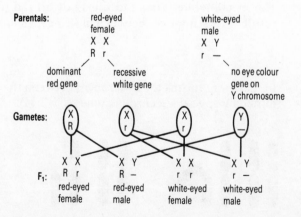

Fig 2.16

**COMMENT ▶** When answering genetics questions involving breeding patterns, it is essential that all the steps be fully explained. The derivation of a particular ratio set out in sketch outline alone, will not score highly – even if perfectly correct.

POPULATION GENETICS

In natural populations it is difficult either to analyse the genotypes of members of the population, or to predict the genotypes and phenotypes of the offspring of random mating within the population.

If the number of double recessives in a population is known, **the Hardy–Weinberg** equation enables the percentage of homozygote dominants and the percentage of heterozygotes for that gene locus in a population to be calculated.

Predictions can then be made about the proportion of genotypes and phenotypes that should appear in the next generation as a result of random mating.

When such predictions prove to be incorrect, it is an indication that some forces are at work which are altering the relative allele frequencies of the dominants and recessives in the population; for example mutation, non-random mating, unequal fertility of different genotypes or selection for or against particular phenotypes.

With respect to a single gene, for example the gene T, the members of a population can have one of three genotypes: TT, Tt, tt.

If the frequency of the allele T in the whole population is p, and that of the allele t is q, then: $p + q = 1$ (where 1 represents the whole population). The relative frequency of the alleles will be the same in both males and females and in their gametes; for example:

100 diploid organisms Tt $\Rightarrow$ 200 alleles:

$$\begin{matrix} 100T \\ \left(\begin{matrix}\text{half the total} \\ p=0.5\end{matrix}\right) \end{matrix} \quad \text{and} \quad \begin{matrix} 100t \\ \left(\begin{matrix}\text{half the total} \\ q=0.5\end{matrix}\right) \end{matrix} \quad (p+q=1)$$

50 males $\Rightarrow$ 100 alleles:

$$\begin{matrix} 50T \\ \left(\begin{matrix}\text{half the total} \\ p=0.5\end{matrix}\right) \end{matrix} \quad \text{and} \quad \begin{matrix} 50t \\ \left(\begin{matrix}\text{half the total} \\ q=0.5\end{matrix}\right) \end{matrix} \quad (p+q=1)$$

50 females $\Rightarrow$ 100 alleles:

$$\begin{matrix} 50T \\ \left(\begin{matrix}\text{half the total} \\ p=0.5\end{matrix}\right) \end{matrix} \quad \text{and} \quad \begin{matrix} 50t \\ \left(\begin{matrix}\text{half the total} \\ q=0.5\end{matrix}\right) \end{matrix} \quad (p+q=1)$$

Assuming the random fusion of gametes:

Gametes	T p	t q
T p	TT p^2	Tt pq
t q	Tt pq	tt q^2

So: $p^2+2pq+q^2=1$

p^2 equals the frequency of homozygous dominants (TT),
$2pq$ the frequency of heterozygotes (Tt), and
q^2 the frequency of homozygous recessives (tt).

In a natural population, the only known value is q^2, the frequency of the homozygous recessives (tt). However, it is possible to substitute values in the equation to obtain the frequency of all the genotypes. For example, consider a population of 100 plants, 70 of which are tall, and 30 of which are short, and where it is known that tall is dominant to short. Then:

Phenotype: tall   short
Genotype: TT or Tt   tt
Percentage: 70   30

$$p^2+2pq+q^2=1$$

$$q^2=\frac{30}{100}=0.3$$

$$q=0.55$$

$$p=1-q=0.45$$

$$p^2=0.2$$

$$p^2+2pq+q^2=1$$

$$0.2+0.5+0.3=1$$

TT   Tt   tt

This means that in the population of 100 individuals, there are 20 homozygous dominant (TT), 50 heterozygous (Tt) and, as was already known, 30 homozygous recessive (tt) individuals.

POLYMORPHISM

Polymorphism occurs when members of a freely interbreeding population of a species have two or more different forms or **morphs** (with no continuous range of intermediates) occurring together in the same habitat in such proportions that the rarest of them cannot be maintained at the observed frequency merely by continuing mutation.

In a stable environment there is usually a stable proportion of the different morphs in a population, and this situation is referred to as **balanced polymorphism.** Examples are red–green colour blindness; human A, B, and O blood groups; and cyanogenesis in clover leaves.

However, the balance between different morphs is sensitive to environmental change, and the polymorphic system can respond rapidly to changes in environmental conditions. When this occurs, the condition is referred to as **transient polymorphism.**

An example is seen in the peppered moth (*Biston betularia*). The peppered moth has two distinct morphs: the light-coloured 'natural' form, and the dark-coloured or 'melanic' form. They are both active at night and during the day they rest on vertical surfaces, usually tree trunks, particularly birch. The proportion of light and melanic forms varies in different parts of the country; in rural areas the light form predominates. In these areas the dark forms are less well camouflaged against the light bark of trees, and are more easily caught and eaten by birds; whereas in industrial areas the light forms are less well camouflaged against pollution-darkened backgrounds. Thus natural selection favours the dark form in industrial areas, and the light form in rural areas.

THE GENETIC MATERIAL

Chromosomes carry genetic information from one generation to the next, and from cell to cell during growth and development. This genetic information has been considered as being in discrete units or genes, carried along the length of the chromosomes rather like beads on a necklace. This model is convenient for interpreting the results of breeding programmes such as those considered by Mendel, but knowledge of the structure of the genetic material reveals it to be more complex.

Chromosomes are composed of special proteins known as histones, and deoxyribonucleic acid (DNA). It is the DNA which carries the genetic information (see Fig 2.17).

Fig 2.17. *Structure and replication of DNA.* DNA is a giant macromolecule much longer than is shown in the diagram. The two strands of the double helix are held together by hydrogen bonds between the bases of each pair. During replication the double helix unwinds and each original strand acts as a template or blueprint for the formation of a new strand. The replication process requires energy (ATP) and the enzyme DNA polymerase. The base pairs are always adenine/thymine and guanine/cytosine. In this illus. the CG connection should be of 3 lines; the AT connection should be of 2 lines.

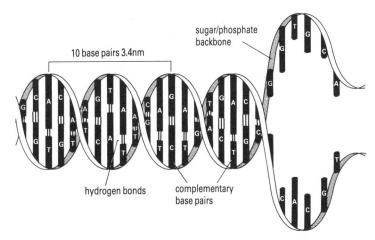

sugar/phosphate backbone

10 base pairs 3.4nm

hydrogen bonds

complementary base pairs

THE GENETIC CODE

The sequence of the four bases, adenine, guanine, cytosine and thymine on a strand of DNA contains a coded message for the construction of proteins, which form the basic structure of the cytoplasm, and all enzymes, which in turn control the functions of the cytoplasm.

All proteins are composed of combinations of about twenty different amino acids joined together by peptide bonds to form long chains. Each one of the twenty amino acids can occur any number of times within a protein.

The sequence of the bases on a particular section of a strand of DNA codes for the sequence of amino acids in a particular protein.

Each amino acid is coded for by a 'code-word' of three bases known as a **triplet codon.** However, there are 64 different combinations of any three letters from four, but only twenty different amino acids to code for.

In fact each amino acid is coded for by more than one triplet codon, and some codons act as 'punctuation' marks between adjacent messages on the DNA.

TRANSCRIPTION AND TRANSLATION

The genetic code has to be expressed in the production of protein. This is achieved by means of ribonucleic acid (RNA) and the ribosomes in the cytoplasm.

The first step in this process is the **transcription** or copying of the coded message into messenger RNA (mRNA). The mRNA is similar in structure to DNA but it is shorter, has an extra oxygen in its sugar, and has the base uracil instead of thymine.

When the DNA code is copied, the opposite base partner is copied into the mRNA molecule. Thus cytosine copies into guanine, guanine is copied into cytosine, and thymine is copied into adenine; adenine however is copied into uracil, as mRNA does not have thymine as part of its structure.

DNA		mRNA
Guanine	→	Cytosine
Cytosine	→	Guanine
Thymine	→	Adenine
Adenine	→	Uracil

EXERCISE ▶

Exercise 2.6

If the sequence of bases on a strand of DNA is: GCATCA; what will be the sequence of bases on the strand of mRNA transcribed from it?

(a)   *CGTAGT*
(b)   *CGUAGU*
(c)   *GCUACU*

The mRNA containing a copy of the genetic code now moves into the cytoplasm and becomes associated with the ribosomes which enable the message to be translated into actual proteins (Fig 2.18). In this process another type of RNA, namely transfer RNA(tRNA), is involved. The tRNA acts as a carrier, bringing the correct amino acid into the correct position in the protein molecule being formed.

The mRNA is usually a short-lived molecule, sometimes lasting only a few minutes. This is necessary, as otherwise, once formed, the mRNA would continue to form the particular protein, perhaps in excess of that required.

Control of the amount of a particular protein produced is achieved by the control of transcription of the DNA message into mRNA in the nucleus.

Fig 2.18. Transcription and translation of the genetic message.

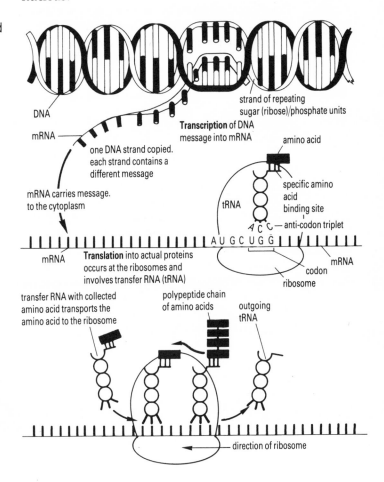

DNA

mRNA

one DNA strand copied. each strand contains a different message

Transcription of DNA message into mRNA

strand of repeating sugar (ribose)/phosphate units

amino acid

specific amino acid binding site

mRNA carries message. to the cytoplasm

tRNA

A C C — anti-codon triplet

A U G C U G G

mRNA **Translation** into actual proteins occurs at the ribosomes and involves transfer RNA (tRNA)

mRNA

codon

ribosome

transfer RNA with collected amino acid transports the amino acid to the ribosome

polypeptide chain of amino acids

outgoing tRNA

direction of ribosome

EXERCISE ▶

Exercise 2.7
Which of the following would it be possible to transfer between members of different species without disruption of normal cell function; DNA, mRNA or tRNA?

Answer tRNA would be universal in its structure and function, as each type of tRNA is specific to a specific amino acid, and all cells contain the same amino acids.

DNA and mRNA contain coded information for the sequence of amino acids in proteins, which are different in each species.

MUTATION

Mutation is a change in the structure of the genetic material, and can occur as a result of changes in individual genes, or changes in chromosomal structure or number.

Most mutations are harmful, or at least of no immediate advantage, as the organism is already adapted to its environment and any change would tend to upset this adaptation. However, the variation produced by mutation could be beneficial under changed circumstances.

GENE MUTATIONS

A gene mutation (point mutation) occurs as a result of an error in the copying of a sequence of bases during the replication of a new DNA strand. Once the error has occurred it is perpetuated by further DNA replications. The altered gene is said to be **allelomorphic** to the original, and thus mutation is the origin of all such alleles of genes.

Dominant gene mutations express themselves immediately, whereas recessive mutations may be masked or hidden for several generations before expressing themselves in a homozygous recessive individual.

The frequency of gene mutations varies, but is of the same order in a wide variety of organisms; that is a gene mutates once in about one million cell generations. This suggests that the same forces are at work in all types, as would be expected considering the universal occurrence of DNA.

The rate of mutation is increased by mutagenic agents such as ionizing radiations and many chemicals.

Ionizing radiations include those elecromagnetic radiations emitted by radioactive materials such as X-rays and γ-rays, and ultraviolet light. As they pass through the genetic material they cause ionizations to occur in the DNA, thus altering its chemical structure and resulting in mutations.

There is a wide range of mutagenic chemicals, including nitrous acid, and chemicals in the mustard gas group. By reacting in one way or another with the DNA and altering its structure and behaviour, mutations result.

CHROMOSOMAL MUTATIONS

CHANGES OF CHROMOSOME STRUCTURE

Changes in the structure of chromosomes usually results in either the loss of genetic material, as in deletions, or in new gene arrangements, as in inversions and translocations.

Deletions involve the loss of a segment of a chromosome. Normally chromosomes have only one centre of movement, the centromere. Therefore if a chromosome gets broken, only that part containing the centromere will move to the pole of the spindle apparatus in meiosis, and the portion without the centromere will be lost. The effect of the deletion depends on the amount and the nature of the genetic material lost.

Inversions involve the breaking off of a segment of a chromosome which then rejoins the wrong way round, so that the gene sequence is reversed. By preventing crossing over within this reversed segment during meiosis, inversions decrease variation in the offspring and act to keep advantageous combinations of gene alleles together so that they are inherited as a unit or '**super-gene**'.

Translocations involve the breaking off of a segment of a chromosome and its rejoining to a non-homologous chromosome. This causes complications during meiosis.

CHANGES IN CHROMOSOME NUMBER

A loss or gain of individual chromosomes of a set is known as **aneuploidy**. A gain of whole sets of chromosomes is known as **euploidy**, of which there are two types, auto(poly)ploidy and allo(poly)ploidy. Such polyploid organisms are usually sterile, as the increased number of chromosome sets causes complications at meiosis, so that fertile gametes cannot be formed. As a result polyploidy is much more common in plants than in animals, as plants often have strong powers of asexual vegetative reproduction which enable them to survive without sexual reproduction.

Autopolyploids have multiple sets of their own chromosomes. This situation usually arises by misdivision at mitosis; the chromatids do not separate to the poles of the spindle. Thus all the chromatids are included in one nucleus, and a diploid (2n) nucleus would become tetraploid (4n).

Allopolyploids are formed by the hybridization of two organisms, usually plants, with different chromosome sets. Usually the organisms must be reasonably closely related. Thus it can occur between members of different species, but is rare between members of different genera. The F1 hybrid is usually sterile, due to problems at meiosis, as the chromosomes will not form homologous pairs. However, if the chromosome number is doubled by the non-disjunction of the chromatids during mitosis (as in autopolyploidy), fertile gametes can be produced, as each chromosome will now have an homologous partner and balanced gametes can be produced by meiosis. Such hybridization between species to form so-called **fertile amphidiploids** would appear to have occurred time and time again in nature to form new species.

COMMENT ▶

Great confidence is required to answer numerical genetics questions under examination conditions. Sometimes the description of the breeding situation is long and involved, and a small error in interpretation could have far-reaching effects on the calculation.

Also, once having solved the problem there is a tendency to give the answers in outline diagram form only. Answers to numerical questions must be fully explained to obtain full marks.

QUESTION ▶

Q. In a particular type of plant, the stem can be either hairy or smooth, and red or green.

The allele for hairy (H) is dominant to the allele for smooth (h), and the allele for red (A) is dominant to the allele for green (a).

(a)　　What are the possible genotypes for,
　　　　(i) hairy and green stemmed plants, and
　　　　(ii) smooth and red stemmed plants? (4)

(b)　　A cross between a hairy and green stemmed plant, and a smooth and red stemmed plant gave rise to offspring in the numbers of;
　　　　100 hairy and red stemmed, 95 hairy and green stemmed, 105 smooth and red stemmed, and 97 smooth and green stemmed.
　　　　(i) What are the genotypes of the parents? (2)
　　　　(ii) Give a reasoned explanation of your answer (11)

(c)　　What is meant by a test or black cross? (3)

COMMENT ▶

This question requires a reasoned explanation of a genetics problem in the main part, and not simply a setting out of the pattern of behaviour of the alleles as you might be more used to doing.

OUTLINE ▶ ANSWER

(a)　　(i) hairy and green stemmed
　　　　HHaa, Hhaa
　　　　(ii) smooth and red stemmed
　　　　hhAA, hhAa (4)

(b)　　(i) genotypes of parents
　　　　Hhaa x hhAa (2)
　　　　(ii) Reasoned explanation (11)

Each gamete can only carry one allele of a pair of alleles; segregation of alleles into gametes produces gametes of different genetic composition;

random fertilization between male and female gametes of different types gives rise to offspring of different genetic composition in certain ratios;

the hairy to smooth, and the red to green ratios are both 1:1 (50:50); perfect ratios seldom being produced;

this ratio is produced by a heterozygous/recessive cross;

therefore the parents must have been heterozygous for hairy (Hh) and red (Aa) and homozygous for the recessive characters smooth (hh) and green (aa) as they showed the recessive characters in the phenotypes.

Parents phenotypes	Hairy green x smooth red
Parents genotypes	Hhaa x hhAa
gametes	Ha ha hA ha
F1	HhAa Hhaa hhAa hhaa
	1: 1: 1: 1

(c)   Test or back cross (3)

cross between an organism pure breeding for a recessive character;

with another of an unknown genotype;

enables homozygous dominant and heterozygous individuals to be identified.

QUESTIONS

1   Outline the process of mitosis, briefly explaining its significance.

(SCE)

2   (a)   Read through the following account of mitosis and then fill in the gaps with the most appropriate word or words to complete the account.

Mitosis is the division of a _____ to give two _____ of identical _____ composition. During the first stage of this process, known as the _____, the chromosomes shorten and _____. They can also be seen to have divided lengthwise into _____. The next stage of the process is marked by the membrane of the _____ breaking down and the chromosomes moving towards the _____ of the cell. The chromosomes become attached to _____ fibres. Meanwhile the _____ divide, initiating the drawing apart of the 'daughter' chromosomes towards the opposite _____ of the cell. Each group of new chromosomes becomes a new nucleus within which one or more _____ are reformed with ribonucleic acid. The chromosomes now become less easily _____. In plant cells, a cell _____ separates the two new cells, whilst in animal cells the cytoplasm _____.

(b)   Give *three* differences between mitosis and meiosis.

(LOND)

3 (a)   In an experiment, the nucleus of a zygote was replaced by a nucleus from a specialised somatic (body) cell of an adult. The resulting cell developed into a complete organism. What does this indicate about the nucleus of the specialised cell?

(b)   (i) The following statements refer to the process of mitosis or meiosis in cells of a dicotyledonous plant. Place a tick (√) against each statement which is true of **meiosis.**

Takes place in meristems.

Homologous chromosomes align in pairs at the equator of the spindle

The chromosome number is halved

Chiasmata occur

The chromosome number of the parent cell is present in each of the new cells formed.

(ii) Name a plant meristem.

(iii) In animals, growth ceases when the adult stage is reached but mitosis still continues. Give one place in adult humans where such mitosis constantly occurs and state the purpose it serves.

(c)   On the leaves of *Bryophyllum* plantlets arise due to mitosis in some of the cells.

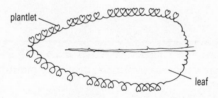

(i) What may be deduced about the genotypes of such offspring.

(ii) Give the term applied to a collection of offspring produced in this way.   (SCE)

4 (a)   Complete the following table of terms commonly used to describe the successive stages in animal gametogenesis. For each stage also give the corresponding chromosome number which would be appropriate for man ($2n = 46$). (See pages 78 and 79.)

Male	Chromosome number	Female	Chromosome number
Primordial germ cell	46	Primordial germ cell	46
Spermatogonium		Oogonium	

Male	Chromosome number	Female	Chromosome number

(*b*)   (i) What is the function of meiosis in the life cycles of plants and animals?

(ii) Describe, concisely, how one diploid cell becomes four haploid cells in the process of meiotic cell division.

(iii) Diagram *A* represents the chromosomes contained in a somatic cell of an animal (2*n* = 6).

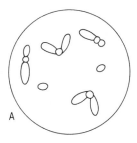

A

Using the same chromosomes shown at *A*, complete diagrams *B* and *C* below to show clearly the essential differences between metaphase of mitosis and metaphase 1 of meiosis.

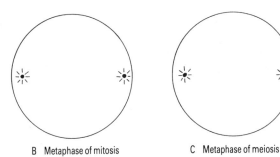

B   Metaphase of mitosis   C   Metaphase of meiosis

(*c*)   Fox breeders have tried to improve particular characteristics in the red fox by hybridising it with the arctic fox and although many hybrids have been produced they are always sterile. The red fox (2*n* = 34) has relatively large and long chromosomes. The arctic fox (2n = 52) has smaller and shorter chromosomes.

(i) What would you expect to be the somatic number of chromosomes of the hybrid?

(ii) How do you account for the sterility of the hybrid?
(CAM)

5 Briefly explain the significance of meiotic cell division.
Describe the ways in which the process of meiosis is different from mitosis. (SCE)

6 Mendel's first law states that an organism's characteristics are determined by internal factors which occur in pairs and only one of a pair of such factors can be represented in a single gamete.

(*a*) Give the modern name for
(i) an internal factor controlling part of an organism's characteristics,
(ii) a pair of such factors.

(*b*) Explain why these factors occur in pairs in organisms rather than singly.

(*c*) Explain why only one of a pair of such factors can be represented in a single gamete.

(*d*) Rewrite Mendel's first law using modern genetic terminology.

(*e*) Explain what is meant by probability. Give a simple example.

(*f*) In a repeat of one of Mendel's experiments a tall, coloured pea plant was crossed with a dwarf, white pea plant. The F_1 was self fertilized and a sample of 20 seeds was collected from the F_2. None of these seeds carried the double recessive characters, dwarf white. Explain why.

(*g*) What is the most probable number of dwarf coloured plants in a sample of twenty taken from the above experiment?

(*h*) Would a cross between parents, each carrying two factors, always produce four types of F_2 offspring? Yes/No.
Explain your answer. (W)

7 In a species of plant, petal colour is determined by one pair of alleles and stem length by another. The following experimental crosses were carried out.

Experiment 1 A purple-flowered plant was crossed with several red-flowered plants. The progeny were all purple-flowered plants.

Experiment 2 A short-stemmed plant was crossed with several long-stemmed plants. The progeny were all short-stemmed.

Experiment 3 A different purple-flowered, short-stemmed plant of the same species was crossed with several red-flowered long-stemmed plants. The following were obtained:
37 purple-flowered short-stemmed
34 red-flowered short-stemmed
41 red-flowered long-stemmed
35 purple-flowered long-stemmed

(*a*) What are the dominant alleles?

(*b*) What are the probable genotypes of the purple-flowered and short-stemmed plants used in experiments 1 and 2?

(*c*) With the aid of diagrams, explain the results obtained in experiments 1 and 2.

(*d*)   With the aid of a diagram, explain the results of experiment 3.

(*e*)   If the purple-flowered, short-stemmed plant used in experiment 3 had been self-fertilized, what proportion of the progeny would you have expected to be red-flowered and what proportion would you have expected to be short-stemmed?

(*f*)   From your knowledge of reproduction in flowering plants explain

  (i) how the crosses required in experiment 3 could be ensured,

  (ii) how self-fertilization could be ensured.   (AEB)

8 (*a*)   How is sex determined in humans?

(*b*)   Colour blindness in humans is a sex-linked recessive character. In a marriage between a colour blind man and a woman with normal colour vision, what types of offspring might be produced? Explain your answer.

(*c*)   Barred plumage in birds is inherited as a sex-linked dominant character. In a cross between a non-barred hen and a barred cock it was found that all the offspring had barred plumage.

Inbreeding among these individuals resulted in a second generation consisting of barred cocks and equal numbers of barred and non-barred hens.

A reciprocal cross between a barred hen and a non-barred cock gave F_1 generation of barred cocks and non-barred hens, and an F_2 generation composed of equal numbers of barred and non-barred individuals of both sexes.

Explain these results.   (LOND)

9 A female *Drosophila* with red eyes and black body was crossed with a male fly having pink eyes and grey body. The F_1 and F_2 offspring were as follows:

F_1 red-eyed grey males and females

F_2 113 red-eyed, grey: 52 red-eyed, black: 47 pink-eyed, grey: 22 pink-eyed, black.

From these results one can deduce that inheritance of these two characters is brought about by

A   one gene affecting both characters.

B   genes on independently segregating chromosomes.

C   linked autosomal genes.

D   sex-linked genes.   (CAM)

10 The two following examples both illustrate inheritance of a sex-linked gene on the X-chromosome. In the parental generation (P) the homogametic sex is homozygous for colour in both examples.

Cat	*Magpie Moth*
(black dominant to yellow)	*(normal colour dominant to pale colour)*
P Black male × yellow female	P Pale male × normal female
F_1 1 yellow male to 1 black female	F_1 1 normal male to 1 pale female

In these crosses the heterogametic sex is

A   male in the cat, female in the moth.

B   female in the cat, male in the moth.

C   male in both cat and moth.

D   female in both cat and moth.   (CAM)

11 In *Drosophila*, a recessive allele which produces miniature wings is found on the X-chromosome. The result of crossing a female with miniature wings with a wild-type male would be

A   all wild-type progeny.

B   all females wild-type, all males miniature.

C   all males wild-type, all females miniature.

D   half the females and half the males miniature.   (JMB)

12 Family trees/pedigree charts are a common means of recording patterns of inheritance in man. In the pedigree charts below, females are symbolized: ♀; males by ♂. The symbols for a parental pair are linked together by a 'marriage line' (thicker horizontal line) and the symbols for their children are represented below the parents beneath a subsidiary horizontal line linked to the marriage line by a short vertical. Individuals represented by a solid black symbol exhibit the trait mentioned.

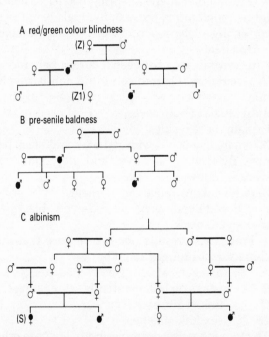

Given that red/green colour blindness, pre-senile baldness, and albinism are inherited in a simple Mendelian way, comment on:

(*a*)   the type of Mendelian inheritance exhibited by pedigree chart **A**,

(*b*)   the genotype(s) of **Z** and **Z1** in pedigree chart **A**,

(*c*)   the way in which pre-senile baldness is inherited in pedigree chart **B**, with special reference to the underlying genetics,

(*d*)   the genotype(s) of the parents of **S** in pedigree chart **C**,

(*e*)   the chance of further brothers and sisters of **S** being albino.

     (O&C)

13 (a)   A part of a ribonucleic acid (RNA) molecule, formed on part of a deoxy-ribonucleic acid (DNA) strand, is shown below.

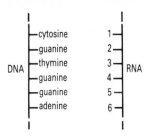

Name the bases numbered 1 and 6 on the RNA strand.

(b)   Other than a difference in bases, give **two** ways in which the structure of RNA differs from that of DNA.

(c)   Occasionally, the arrangement of bases in a molecule of DNA is changed. What is the genetic significance of such a change when it occurs in a reproductive cell?

(d)   (i) Name the sub-cellular structure at which protein synthesis takes place and state its location.

(ii) How many bases on the RNA molecule are required to code for an amino acid?

(iii) What determines the **order** in which the amino acids link up to form a protein?

(iv) Give one function of a protein in a cell.   (SCE)

14 What are the properties of DNA which make it so suitable (a) as hereditary material (b) for encoding genetic information? Describe how this information is transcribed and translated.   (O)

15 Describe how a deoxyribonucleic acid (DNA) strand in the nucleus is able to effect the synthesis of a protein fibre in the cytoplasm of a cell. Explain the effects of a mutation in the DNA.   (SU)

16 A mutation is the result of

A   a spontaneous change in a chromosome or gene.

B   evolution.

C   natural selection.

D   crossing over.   (CAM)

17 Briefly describe what is meant by (a) Hardy–Weinberg Law; (b) sickle cell anaemia. In a certain N. African country a medical investigation revealed that 0.04% of the population suffered from sickle cell anaemia. Sickle cell anaemia is determined by a single pair of alleles H and h where individuals with the trait have the genotype hh and those with normal red blood corpuscles are either HH or Hh.

(a)   Using the Hardy–Weinberg equations $p^2 + 2pq + q^2 = 100\%$ (total population) and $p + q = 100\%$ (where p and q represent the allele frequencies, and p^2, $2pq$ and q^2 represent the genotype frequencies), calculate the percentages of the total population of the two genotypes for normal blood.

(b)   In a few very isolated areas the proportion of individuals in the population with sickle cell anaemia was found to be as high as 4%. Calculate (*i*) the proportions of homozygous to heterozygous normal blood types and (*ii*) the ratio of the two phenotypes.

(O)

REPRODUCTION AND GROWTH

CONTENTS

ASEXUAL REPRODUCTION

Asexual reproduction requires only a single parental organism which gives rise to offspring by mitotic cell division (during which the complete adult number of chromosomes is exactly replicated and passed on, so that the offspring are genetically identical to the parent).

Binary fission, which is seen in bacteria and many protozoa, is perhaps the simplest form of asexual reproduction. For example, when an amoeba has grown to a certain optimum size, the nucleus undergoes mitotic division and the cytoplasm undergoes cleavage into two halves producing two new daughter amoebae.

The production of specialized asexual reproductive **spores** is commonly seen, especially in parasitic and saprophytic micro-organisms such as the bacteria and the fungi, where the production of vast numbers of easily dispersible spores ensures successful transference to a new food source.

When, in plants, a part of the parental vegetative plant body separates and grows into a new individual, the term **vegetative reproduction** or propagation is used. This is seen in the fragmentation of the filamentous algae (e.g. *Spirogyra*) and of the gametophyte thallus of mosses and liverworts; and in a wide variety of specialized structures such as **runners** (surface horizontal stems, e.g. strawberry) **stolons** (ends of shoots which root, e.g. blackberry), **rhizomes** (horizontal underground stems which become swollen, e.g. iris), **bulbs** (swollen leaves, e.g. daffodil), **corms** (vertical underground swollen stem, e.g. crocus), **tubers** (underground swollen shoot tips, e.g. potato), and **swollen tuberous roots** (e.g. dahlia).

Many of the structures mentioned are organs of **perennation**, that is they store food for the future growth of the plant. Vegetative reproduction only truly occurs when parts separate from these structures to give rise to new individuals.

Apomixis is a form of asexual reproduction which has a superficial similarity to normal sexual reproduction.

It includes **parthenogenesis**, in which the female gametes develop into offspring without fertilization. For example aphids habitually produce diploid eggs by mitosis, which develop without fertilization by male gametes, into wingless females. In the honeybee the fertile male drones develop from unfertilized haploid eggs at certain times.

Sexual reproduction involves the fusion of the nuclei of male and female sex cells or gametes, in a process known as **fertilization.**

The gametes are **haploid,** that is they each contain one complete set of chromosomes, and they fuse to form a **diploid zygote** with two complete sets of chromosomes.

Diploid cells form haploid cells by a process of **meiosis** or reduction division, in which the chromosome number is halved. In animals, meiosis occurs during gametogenesis, shown in Fig 3.1 and 3.2.

In plants, if there is an alternation of generations between a diploid sporophyte and a haploid gametophyte, meiosis occurs during spore formation (sporogenesis).

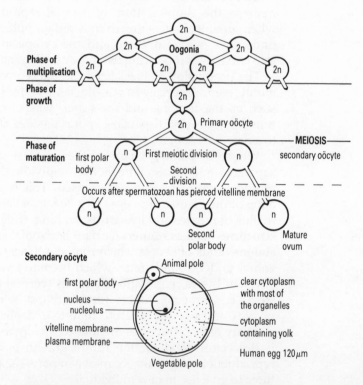

Fig 3.1. *Gametogenesis in the mammalian female (oogenesis).* The polar bodies take no part in reproduction and disappear, thus only one functional female gamete (ovum) is produced from each primary oocyte.

Certain genetic 'mixing' events, which occur during meiosis and the subsequent random fusion of gametes, result in genetic variation in the offspring which can be of adaptive advantage.

In most plants and animals the female gamete is larger and non-motile, and the male gamete is smaller and motile, that is they are

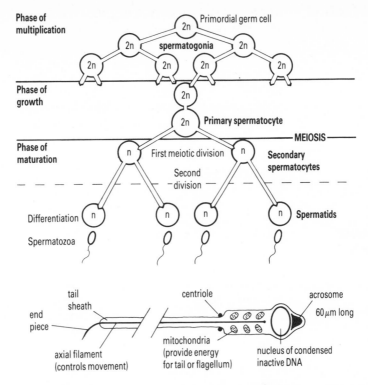

Fig 3.2. *Gametogenesis in the mammalian male (spermatogenesis).* During copulation the spermatozoa are deposited in the vagina of the female and swim up through the uterus and fallopian tubes by lashing movements of the tail.

anisogamous or **heterogamous**, and the type of fertilization is known as **oogamy**. Individual organisms can be either single sexed (dioecious) or **hermaphrodite** (monoecious) with both male and female organs. Hermaphrodite organisms may be self-fertilizing, or they may have outbreeding mechanisms which favour or compel cross fertilization with another hermaphrodite organism.

Where an animal species has separate sexes, the males and females usually have distinctly different appearances (sexual dimorphism).

EXERCISE ▶

Exercise 3.1

Which of the following statements is false?

(*a*)   *Asexual reproduction involves mitotic cell division.*

(*b*)   *Asexually produced offspring are genetically identical to their parents.*

(*c*)   *Sexual reproduction involves meiotic cell division.*

(*d*)   *Sexually produced offspring show genetic variation.*

(*e*)   *In all organisms with sexual reproduction, meiosis immediately precedes gamete formation.*

SEXUAL REPRODUCTION IN PLANTS

There is a variety of patterns of life cycles in the plant kingdom. The primitive algae and many fungi have haploid adult stages which arise as a result of meiosis occurring in the diploid zygote; such a life cycle is known as **haplontic.**

Some algae and fungi have **diplontic** life cycles in which the adults are diploid and produce haploid gametes by meiosis (as in all animals).

All other plants have **diplohaplontic** life cycles with **alternating diploid sporophyte** and **haploid gametophyte** generations.

If the two generations are vegetatively similar such alternation of generations is referred to as **isomorphic**, and if they are dissimilar it is referred to as **heteromorphic.**

ALTERNATION OF GENERATIONS

In the alternation of generations the haploid gametophyte stage produces haploid gametes which fuse to form a diploid zygote. This develops into a diploid sporophyte stage which in turn produces haploid spores by meiosis. The haploid spores develop into another haploid gametophyte plant body or thallus.

This is most clearly seen in the Bryophytes and Pteridophytes, and can be traced through to the development of the seed habit in the Spermatophyta.

BRYOPHYTES

In the Bryophytes (liverworts and mosses) the gametophyte generation is the dominant generation, and the sporophyte generation is completely dependent upon it (Fig 3.3).

In liverworts e.g. *Pellia* the gametophyte generation is represented by a small, green, heart-shaped prothallus about 10 mm long. Male gametes (spermatozoids or antherozoids) are produced in antheridia and female gametes (oospheres) are produced in archegonia. Fertilization is achieved by the spermatozoids swimming in a film of moisture towards an oosphere in an archegonium, attracted by a chemical secretion (**chemotaxis**). Thus fertilization is dependent on the presence of water in which the male gametes can swim (**zoidogamous fertilization**).

The diploid zygote resulting from fertilization develops into the sporophyte generation, which is represented by a simple sporangium with a foot to absorb water and nutrients from the gametophyte and a stalk or seta which raises the sporangium capsule into the air. Inside the capsule, diploid spore mother cells give rise to haploid spores by meiosis.

The spores are released by the dehiscence of the capsule, and germinate under suitable conditions to form new gametophyte prothalli.

The life cycle of mosses is essentially the same, except the gametophyte is represented by a more elaborate plant with root-like rhizoids, a stem, and leaf-like structures (there are 'leafy' liverworts as well). Also the sporangium capsule has a more complex dehiscence mechanism with an elaborate toothed peristome which opens when dry and closes when moist.

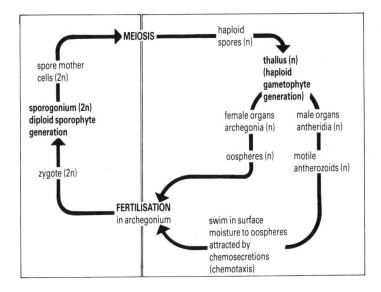

Fig 3.3. *Bryophyte life cycle.* Note that the sporophyte is completely dependent upon the gametophyte.

PTERIDOPHYTES

In the Pteridophytes the gametophyte is also an inconspicuous green prothallus 6–12 mm long and fertilization is zoidogamous, but the diploid sporophyte is only dependent on the haploid gametophyte for the early part of its development. At a very early stage it develops true roots, stems and leaves, and grows into the completely independent and dominant sporophyte plant. The sporangia are borne on leaves known as **sporophylls**, and produce haploid spores by meiosis (Fig 3.4).

Asexual vegetative reproduction of the gametophyte thallus of the Bryophyta (liverworts and mosses) and of the sporophyte plant of the Pteridophyta (ferns and bracken) can perpetuate the species without the alternation of generation necessarily occurring. For example, bracken can grow and spread by means of its strong rhizome in dry sandy soil, where conditions prevent the germination of the spores into the haploid gametophyte.

EXERCISE ▶

Exercise 3.2
Which of the following statements is incorrect:
(a) *The gametophytes of both Bryophytes and Pteridophytes are capable of photosynthesis.*

(i)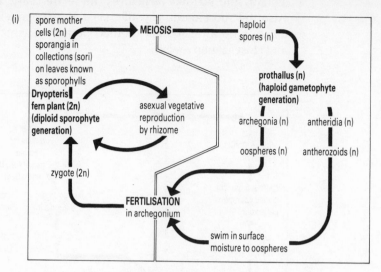

(ii)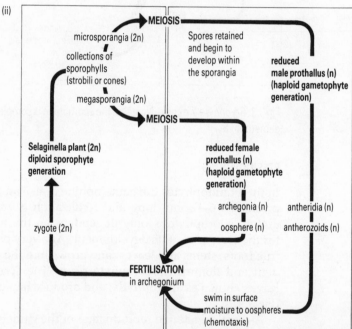

Fig 3.4. *Pteridophyte life cycles* (i) *Life cycle of Dryopteris felix mas (Class Filicatae).* Note that the dominant sporophyte is only dependent on the gametophyte for a short time after fertilization. The sporophyte soon develops true roots, leaves and stem (an underground rhizome) and becomes a fully terrestrial plant. (ii) *Life cycle of Selaginella (Class Lycopodiatae).* Note that the early development of the gametophyte is dependent on the sporophyte.

(b)   The 'leaves' of a moss plant are not homologous with the leaves of a fern plant, i.e. they are not of the same developmental origin.

(c)   In the Bryophytes and the Pteridophytes new sporophytes only arise from the diploid zygote of the gametophyte generation.

(d)   The sporophyte of Bryophytes is dependent upon the gametophyte, but in the Pteridophytes the sporophyte becomes an independent plant.

SIGNIFICANCE OF HAPLOIDY AND DIPLOIDY IN PLANT LIFE CYCLES

HAPLOIDY

The haploid phase has only one set of chromosomes, therefore:

1 all the genes are expressed in the phenotype.
2 any mutations will be expressed in the phenotype.

DIPLOIDY

The diploid phase has two sets of chromosomes, therefore:

1 dominant alleles are expressed in the phenotype
2 recessive alleles are only expressed in the phenotype when present in double dose (homozygous recessive).
3 only dominant mutations will be expressed as they arise; recessive mutations will only be expressed when two come together to form a homozygous recessive as a result of fertilization.

DEVELOPMENT OF THE SEED HABIT

The seed-bearing plants, or Spermatophyta (the Gymnosperms and the Angiosperms) are the dominant terrestrial group of plants. The plants themselves are the diploid sporophyte generation, and the gametophyte generation is greatly reduced and enclosed by the sporophyte issues (Fig 3.5).

Some Pteridophyta, for example *Selaginella* in the class Lycopodiatae, are **heterosporous**, that is they produce two different types of spores: the smaller microspores and the larger megaspores. The microspores give rise to the male gametophytes which bear only male reproductive organs (antheridia), and the megaspores give rise to the female gametophytes which bear only female reproductive organs (archegonia).

In *Selaginella* both types of spores begin their development into gametophytes whilst still inside the microsporangia and megasporangia of the sporophyte (which are borne on the sporophylls grouped together to form strobili or cones). This development is dependent upon food reserves stored in the spores by the sporophyte plant. Both gametophytes are eventually released from the sporophyte and fertilization is achieved by the motile male gametes (antherozoids) swimming in a film of moisture to the female gametes (oospheres) in the archegonia of the female gametophyte.

In the Spermatophyta this trend towards the retention of the gametophyte by the sporophyte, and the consequent dependence of the gametophyte on the sporophyte, is carried to completion.

In the Spermatophyta the gametophytes are very reduced and develop within the walls of the spores. The megaspore and the female gametophyte are completely retained in the megasporangium, on the megasporophyll of the sporophyte; and the microspore and its male gametophyte (reduced to one or two nuclei), are transferred as pollen to the megasporophyll in the process of **pollination.** The microspore or pollen grain develops a pollen tube down which the male gametes pass to the female gametes, in a process of **siphonogamous fertilization** which is not dependent on the presence of free water, and is thus well adapted to the terrestrial environment. The fertilized zygote (oospore) develops into the embryo sporophyte of the next generation within the megasporangium walls, which form the protective coverings or integuments of the structure now known as the seed.

In the Gymnosperms the seed remains exposed on the surface of the megasporophyll (or ovuliferous scale), collections of which form the female cones; whereas in the Angiosperms the megasporophyll

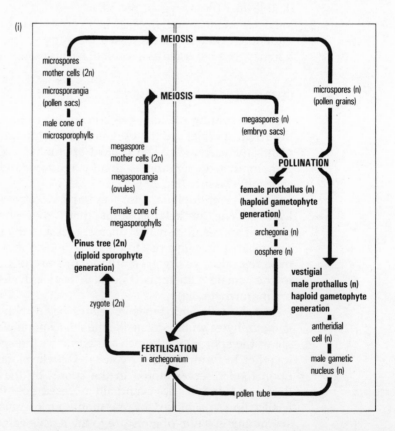

Fig 3.5. *Spermatophyte life cycles* (i) *Gymnosperm life cycle, Pinus sylvestris (Class Pinatae).* (ii) *Angiosperm life cycle.*

(ii)

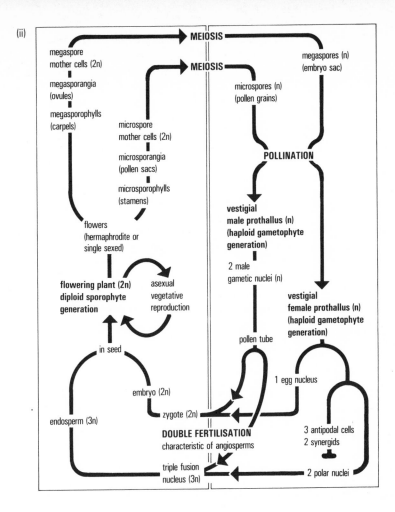

encloses the seed in an ovary, the wall of which develops into the fruit after fertilization.

EXERCISE ▶

Exercise 3.3
Match the following lettered items, which refer to various structures in the reproductive parts of flowering plants, to the appropriate numbered items which refer to various homologous structures in the alternation of generation.
A: Stamens, B: Pollen sac, C: Pollen grains, D: Carpel, E: Ovule.
1: Microspore, 2: Megasporophyll, 3: Microsporophyll, 4: Megasporangium, 5: Microsporangium.

COMMENT ▶

The alternation of generations in plant life cycles is a major concept of biology. Once the basic pattern of the alternation of generations is understood, it provides a unifying theme for the study of the plant life cycles, from the Bryophyta to the Spermatophyta, which enables them to be learned more easily.

FLOWER STRUCTURE

There are four sets of floral parts, the female **gynoecium** of carpels, the male **androecium** of stamens, the **corolla** of petals, and the **calyx** of sepals, which are borne either in whorls (circles) or in spirals on the swollen receptacle of the flower stalk or pedicel. Flowers may be solitary, or occur in groups known as **inflorescences**.

Fig. 3.6. Half flower (e.g. buttercup).

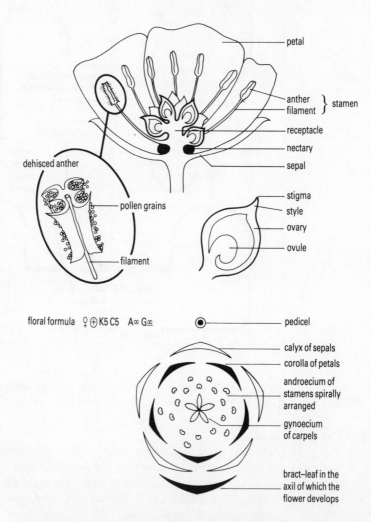

Fig 3.7. *Floral structure and floral formulae.* A floral diagram is a 'ground plan' of the flower showing the relative positions of the parts. A floral formula is a 'shorthand' way of describing the floral structure. Flowers with separated or free floral parts are considered to be less highly developed than those with fused and often reduced floral parts. Dicotyledon flowers usually have floral parts in fours or fives or multiples of these numbers.

Monocotyledon flowers usually have floral parts in threes or multiples of threes. Flowers can be single-sexed or hermaphrodite.

POLLINATION

Pollination is the transfer of pollen from the anther lobes of the stamens to the stigma of the carpel(s), either of the same flower (self-pollination) or a flower on another plant of the same species (cross-pollination) (Fig 3.8).

Self-pollinating flowers often have the stamens arranged so that the pollen can fall onto the stigma(s), and many self-pollinate in the bud before the flower opens (e.g. garden pea).

Cross-pollinating flowers may be either single sex, where cross-pollination is inevitable (e.g. willow); or hermaphrodite, where various devices favour cross-pollination and decrease the chances of accidental self-pollination (e.g. most Angiosperm flowers).

Some flowers have their parts so arranged as to lessen the chance of self-pollination (e.g. primrose); in some the anthers mature first (**protandry**) (e.g. daisy).

In others (less commonly) the carpels mature first (**protogyny**), (e.g. hawthorn).

Some have genetically controlled self-sterility incompatibility mechanisms by which the growth of the pollen tube of their pollen is slowed or stopped on their own stigma (e.g. primrose).

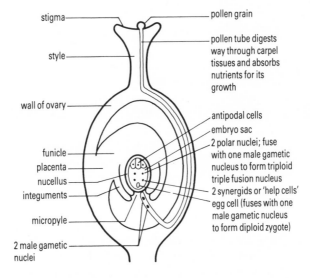

Fig 3.8. *Pollination and fertilization in Angiosperms.* One male gametic nucleus fuses with the ovum nucleus, and the second male nucleus fuses with the two polar nuclei, in a process of double fertilization which is unique to the Angiosperms. The triploid 'triple fusion nucleus' can divide to give the endosperm food store tissue of endospermous seeds e.g. maize or it can degenerate, as in non-endospermous seeds e.g. pea. The fertilized ovum develops into the embryo plant. The integuments develop into the seed coats or testa. The ovary wall develops into the pericarp or fruit.

Table 3.1 Comparison of wind- and insect-pollinated flowers

Wind-pollinated (anemophilous)	Insect-pollinated (entomophilous)
(1) Relatively small inconspicuous flowers, with no scent or nectar. Often pendulous inflorescences of male flowers (catkins) hanging in wind.	Relatively large, brightly coloured flowers, with scent and nectar.
(2) Large, loose, protruding anthers.	Smaller anthers arranged so as to come in contact with insect visitors.
(3) Large amounts of small, light, smooth pollen grains easily carried by wind.	Smaller amounts of larger, ridged or spiked pollen grains to attach to insects.
(4) Large, protruding, feathery stigmas to catch wind-borne pollen.	Smaller, often sticky, stigmas arranged to come in contact with insect visitors.
e.g. Grasses, willow, hazel	e.g. Buttercup, clover

FRUITS AND SEEDS

After pollination and fertilization the ovule develops into a seed and the ovary wall develops into the fruit or pericarp. Sometimes the receptacle enlarges to form a false fruit.

Fruits are classified according to the number of carpels involved in their structure, their nature (i.e. dry or succulent), and type of dehiscence.

TYPES OF FRUIT

1 **Dry** (i)**Indehiscent**, pericarp does not open to allow seed to escape, both pericarp and test are ruptured when the embryo germinates.

(*a*) **Single carpel**

Achenes with thin or leathery pericarp.

Nuts: achenes, typically with woody pericarp, e.g. oak (*Quercus*), beech (*Fagus*), hazel (*Corylus*).

Caryopsis: achenes in which pericarp is fused to the testa, e.g. cereal grains (wheat, oat, barley, maize, rice).

Samara: achene with pericarp expanded into one or more membranous wings, e.g. elm (*Ulmus*), ash (*Fraxinus*).

Cypsela: formed from an inferior ovary, often with persistent plumed calyx used in dispersal, typical of the Compositae, e.g. dandelion.

(*b*) **Two or more carpels**

Schizocarps: many seeded fruits which on ripening split up into a number of one-seeded achene-like parts, e.g. sycamore (*Acer*).

(ii)**Dehiscent**, pericarp breaks open naturally while still on plant to allow seeds to escape.

(*a*) **Single carpel**

Follicle: pod which splits down one side, e.g. delphinium.

Legume: pod which splits down both sides e.g. bean.

(*b*) **Two carpels**

(i) **Siliqua:** special type of capsule with two carpels divided by a central false septum, e.g. wallflower.

(ii) **Silicula:** shorter and broader form of siliqua, e.g. shepherd's purse.

(c) **Two or more carpels**

Capsules: carpels open by slits, pores or teeth to allow escape of the seeds, e.g. poppy.

2 Succulent

The pericarp wall is swollen and succulent.

(*a*) **Drupes** or **'stone' fruits**, formed from a single carpel. Pericarp has outer epicarp or skin, a middle fleshy mesocarp and a hard woody endocarp forming the 'stone' which encloses the seed, e.g. plum, cherry, peach.

(*b*) **Berries** differ from drupes in not having a stony endocarp, the hard seeds are embedded in the pulpy mesocarp and endocarp, e.g. tomato, marrow, gooseberry.

3 False fruits

In some the receptacle enlarges and becomes succulent whilst the true fruits may be relatively inconspicuous, e.g. the 'seeds' of strawberries are in fact the true fruit (achenes); and the apple, where the 'core' corresponds to the true fruit. In others the inflorescence becomes fruit-like, e.g. pineapple and fig.

DISPERSAL

Indehiscent fruit are dispersed with the seeds, whereas with dehiscent fruit the seeds alone are dispersed.

Wind dispersal

Many fruits are winged, as in elm, ash and sycamore; or plumed as in dandelion, to aid their lift. Some seeds are dust-like and are easily blown away, and yet others are ejected into air currents as the fruit sways in the wind, e.g. censer mechanisms as in the poppy capsule.

Mechanical dispersal

Some fruits are explosive, dispersing their seeds by some sudden mechanical action, often generated by tensions set up by the drying of the fruit wall, e.g. pods of leguminous plants such as gorse and broom, and lupin.

Animal dispersal

Many seeds and fruits have hooks and spines to attach to animal fur; and the seeds of succulent fruits are dispersed by the animals feeding on them, either by sticking to their beaks and feet, or by passing through their intestine undigested.

Water dispersal

Many fruits and seeds are dispersed 'accidentally' by water, but some are especially adapted with air cavities and buoyant outgrowths, e.g. alder and water lily.

EXERCISE ➤

Exercise 3.4

Which of the following statements is incorrect?

(*a*)   *After pollination and fertilization the ovary wall develops into the fruit.*

(*b*)   *Indehiscent fruit open when ripe to allow the seeds to escape.*

(*c*)   *The receptacle can enlarge to form a false fruit.*

(*d*)   *The seeds of succulent fruits are often dispersed by animals.*

(*e*)   *In some plants the entire inflorescence can become fruit-like.*

SEXUAL REPRODUCTION IN MAMMALS

MALE REPRODUCTIVE SYSTEM

The male urinogenital system is shown in Fig 3.9. The testis is a tubular organ, composed of semeniferous tubules which produce spermatozoa by the process of spermatogenesis.

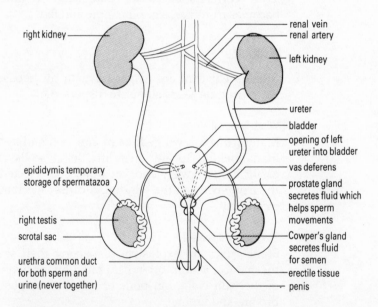

Fig 3.9. Male mammalian urinogenital system (ventral view).

FEMALE REPRODUCTIVE SYSTEM

The female urinogenital system is shown in Fig 3.10, and the structure of the mammalian ovary in Fig 3.11.

Pituitary gonadotrophic hormones control the cyclic activity of the ovary, which in turn regulates the cyclic changes in the rest of the female system by the secretion of the ovarian hormones.

During the first half of the cycle the developing **Graafian follicle** secretes **oestrogen** which stimulates the growth and blood supply of the lining of the uterus.

These changes prepare the uterus for the reception of the developing egg, should fertilization occur.

After ovulation the Graafian follicle becomes the **corpus luteum** and secretes the hormone **progesterone** which maintains and reinforces the preparations for pregnancy.

Fig 3.10. Female mammalian urinogenital system (ventral view).

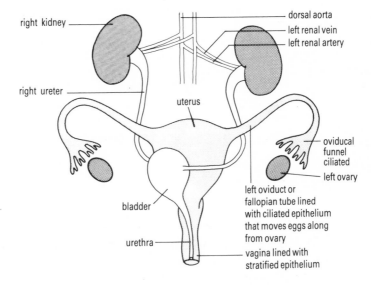

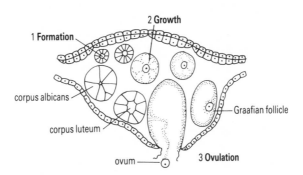

Fig 3.11. *Structure of the mammalian ovary.* (1) *Formation*: the germinal epithelium produces follicles. (2) *Growth*: the follicle enlarges to form a mature Graafian follicle, the wall of which secretes the oestrogen which controls the changes in the female system in the first half of the menstrual cycle. (3) *Ovulation* in the human female occurs on the 14th day of the 28-day cycle.

The corpus luteum secretes progesterone which controls changes in the second half of the cycle.

If fertilization does not occur, the corpus luteum degenerates, the levels of oestrogen and progesterone drop, and the lining of the uterus breaks down and is eliminated as the menstrual flow in humans.

If fertilization occurs (usually in the oviducts), the developing zygote embeds itself in the wall of the uterus (**implantation**). In the ovary the corpus luteum persists and enlarges, and continues to secrete progesterone which maintains the pregnancy until the placenta develops and begins to secrete **placental progesterone** which maintains the pregnancy until birth.

EXERCISE ▶

Exercise 3.5

The events occurring in the female system following fertilization of the egg are best illustrated by the sequence:

(a)   Graafian follicle → progesterone → implantation of the fertilized egg → disappearance of the corpus luteum → low level of oestrogen.

(b)   Graafian follicle → oestrogen → proliferation and vascularization of the uterus → implantation of the fertilized egg → persistence and enlargement of the corpus luteum → high level of progesterone maintained.

(c)   Graafian follicle → oestrogen → implantation of the fertilized egg → proliferation and vascularization of the uterus → persistence and enlargement of the Graafian follicle → low level of progesterone.

PLACENTA

The placenta is composed of both fetal and maternal tissues, and serves for attachment and physiological exchange by a combination of diffusion and active transfer processes over the large surface area of the placental villi.

Functions

1   Embryo takes up:

(*a*)   nutrients e.g. monosaccharides, amino acids, fatty acids, vitamins, mineral ions, water.

(*b*)   oxygen, as foetal haemoglobin has a greater affinity oxygen than maternal haemoglobin.

(*c*)   antibodies.

(*d*)   heat.

2   Embryo gets rid of

(*a*)   carbon dioxide.

(*b*)   nitrogenous wastes e.g. urea.

3   Produces hormones that prevent ovulation and menstruation e.g. progesterone.

4   Prevents mixing of the foetal and maternal circulations which is necessary because:

(*a*)   maternal blood pressure would be too high.

(*b*)   maternal hormones would be incompatible with the foetus, especially if male.

(*c*)   pathogens from the mother would infect the foetus (some in fact do e.g. German measles, VD).

(*d*)   toxins could be passed on from the mother (some in fact are e.g. alcohol, drugs, nicotine etc.)

(*e*)   maternal antibodies and white blood cells would attack the 'foreign' protein of the foetus.

(*f*)   maternal Rhesus blood groups may be incompatible.

(*g*)   maternal waste products would be toxic.

This type of development with a placenta and the young being born alive is known as **viviparity.** Other animals such as some insects, snails, fish, lizards, and snakes can retain their eggs inside their body until they hatch and the young are subsequently born alive. However in this process (known as **ovoviviparity**) the developing young are always separated from the parent by the egg membrane.

MAMMALIAN SEX HORMONES

1 **Pituitary gonadotrophins** Pituitary hormones controlling the gonads

(*a*)   **Follicle stimulating hormone (FSH)** Stimulates growth and development of Graafian follicles in ovary and the secretion of oestrogen. In males it initiates sperm formation.

(*b*)   **Interstitial cell stimulating hormone (ICSH) or luteinising hormone (LH)** Stimulates ovulation and the formation of the corpus luteum. In males it stimulates the secretion of testosterone by the testes.

2 **Testes hormones**

Androgens, e.g. **testosterone** Controls development of primary and secondary sexual characteristics.

3 *Ovarian hormones*

(*a*)   **Oestrogens** Control development of primary and secondary sexual characteristics, and the development of the lining of the uterus in the first half of the oestrous cycle. Stimulates pituitary to secrete LH.

(*b*)   **Progesterone** Controls the development of changes in the second half of the oestrous cycle, which it maintains in the event of pregnancy. Inhibits FSH and therefore other follicles are stopped from developing (this is the basis of the contraceptive pill).

GROWTH

The definition of growth presents certain difficulties. The definition of growth as an increase in size, volume, or fresh weight, is not specific enough; as organisms may take up extra water which would produce the same effect; also non-living things may grow in this sense.

An increase in dry weight can also occur in non-living objects; and also it is possible for organisms to be growing and yet to be losing dry weight, for example germinating seedlings.

A more accurate definition of growth would be an increase in size accompanied by an irreversible increase in complexity.

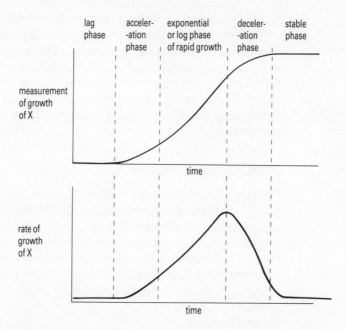

Fig 3.12. General growth curve typical of individuals and populations.

GROWTH AND DEVELOPMENT IN PLANTS

GERMINATION

Some seeds germinate as soon as conditions are right, but others remain dormant for a certain period of time before germinating.

Requirements for germination

1 Moisture.
2 Oxygen.
3 Temperature of a suitable level.
4 Some require presence or absence of light.
5 Removal of any inhibitors in fruit or testa.
6 Some require mechanical abrasion of testa.

Once germination begins there are two major phases:

the **hydration phase** whereby water enters the seed and the cytoplasm regains its activity;

the **metabolic phase** in which the enzyme controlled hydrolysis of the food stores and their resynthesis into the materials for growth and development occurs.

In **hypogeal** germination the cotyledons remain below the soil surface, e.g. broad bean.

In **epigeal** germination the cotyledons are raised above the ground and act as the first photosynthetic leaves of the seedling, e.g. sunflower.

GROWTH OF DICOTYLEDONS

All Dicotyledons have the same basic pattern of early growth, however herbaceous Dicotyledons generally lack the secondary thickening seen in shrubs and trees.

Stems

The stem grows by means of divisions of its apical meristem, and procambial strands of dividing meristem cells are produced which differentiate into the xylem and phloem of the vascular bundle.

The vascular elements differentiated from the meristem cells of the procambial strand are known as **primary tissues.** Primary xylem consists of elements differentiated in the zone of elongation (protoxylem), and those differentiated when the stem has stopped elongating in that zone (metaxylem).

The same terms apply to the phloem tissues.

Secondary xylem and phloem are produced by divisions of the vascular cambium after the primary tissues have differentiated.

With secondary thickening, the outer regions are stretched and ruptured, and a protective layer of cork (phellem) is formed by the cock cambium (phellogen) which arises in the outer regions of the stem. At intervals lenticels of loosely packed cork cells allow for gaseous exchange through the otherwise impermeable cork layers.

Monocotyledons differ from the Dicotyledons in having irregularly arranged vascular bundles which have no cambium. There is therefore no secondary thickening and Monocotyledons are generally herbaceous. Intercalary meristems at the bases of internodes of shoots produce increase in length, for example in grasses where the arrangement allows grass to be continually cut or grazed.

EXERCISE ▶

Exercise 3.6
Which of the following statements is correct?
(a)   Primary tissues are formed by divisions of the vascular cambium.
(b)   Protoxylem and protophloem are formed in the zone of elongation.
(c)   Secondary tissues are formed by divisions of the apical meristems.
(d)   Secondary xylem repeatedly divides to form concentric rings during secondary thickening.

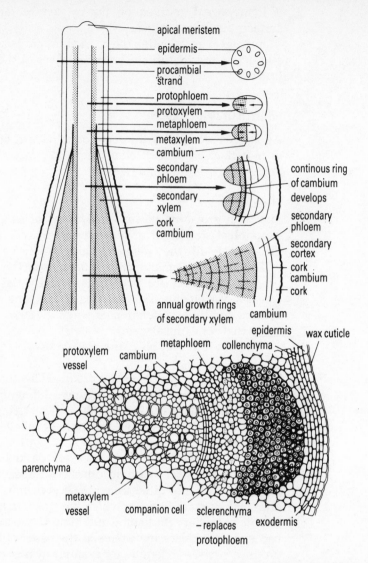

Fig 3.13. *Structure of the dicotyledon stem (LS and TS).* The arrows indicate the position of the transverse sections shown on the right of the longitudinal section.

Roots

Roots also grow by means of apical meristems. As the root grows by divisions of its apical meristem, a protective root cap is continually being formed and worn away as the root pushes through the soil. At the same time a central procambial strand is produced which gives rise to the vascular tissue.

COMMENT ▶ Try to understand the sequence of events in secondary thickening. Once the sequence is understood the details fall into place and are more easily learnt. Also familiarize yourself with slides and photomicrographs of the various stages, as these frequently appear in examinations.

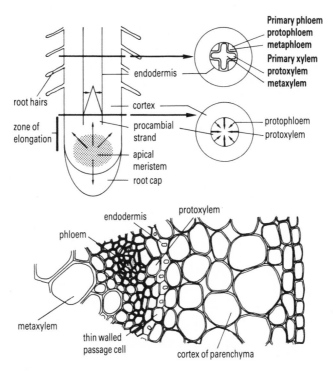

Fig 3.14. *Structure of the dicotyledon root (LS and TS).* The arrows indicate the position of the transverse sections shown on the right of the longitudinal section.

GROWTH AND DEVELOPMENT IN ANIMALS

METAMORPHOSIS IN INSECTS

Incomplete or **hemimetabolous metamorphosis** is said to occur when the young (**nymphs**) resemble the adult, and change gradually through a number of stages (**instars**) between moults (**ecdyses**). Wings, when present, develop externally, and these insects are known as the **Exopterygota**, e.g. locust.

LOCUST LIFE CYCLE

The eggs are laid in damp sand and take about 12 days to hatch (at

30°C). A small vermiform (worm-like) larva emerges, wriggles to the surface and almost immediately undergoes a first moult to give the first instar. There follows a period of feeding and growing in which the flightless nymphs (known as 'hoppers') undergo a series of moults and instars before emerging from the last moult as the winged adult. After a further 2–4 weeks the young adults can mate.

Egg→ vermiform larva

1st moult→ 1st instar (5 days)*

2nd moult→ 2nd instar (4 days)

3rd moult→ 3rd instar (4 days)

4th moult→ 4th instar (5 days)

5th moult→ 5th instar (8 days)

6th moult→ young adult (or imago)

*Lengths of stages at 34°C.

Complete or **holometabolous metamorphosis** is said to occur when the young (**larvae**) do not resemble the adults, into which they change during a **pupal stage.** Wings when present, develop internally, and these insects are known as the **Endopterygota**, e.g. butterflies and moths.

Metamorphosis is under hormonal control.

In the head a pair of glands known as the **corpora allata** secrete the hormone **neotonin** or juvenile hormone, which favours the growth of larval structures and suppresses the development of adult structures.

Another pair of glands in the head secrete a trophic hormone which stimulates the prothoracic or **ecdysial glands** in the first segment of the thorax.

These secrete **ecdysone** or moulting hormone, which initiates ecdysis and stimulates the growth of adult structures.

METAMORPHOSIS IN AMPHIBIA

The pituitary secretes the hormone **prolactin** which promotes the growth of the larval stages (tadpoles) but retards the onset of metamorphosis into the adult.

Eventually the hypothalamus of the brain secretes a neurosecretion which stimulates the pituitary to secrete **thyroid stimulating hormone** (TSH).

This stimulates the thyroid to increase the secretion of **thyroxine** which is involved in the metamorphosis of the tadpole into the adult.

EXPERIMENTAL WORK

GERMINATION

Simple experiments with germinating seeds can demonstrate the conditions necessary for germination. For example a bag of soaked seeds suspended in a closed vessel, over a fresh solution of pyrogallate of potash (pyrogallic acid crystals dissolved in excess potassium hydroxide) which absorbs oxygen, will not germinate; whilst those in a control vessel without pyrogallate do germinate.

The action of enzymes in the metabolic phase of germination can be demonstrated by placing germinating seeds on 1% starch agar, incubating for a few days, and then flooding the plate with iodine solution (see Chapter 1).

GROWTH

The growth in length of a flowering plant stem can be measured over a period of several days or weeks by means of a growth lever (Fig 3.15).

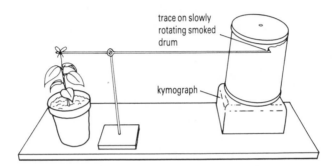

Fig 3.15. *The growth lever.* The unequal arms are balanced by adding weights to the short arm. As the shoot grows the pointer travels downwards. The ratio of the long arm to the short arm equals the ratio of the amount moved by the long arm to the amount of actual growth. Such experiments can be used to show the daily periodicity of plant growth by which plants grow more rapidly at night than they do in the day (in constant temperature).

Although the length of time this experiment takes precludes its direct use in practical examinations, it could (like other long lasting experiments) be set up as a demonstration, and/or a copy of the trace could be supplied for interpretation.

The actual zone of elongation of a stem (or a root) in which the growth in length occurs can be demonstrated by marking the stem with close, equally spaced, parallel inked lines, which spead out as the cells in the zone of elongation extend.

QUESTION ▶

Q.   Show by means of a labelled diagram the internal structure of an ovule in a flowering plant. (8)
Give an outline account of the development of the seed in dicotyledonous plants. (12)

This question requires an 'outline account' of a complex process that varies in detail in different dicotyledons, therefore the principle processes must be described here in general.

OUTLINE ▶ ANSWER

Ovule structure (8)
See Fig 2.8 p. 54
Seed development. (12)
Note that details of fertilization are not required.
Fertilized diploid zygote undergoes nuclear and cell division;
gives rise to a row of cells the pro-embryo;
the cell at the end furthest from the micropyle divides into eight cells (octants) known as the embryonal mass;
remaining cells of pro-embryo constitute the suspensor which can act as a food absorbing organ;
embryonal mass differentiates into embryo, with plumule, two cotyledons (seed leaves) and hypocotyl (seedling stem below cotyledons);
radicle grows from terminal cell of suspensor or hypophysis cell;
triple fusion nucleus gives rise to triploid endosperm;
endosperm may or may not develop into a food storage tissue;
nucellus typically disappears (may form food store – perisperm);
integuments form protective coverings, inner tegmen and outer testa or seed coat;
micropyle persists as a pore in the testa.

QUESTIONS

1 'Non-sexual reproduction produces offspring identical with the parent, whereas sexual reproduction produces variation'. Discuss this statement.   (LOND)

2 Which one of the following statements about gametogenesis in Man is the most accurate?
    A   The primary spermatocyte gives rise to 4 sperms and the primary oocyte gives rise to 4 ova.
    B   The primary spermatocyte gives rise to 4 sperms and the primary oocyte gives rise to one ovum.
    C   The spermatids give rise to sperms by meiosis.
    D   The spermatids give rise to sperms by mitosis. (CAM)

3 Write a comparative account of gametogenesis and fertilization in the flowering plant and the mammal.   (W)

4 With reference to the life cycles of a moss or liverwort, a fern and a flowering plant explain the term 'alternation of generations'.
                                                                   (LOND)

5 What do you understand by the term *gametophyte generation*?
    Describe and compare the gametophyte generation in three different types of plant.   (O&C)

6   In the life history of ferns, meiosis occurs during
    A   germination of the zygote
    B   formation of the spores
    C   germination of the spores
    D   formation of the gametes   (CAM)

7   Which one of the following usually has the haploid number of chromosomes during the vegetative phase of its life cycle?
    A   green alga
    B   fern
    C   herbaceous Monocotyledon
    D   woody Dicotyledon   (CAM)

8   (*a*)   In angiosperms the microsporophyll is represented by the anther.
What represents the megasporophyll?
(*b*)   The mature female gametophyte consists of an embryo sac containing eight haploid nuclei; one of these is the egg nucleus and two others form the primary endosperm nuclei.
Of what does the mature male gametophyte consist?
Using the information given in part (*b*) of the question, and your answer to it, briefly explain how fertilization in flowering plants is brought about.   (O)

9   The diagram below shows a vertical section of an angiosperm ovary with two ovules at the time of fertilization.

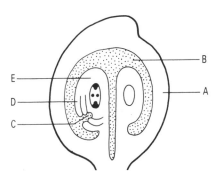

(i) Name the features labelled **A, B, C, D** and **E.**
(ii) State what happens to each of these features after fertilization has occurred.

10 The diagram shows a longitudinal section of a fruit containing a single seed.

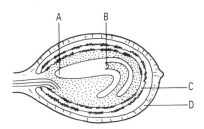

Use the letters in the diagram to indicate which part
    (i) will form the root system.
    (ii) will form the shoot system.
    (iii) is formed from the ovary wall.
    (iv) is formed from the integuments of the developing ovule.
                    (JMB)

11   The diagram shows a half flower which is insect pollinated.

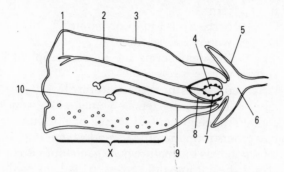

(*a*)   Name the parts labelled 1–10.
(*b*)   Give *one* function for each of the parts numbered 1, 5, 7 and 8.
(*c*)   Suggest a possible function for the pattern of markings in the
region marked X.
(*d*)   Give *three* changes in the flower that result from pollination.
(*e*)   Give *four* differences between this flower and a typical wind-
pollinated flower.   (LOND)

12   (*a*)   (i) In the list below underline **all** of the features which relate
to wind-pollinated flowers.
inconspicuous flowers
long feathery stigmas
nectar present
small heavy pollen grains
abundant pollen produced
stamens enclosed within the petals
dangling, exposed anthers.
(ii) Self-pollination in a wild population often bestows a biological disadvantage on that population. Outline the reason
for this.

(*b*)   The diagrams below, not drawn to scale, show sections
through (I) a germinating pollen grain and (II) a carpel with a single
ovule.
(i) Label the male and female gametes with the letters **M** and
F respectively.
(ii) In diagram (II), draw in a single line to represent the route
taken by the pollen tube from its germination to the time of
fertilization.
(iii) 1 What is a tropism?
      2 The pollen tube exhibits **positive chemotropism.**
Explain what this means.

(I)   (II)

(iv) After fertilization has occurred, into what do carpel and ovule develop? (SCE)

13 Distinguish between pollination and fertilization in a flowering plant. Describe the pollination mechanism of a *named* insect-pollinated flower. To what extent do insects and flowering plants depend on each other? (LOND)

14 Describe an experiment which you might perform to demonstrate the necessity for one of the conditions required for the germination of the seed of a named plant. (SU)

15 The diagrams show two transverse sections of stem taken from the **same** twig.

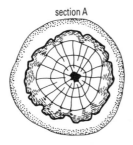
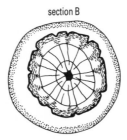

section A   section B

(i) Calculate the number of years' growth for each section.
(ii) Name the tissue you examined in order to make this calculation.
(iii) Account for the difference in age of these two sections from the same twig.
(iv) What is the structural difference between wood formed at different seasons?
(v) How does the location of areas of growth differ in animals and plants? (SCE)

16 Outline the method by which a Dicotyledonous tree increases in girth. Refer to its significance in estimating the age of the tree and the kind of growth conditions it has encountered during its life.
(SCE)

17 Phellogen is an actively dividing tissue present in some angiosperms. Where is it found?
A   in the apical zone of branches of young stems

B   in the deeper layers of the cortex between the vascular bundles of young stems

C   immediately external to the phloem in older stems

D   immediately internal to the suberized cells in older stems.

(CAM)

18   (a)   Below is a diagram of a transverse section of a woody stem.

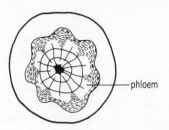

phloem

(i) Insert in the diagram a line to **represent** the cork cambium.

(ii) State the function of cork in such stems.

(iii) **Explain** why lenticels are present in cork.

(b)   The diagram shows a log of wood which has been cut in three different planes as a result of which various patterns, **X, Y** and **Z**, on the cut surfaces can be seen.

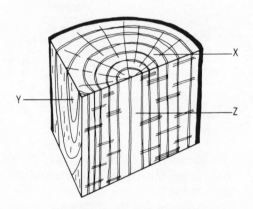

(i) Face **X** clearly shows two structural features in the xylem. What are these features?

(ii) Pattern **Z** is produced by vascular tissue and medullary rays. State the function of a medullary ray.

(iii) Such patterns, especially **Y**, are used in the manufacture of furniture to make it look more attractive. What name is given to these wood patterns?

(c)   **Briefly**, describe how water-soluble dyes can be used to provide evidence for the pathway of water movement in stems.

(SCE)

19 Explain why it is **incorrect** to state:
(*a*)   that the pollen grain of the flowering plant is equivalent to the spermatozoon of a mammal.
(*b*)   that the anther is the male organ of the flowering plant,
(*c*)   that the ovum of a mammal is equivalent to the ovule of a flowering plant.   (CAM)
20 The placenta serves as a link between foetus and mother. At the same time it acts as a barrier between them. By reference to the functions of the placenta, explain what these statements mean.   (SU)
21 The relative concentrations of certain hormones in the blood during a human oestrous cycle are shown below:

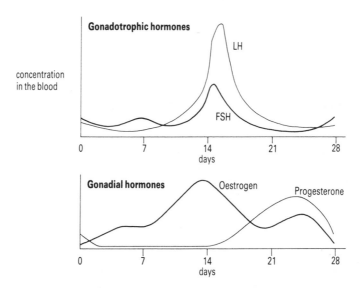

(*a*)   Indicate, on the graphs above, the positions of ovulation and menstruation in the oestrous cycle   [2]
(*b*)   State precisely where the four hormones are produced.
Follicle stimulating hormone (FSH)
Luteinising hormone (LH)
Oestrogen
Progesterone   [4]
(*c*)   State **two** effects of the increase in the levels of **each** of the gonadotrophic hormones during the early stages of the cycle.
          FSH (i)
                 (ii)
          LH (i)
                 (ii)   [4]
(*d*)   Account for the rapid fall during the fourth week of the cycle in the levels of
                 (i) oestrogen
                 (ii) progesterone   [4]

(*e*)　　Comment on the relationship between the levels of oestrogen and progesterone as shown on the graph.　　　　　　　　　[2]

(*f*)　　State **two** effects which the continued secretion of progesterone will have if the fertilised egg becomes implanted in the uterine wall.

　　　(i)

　　　(ii)　　　　　　　　　　　　　　　　　　　　　　　　　　[2]

23　In 1911, Gudernatsh, a German biologist studying the effects of different dietary conditions on tadpoles, discovered that feeding extracts of mammalian thyroid glands to the tadpoles caused them to turn abruptly into frogs and that removal of iodine from the water in which the tadpoles were living resulted in their failure to metamorphose.

(*a*)　　Comment on the likely roles of thyroid hormone and iodine in controlling metamorphosis under normal dietary conditions.

(*b*)　　Describe a series of laboratory experiments which you could carry out to investigate:

　　　(i) the effects of thyroid hormone on the metamorphosis of mature tadpoles,

　　　(ii) the role of iodine in the metamorphosis of young tadpoles.

　　　(iii) *two* other environmental factors which may stimulate the onset of metamorphosis.　　　　　　　　　　　(AEB)

NUTRITION

CONTENTS

All organisms require a supply of organic and inorganic materials to exist.

Holophytic organisms (most plants, some bacteria) synthesize all their organic materials from inorganic substances, using energy from sunlight, in the process of photosynthesis. The simplified equation of photosynthesis is:

$$CO_2 + H_2O \xrightarrow[\substack{\text{Chlorophyll} \\ \text{Enzymes}}]{\substack{\text{Light} \\ \text{energy}}} \text{Organic compounds} + O_2$$

Other inorganic nutrients are also required for the further synthesis of more complex organic compounds, such as amino acids, proteins and oils, etc.; and for general metabolism.

Chemosynthetic bacteria synthesize their organic material from inorganic substances, using energy from inorganic chemical reactions, in the process of chemosynthesis. Some of these are important in the nitrogen cycle, for example *Nitrobacter* utilizes energy released during the oxidation of nitrite to nitrate.

Photosynthetic and chemosynthetic types are also called **autotrophic** (or self feeding).

EXERCISE ▶

Exercise 4.1

How does the synthesis of organic compounds by chemosynthesis differ from the synthesis of organic compounds utilizing energy from respiration?

Answer Chemosynthesis utilizes energy from **inorganic reactions**, whereas respiration releases energy from some **organic compounds** which can subsequently be used for the synthesis of other organic compounds from simpler organic compounds. For example, in heterotrophs carbohydrates are oxidized in respiration to release energy, and this energy can be used to synthesize new protein from amino acids in the cell.

Heterotrophic organisms (animals, fungi and some bacteria) are unable to carry out photosynthesis or chemosynthesis and require a supply of organic and inorganic nutrients. Saprophytic organisms obtain their nutrients from the bodies of dead organisms by secreting enzymes and absorbing the soluble end products of digestion by diffusion through their surface. Parasitic organisms obtain their nutrients by living on or in organisms of another species.

Holozoic animals actually engulf or swallow organic matter into a cavity, in which digestion occurs.

All heterotrophic organisms ultimately depend, either directly, or indirectly via food chains, upon autotrophic organisms for their organic nutrients.

Photosynthesis is also the only source of oxygen in the environment, which is essential for the aerobic respiration of both plants and animals.

PLANT NUTRITION

INORGANIC NUTRIENTS

Various chemical elements and inorganic ions are required by plants. These elements and ions, which are sometimes referred to generally as 'minerals', are obtained by non-parasitic plants from the soil.

UPTAKE

Although the necessary mineral nutrients may be present in the soil, a complex of interactions between the minerals, and between the minerals and the soil particles, affect their availability to the plant. For example, generally clay particles in the soil have a net surface negative charge which holds positively charged cations (e.g. calcium, Ca^{2+}, magnesium, Mg^{2+}, ammonium, NH_4^+, etc.). These represent a cation store in the soil. Their uptake by the plant is usually via cation exchange mechanisms, by which the plant exchanges an unwanted cation for one that is required. The unwanted cation (e.g. hydrogen, H^+) displaces the required one (e.g. potassium, K^+) from the soil particle, and the required one is then free to be taken up.

In general, negatively charged anions (e.g. nitrate, NO_3^-, sulphate, SO_4^{2-}, etc.) are not held by the soil particles, and most are free in the soil solution. They are thus easily leached or washed from the soil and must be replaced continuously from decomposing organic matter via natural cycles, for example the nitrogen cycle.

There is no single pathway of mineral uptake. Some minerals are drawn up to the leaves in the transpiration stream through the cellulose cell walls and intercellular spaces, only passing through cell membranes and cytoplasm at the endodermal passage cells. Others are taken up into the root hair cytoplasm and then from cell to cell across the cortex to the vascular tissue, by a complex of passive and active mechanisms.

Passive uptake is mainly by diffusion, with substances passing from regions of their high concentration to regions of their low concentration, down their concentration gradient.

Active uptake mechanisms usually involve carriers which transport the minerals across the cell membrane, against their prevailing diffusion gradient, using energy from respiration.

EXERCISE ➡

Exercise 4.2
How would it be possible to determine whether the uptake of a particular mineral by a plant is passive or active?

Answer If the uptake is active, then anything that inhibits the metabolism of the plant in general and its respiration in particular, would depress the rate of uptake. If the uptake is passive, the rate of uptake should be relatively unaffected by the rate of metabolism.

TRANSPORT WITHIN THE PLANT

Once the minerals reach the xylem they are distributed in the transpiration stream to the various **sinks** or points of utilization. They mainly go to young growing regions, which actively accumulate them. Once they have reached a particular destination they may be removed by competition to another more active region, depending upon their mobility.

The mobility of the various minerals within the plant varies considerably. Sulphur, phosphorus and nitrogen are easily moved from one tissue to another; but calcium and iron are only moved with difficulty, and new regions of requirement must be supplied from the root.

These differing mobilities are reflected in the pattern of the appearance of deficiency symptoms in the leaves of plants growing in soils deficient in certain minerals. For example, the deficiency symptoms of mobile substances appear first in older leaves, and those of immobile substances appear first in the young, growing leaves.

PHOTOSYNTHESIS

In photosynthesis, light energy is trapped as chemical energy in a wide variety of stable chemical compounds.

Photosynthesis occurs in two main stages:
(a)   **A light-dependent stage** and
(b)   **a non-light dependent stage** or so-called '**dark stage**'.

Photosynthesis occurs in the chloroplastids (Fig 4.1), the 'light stage' occurring in the grana and the 'dark stage' in the stroma.

LIGHT STAGE

The light stage is summarized in Fig 4.3. Light is absorbed by the chlorophyll in the grana of the chloroplastids; accessory pigments such as the carotenoids are also involved in the process.

The light excites the chlorophyll molecules (photoactivation) and in each molecule electrons are raised to higher energy levels.

The chlorophyll is also involved in the light dissociation or photolysis of water, which provides hydrogen ions (H^+) and hydroxyl ions (OH^-).

Table 4.1. Mineral nutrients of plants: macronutrients and micronutrients

Element Macronutrients	Form in which absorbed	Role in plant	Deficiency symptoms	Notes
Potassium	K^+	Catalyst in protein synthesis, chlorophyll formation, and carbon assimilation. Role in cell membranes and disease resistance.	Leaves have pale yellow edges, necrosis or breakdown of leaf margins and tips. Increased amount of soluble carbohydrate and 'leaf scorch' due to low water content.	Most available in acid soils. Balance of nitrogen, phosphate, and potassium (NPK) very important.
Calcium	Ca^{2+}	Component of middle lamella of cell walls, thus important in meristems.	Necrosis of terminal growing points, distortion of young leaves, chromosome abnormalities. Its absence may result in toxic amounts of magnesium entering.	Deficient in acid soils. Balance of sodium, potassium, and calcium important.
Nitrogen	NO_3^- NH_4^+	Part of amino acids, proteins, vitamins, nucleic acids, ATP, and chlorophyll.	Very marked chlorosis, stunted growth, loss of lower leaves in extreme deficiency due to removal of amino acids from older leaves to growing regions.	Often deficient. Nitrogen from organic manures less easily leached than fertilizers, e.g. ammonium sulphate, sodium nitrate, gaseous ammonia injection into soil. Root nodules of legumes are a good source.
Phosphorus	H_2PO_4	Part of cytoplasm, nucleic acids, ATP. High concentration in fruits and seeds.	Dark green dead patches on leaves. Stunted growth.	Often deficient, not readily available in alkaline soils.
Magnesium	Mg^{2+}	Part of chlorophyll molecule and enzyme activater in phosphate metabolism.	Chlorosis of older leaves, i.e. from base up; as Mg^{2+} is removed from older leaves by competition from younger leaves. Veins remain green.	Often deficient in acid soils.
Sulphur	SO_4^{2-}	Part of some proteins and cofactors.	Chlorosis of young leaves, as SO_4^{2-} cannot be withdrawn from older leaves. Roots often enlarge.	Sulphuric acid in rain from SO_2 pollution prevents widespread deficiency.
Micronutrients Iron	Fe^{2+}	Involved in chlorophyll synthesis. Part of cytochrome pigments and some prosthetic groups.	Chlorosis of young leaves, as iron cannot be withdrawn from older leaves.	Less available on chalky soils as it is bound as insoluble ferric hydroxide.
Boron	BO_3^{3-} $B_4O_7^{2-}$			
Chlorine Copper Cobalt Manganese Molybdenum Zinc	Cl^- Cu^{2+} Co^{2+} Mn^{2+} Mo^{3+} Zn^{2+}	Complex interactions, the role of many is not known. Mo is important in nitrogen fixation.	Difficult to identify direct and indirect effects.	These are the trace elements required in very small amounts.

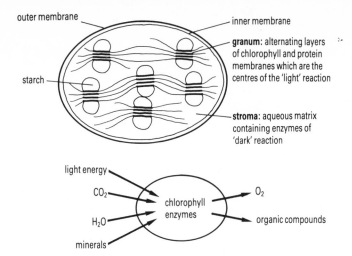

Fig 4.1. *Chloroplastid structure.* The diagram is based on structures seen in sections under the electron microscope (see also Chapter 1).

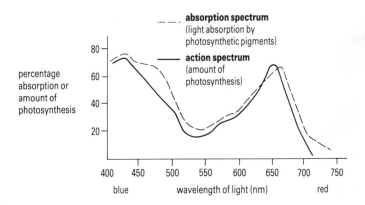

Fig 4.2. Absorption and action spectra.

The excited electrons from the chlorophyll pass along a chain of electron carriers and combine with the hydrogen ions to convert a substance NADP to NADPH$_2$ which is used in the dark stage for the synthesis of organic compounds.

Electrons pass from the hydroxyl ions (OH$^-$) down an electron carrier system to the chlorophyll molecule, replacing the excited electrons that were removed.

As the electrons pass along the electron carrier system, energy-rich ATP is generated from ADP and P. This ATP is used in the dark reaction in the synthesis of organic compounds as an energy source.

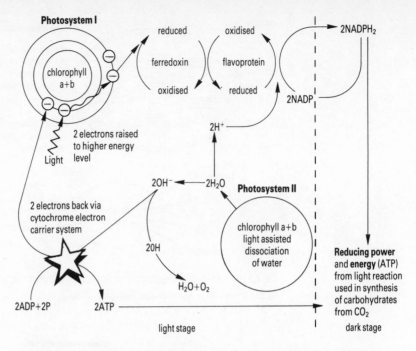

Fig 4.3. *Outline of the light-dependent stage of photosynthesis.* The chlorophyll is activated by the absorption of light. The photo-excited chlorophyll yields electrons which pass along a series of carriers, join up with protons (H^+) from the water, and reduce the co-factor NADP to $NADPH_2$. This provides the so-called 'reducing power' for the dark reaction. Electrons from the hydroxyl ions (OH^-), which come from the dissociation of water, pass back to the chlorophyll molecule; in so doing they yield energy which is trapped in ATP. This ATP is used to provide energy for the synthetic processes of the dark reaction. The addition of phosphate to ADP to form ATP is called **phosphorylation**, and this method of ATP formation involving light is referred to as **photo-phosphorylation**.

EXERCISE ▶

Exercise 4.3
What other source of ATP is there in a photosynthetic plant?

Answer Respiration, which proceeds both in the dark and the light, also produces a supply of ATP. This occurs in the mitochondria, and the extent to which the ATP from each of these processes is 'intermingled' is not clear.

DARK STAGE

The dark stage, or rather the non-light dependent stage, utilizes the products of the light reaction, namely $NADPH_2$ (a reducing agent) and ATP (an energy-rich carrier), in the synthesis of complex organic compounds using carbon dioxide. It is summarized for C3-type plants in Fig 4.4.

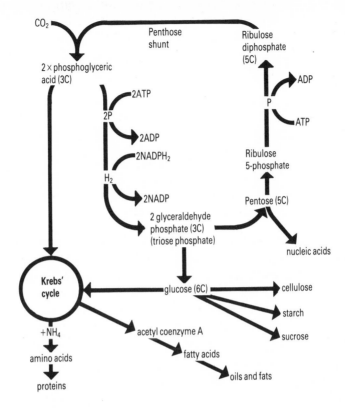

Fig 4.4. *Outline of C3 non-light dependent (dark) stage of photosynthesis.* The complex series of steps in the **Pentose Shunt** are not shown, therefore the carbon atoms do not 'balance' in the flow chart.

The carbon dioxide in the air must first be trapped by an acceptor molecule. There are two main pathways by which this occurs.

In C3-type plants, the carbon dioxide combines with a five-carbon (5C) acceptor substance to form a six-carbon (6C) compound, each molecule of which then breaks down into two molecules of a three-carbon (3C) compound. Examples of C3-type plants are broad bean, tomato, wheat.

In C4-type plants the carbon dioxide combines with a three-carbon acceptor substance to form a four-carbon compound which leads into the synthetic pathways. At high intensities C4-type plants have a photosynthetic rate two to three times greater than C3-type plants, giving them a much more rapid growth rate. Examples of C4-type plants are maize and sugar cane.

COMMENT ▶	Questions are often set which require an explanation of how a study of the external factors affecting the rate of photosynthesis leads to an understanding of the biochemical pathways involved. Some of the experimental work which led to an understanding of these pathways is set out at the end of this chapter.

FORMATION OF AMINO ACIDS IN PLANTS

Photosynthetic plants can synthesize all their required amino acids from inorganic materials (unlike animals that must have a supply of ready-made amino acids in their diet).

Plants take up nitrogen mainly in the form of nitrate ions (NO_3^-) and sometimes ammonium ions (NH_4^+).

If nitrate ions are taken up they are reduced to nitrite ions and then to ammonium ions. If ammonium ions are taken up these reduction processes are not necessary.

$$\text{Nitrate ions} \xrightarrow[\text{reductase}]{\text{nitrate}} \text{Nitrite ions} \xrightarrow[\text{reductase}]{\text{nitrite}} \text{Ammonium ions}$$

The ammonium ions are combined with alpha-oxoglutaric acid from the Krebs' cycle and reduced to form an amino acid (glutamic acid).

Other amino acids are then formed by transamination.

$$\begin{array}{ccc} \text{AMINO ACID A} & \underset{\text{GROUP}}{\overset{\text{AMINO}}{}} & \text{KETO ACID B} \\ \downarrow & \rightarrow & \downarrow \\ \text{KETO ACID A} & & \text{AMINO ACID B} \end{array}$$

ANIMAL NUTRITION

All animals are heterotrophic, that is they require a supply of ready synthesized organic matter, either directly, or indirectly via food chains, from plants.

Most animals are holozoic – that is they actually engulf or swallow organic matter into a cavity in which digestion occurs.

NUTRIENTS

There is a wide range of nutritional requirements throughout the animal kingdom, but all animals require energy-yielding compounds (usually carbohydrates and fats), amino acids, vitamins, mineral salts, and water.

CARBOHYDRATES

These are composed of carbon, hydrogen, and oxygen only, usually with the hydrogen and the oxygen in the same proportion as in water

$(C_x(H_2O)_y)$. They are used as a source of structural materials and as a source of energy in respiration.

Monosaccharides (e.g. glucose and fructose) are the simplest carbohydrates. They require no digestion to render them diffusible, and are the end-products of the digestion of other carbohydrates.

Disaccharides (e.g. sucrose and maltose) consist of two monosaccharide molecules joined together with the loss of water. They are hydrolysed to monosaccharides during digestion. For example

$$\text{sucrose} + \text{water} \xrightarrow[\text{(invertase)}]{\text{sucrase}} \text{glucose} + \text{fructose}$$

$$\text{maltose} + \text{water} \xrightarrow{\text{maltase}} \text{glucose} + \text{glucose}$$

Polysaccharides (e.g. starch, glycogen and cellulose) consist of many monosaccharide molecules joined together, with loss of water molecules. They are hydrolysed to monosaccharides during digestion. For example

$$\text{starch (amylose)} + \text{water} \xrightarrow{\text{amylase}} \text{maltose} + \text{water}$$

$$\text{maltose} + \text{water} \xrightarrow{\text{maltase}} \text{glucose} + \text{glucose}$$

Few animals possess cellulase enzyme. Those that do not, but which consume plant material (with its cellulose cell walls) harbour symbiotic bacteria in the gut which produce cellulase enzyme.

FATS

These are combinations of glycerol and fatty acids. Saturated fats are unreactive and accumulate in the fat stores of the body, unsaturated fats (and polyunsaturated fats) are very reactive in metabolism.

Most animals survive with little or no dietary fats, as they are readily synthesized from carbohydrates. However, some animals require certain fatty acids in their diet as they are essential for their metabolism and cannot be synthesized from carbohydrates.

Fats are also a source of fat-soluble vitamins, e.g. vitamin A.

AMINO ACIDS

These provide the organic nitrogen required by animals. Apart from some colourless flagellates which can obtain nitrogen from ammonia or nitrates, all animals require some ready synthesized amino acids as part of their diet, these are known as **essential amino acids**.

From these the full range of necessary amino acids can be synthesized by means of various interconversions. Most animals require up to twelve essential amino acids in their diet, but some of the non-essential amino acids stimulate growth and may be essential only at certain stages of development.

Amino acids are taken up in the diet of most animals as proteins, which are hydrolysed to their constituent amino acids. These are then absorbed and resynthesized into the protein of the animal for growth, repair and general metabolic replacement.

EXERCISE ▶

Exercise 4.4

A supply of nitrates (containing nitrogen) is essential to photosynthesising plants. What nitrogen-containing compounds are required by heterotrophic organisms (fungi and animals)?

Answer The nitrogen-containing compounds required by heterotrophic organisms are amino acids. These are obtained from the digestion of proteins which consist of long chains of amino acids, the amino acids having been synthesized originally as a product of photosynthesis, utilizing inorganic nitrate.

MINERALS

These are only required in small amounts, but are essential for the healthy functioning of the body.

VITAMINS

These are organic compounds which animals must obtain in their diet. They are needed only in very small amounts, but are extremely important in promoting and maintaining normal growth, development and reproduction.

As different animals have different requirements, the term vitamin can only be used with reference to specific animals, for example vitamin C is required by man but not by rats. The vitamin requirements of most animals are unknown. However, the B group vitamins, which generally act as co-enzymes in fundamental chemical processes, are needed by most animals including the invertebrates.

BALANCED DIET IN MAN

CARBOHYDRATES

These are not essential to man's diet, but they normally provide most of the energy of the diet and are necessary for the correct utilization of a limited protein supply.

The largely indigestible polysaccharide cellulose provides the dietary fibre or roughage which gives bulk to the diet and which satisfies the appetite, and provides resistance for the gut wall muscles during peristalsis. It also retains water in the contents of the colon, and thus the transit time of the food through the gut is shortened. This is thought to prevent the accumulation of putrefactive bacteria and consequent gut disorders.

FATS

These are a good source of energy and the fat-soluble vitamins A, D, E, and K.

The polyunsaturated fatty acids, linoleic and linolenic acids, cannot be synthesised by the body and must be supplied in the diet. They are known as 'essential fatty acids'.

AMINO ACIDS

Proteins from animal sources yield the full range of essential amino acids and are therefore known as proteins of **high biological value**. Proteins from most plant sources do not yield the full range of amino acids essential for growth in sufficient amounts and are therefore known as proteins of **low biological value** (notable exceptions are soya beans and wholewheat).

If carbohydrates and fats are in short supply, proteins are used as the major energy source.

Table 4.2. Minerals: source, function, and daily intake

Mineral	Main sources	Function	Estimated average adult daily intake	Total body content (in g)
			Macronutrient (daily intake in g)	
Calcium	Dairy products Bread	Formation of bones and teeth; blood clotting, muscle contraction	1.1	1000
Phosphorus	Cheese Yeast extract	Formation of bones and teeth; part of DNA, RNA, ATP; acid-base balance	1.4	780
Sulphur	Dairy products Legumes	Part of thiamin; part of keratin	0.85	140
Potassium	Meats Potatoes	Osmoregulation; acid-base balance; nerve transmission	3.3	140
Sodium	Cheese Salt	Osmoregulation; acid-base balance; nerve transmission	4.4	100
Chloride	Meats Salt	Osmoregulation; acid-base balance; gastric acid	5.2	95
Magnesium	Cheese Greens	Energy metabolism; calcium metabolism	0.34	19

Mineral	Main sources	Function	Estimated average adult daily intake	Total body content (in g)
			Micronutrient (daily intake in mg)	
Iron	Liver Cocoa	Haemoglobin and myoglobin; cytochromes; intracellular bacteriocide	16.0	4.2
Fluoride	Sea-food Water Tea	Bone and teeth formation; prevention of decay	1.8	2.6
Zinc	Meats Legumes	Many enzymes; protein metabolism	13.0	2.3
Copper	Liver Legumes	Formation of haemoglobin; energy release, formation of melanin	3.5	0.07
Iodine	Fish Iodized salt	Thyroxine	0.2	0.01
Manganese	Tea Cereals	Bone development; amino acid metabolism	3.7	0.01
Chromium	Meats Cereals	Glucose uptake by cells	0.15	0.001
Cobalt	Meats Yeast Comfrey	In vitamin B_{12}	0.3	0.001

N.B. Intakes will generally be greater than requirements.

Table 4.3. Vitamins: their sources, functions, and deficiency symptoms

Vitamin name	Letter	Main sources	Function	Deficiency symptoms
Retinol	A	Liver, milk, greens, carrots	(a) Formation of visual purple (b) Healthy membranes (c) Resistance to disease (d) Normal growth	(a) Night blindness (b) Xerophthalmia (c) Infection (d) Poor growth
Calciferol	D	Fish-liver oil, butter, sunlight on skin	(a) Uptake of calcium and phosphorus (b) Calcification of bone	Rickets in children Osteomalacia in adults

Vitamin name	Letter	Main sources	Function	Deficiency symptoms
Tocopherol	E	Milk, egg yolk, wheatgerm, greens	(a) As an antioxidant (it is easily oxidized and conserves vitamins A, C, D, K and polyunsaturated fatty acids)	Never demonstrated in man Sterility in rats
Phylloquinone	K	Liver, egg yolk, greens	Involved in blood clotting	Impaired clotting, and haemorrhage
Thiamine	B_1	Meat, milk, cereals, yeast	Coenzyme in release of energy	1. Beri-beri
Riboflavine	B_2 (USA old G)	Milk, fish, greens	Coenzyme in release of energy	1. Araboflavinosis
Niacin	(Part of old B_2)	Meat, fish, greens, wheatgerm	Coenzyme in release of energy	1. Pellagra
Pantothenic acid	B_5	Eggs, cereals	Coenzyme in release of energy	Fatigue, poor muscle coordination 'Burning feet' syndrome
Pyridoxine	B_6	Meats, potatoes, cabbage	(a) Coenzyme for amino acid metabolism (b) Catalyses conversion of amino acid tryptophan to niacin (c) Aids in release of energy from glycogen	Anaemia Hyper-irritability Loss of weight Convulsions
Biotin	(old H)	Milk, egg yolk, cereals, legumes	(a) Coenzyme in release of energy (b) Metabolism of fatty acids	Lassitude Dermatitis
Folic acid	Bc	Liver, kidney, greens	(a) Synthesis of adenine, guanine and thymine (b) Amino acid synthesis	Macrocytic anaemia
Cobalamin	B_{12}	Meat, liver, yeast, comfrey	(a) Maturation of red blood corpuscles (b) Carbohydrate metabolism (c) Growth factor	Pernicious anaemia
Ascorbic acid	C	Citrus fruits, greens	(a) Forms collagen and inter-cellular materials (b) Promotes use of calcium in bones and teeth	Scurvy

Vitamins are classified according to their solubility, thus, A, D, E, and K are fat-soluble, while the B complex (8) and C are water soluble.

MINERALS

A complex of factors affects the uptake of minerals, so that it is difficult to determine the exact daily requirements. For example, the presence of cellulose fibres and phytic acid (found in wholemeal bread) decreases the uptake of available calcium, zinc, and iron; and calcium uptake is increased by the presence of vitamins D and C.

VITAMINS

A complex of factors also affects the uptake of vitamins, so again it is difficult to assess the exact daily requirements. For example, anti-vitamins oppose vitamin activity; provitamins are converted to vitamins by the body at different rates; some vitamins are in a bound form and not available to the body; and synthesis by symbiotic bacteria of vitamins K, B_1, nicotinic acid, riboflavin, and folic acid occurs in the large intestine.

FEEDING MECHANISMS

A variety of feeding mechanisms are employed to obtain the necessary food material. The main types are given here.

MICROPHAGOUS FEEDERS

(a)   Filter feeders These are aquatic animals that feed on relatively small food particles usually suspended in the water. Due to the relatively minute size of the food particles, they tend to have to feed continuously in order to obtain sufficient nutrients.

They filter the food particles from the water by means of cilia, or bristles or 'hairs', often in conjunction with the secretion of mucus in which the particles are actually trapped and swept along to the mouth by the rhythmically beating cilia.

Examples of this type of feeding are found in *Paramecium* and *Mytilus* (the marine mussel) (Fig 4.5).

Fig 4.5. *Filter feeding in Mytilus*. The gill filaments are covered in cilia which beat in a rhythmic manner to create a flow of water, in through the inhalent siphon and out through the exhalent siphon. As the current of water passes over the gills, small food particles are trapped in mucus and swept by ciliary action to the mouth.

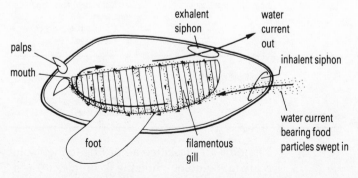

(b)   Deposit feeders These feed on small nutrient particles that have settled on or become mixed with the substratum of the environment.

They also tend to feed continuously to obtain a sufficient volume of food. An example of this type of feeding is found in earthworms, which digest organic material in the soil they swallow.

(c)   Fluid feeders These feed on nutritive fluids obtained from other living, or recently dead, organisms. Some, such as the butterflies, feed on the fluid secretions of flowers (nectar). Those that feed on the fluids of living organisms have sharp piercing mouthparts as well as tubular 'sucking mouthparts'.

Most animals that feed on fluids are in fact parasitic insects, e.g. *Pediculus capitis* (head louse), Aphid species (greenfly and blackfly), and *Anopheles gambiae* (malarial mosquito) (Fig 4.6).

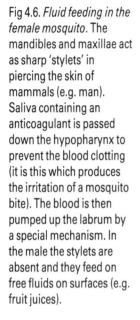
Fig 4.6. *Fluid feeding in the female mosquito.* The mandibles and maxillae act as sharp 'stylets' in piercing the skin of mammals (e.g. man). Saliva containing an anticoagulant is passed down the hypopharynx to prevent the blood clotting (it is this which produces the irritation of a mosquito bite). The blood is then pumped up the labrum by a special mechanism. In the male the stylets are absent and they feed on free fluids on surfaces (e.g. fruit juices).

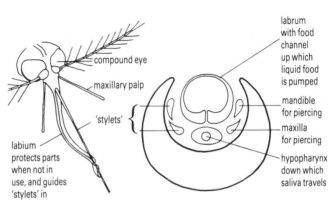

compound eye
maxillary palp
'stylets'
labium protects parts when not in use, and guides 'stylets' in

labrum with food channel up which liquid food is pumped
mandible for piercing
maxilla for piercing
hypopharynx down which saliva travels

EXERCISE ▶

Exercise 4.5
What is one of the main problems fluid feeders have in sucking fluids, particularly blood, up long narrow tubular mouthparts?

Answer One of the main problems is the coagulation of the fluid, particularly blood, in the long, narrow, tubular mouthparts. This problem is overcome by a secretion of anticoagulant saliva down the mouthpart. It is in this way that viruses, bacteria, protozoa, and even small nematodes can be introduced into a new host by insect vectors.

MACROPHAGOUS FEEDERS

These feed on relatively large food particles, and thus only need to feed occasionally, since when they do feed they take in relatively large amounts of nutrients. The food is detected by specific mechanical or chemical stimuli and often has to be broken down by mechanical means, such as by specialized mouthparts in crustaceans and insects, and by teeth in vertebrates – particularly mammals.

Mammals have a **heterodont dentition** with different teeth specialized for different functions, and also have the entire dentition adapted to a particular diet, for example.

1   **CARNIVORES – MEAT EATERS**

2   **HERBIVORES – PLANT EATERS**

3   **OMNIVORES – MIXED DIET.**

1. CARNIVORES

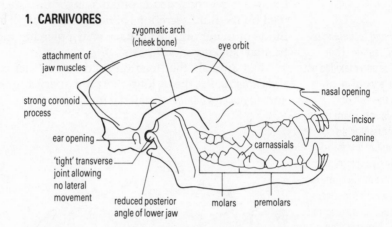

Fig 4.7. *Carnivore (dog) dentition*. The incisors and strongly developed canines are adapted for holding, killing and tearing the prey. The premolars and molars are sharp-edged and the last upper premolars and first lower molars are particularly strongly developed as cutting and shearing teeth and are known as the carnassials. The 'tight' joint of the lower jaw only allows an up-and-down 'scissor-like' action, which is necessary for the cutting action of the carnassials. The large coranoid process and strong zygomatic arch allow for the attachment of the strong jaw muscles and the reduced posterior angle allows for a wide gape.

2. HERBIVORES

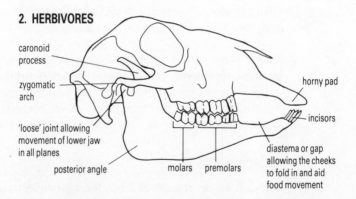

Fig 4.8. *Herbivore (sheep) dentition*. Vegetation (grass in particular) is relatively hard to masticate and is relatively low in nutritional value when compared to meat. Therefore the herbivorous dentition shows many adaptations for the mastication of large volumes of plant material. The premolars and molars have broad, ridged surfaces and the vegetation is crushed by the grinding action of the side to side movement of the lower jaw. To offset the wearing down of the surfaces the teeth continue to grow throughout life.

Differences between herbivores and carnivores

Herbivores	Carnivores
Vegetation is hard to masticate and low in nutritional value. Therefore skull, dentition and gut show adaptations for dealing with large volumes of vegetation	Meat easily digested and high in nutritional value, but generally has to be caught and killed. Therefore skull, dentition and gut show adaptations for dealing with prey which is relatively easy to digest
1 Pulp cavities of teeth open so teeth grow throughout life to offset wear from chewing vegetation	1 Pulp cavities of teeth closed so teeth do not grow throughout life
2 Extra layer of surface cement to offset wear	2 None
3 Canines reduced or absent producing a gap (diastema)	3 Canines strongly developed for piercing and tearing
4 Premolars and molars with broad ridged surfaces for grinding vegetation	4 Premolars and molars modified as sharp cutting carnassials
5 Lower jaw can move sideways for grinding action of cheek teeth	5 Lower jaw can only move up and down for shearing action of carnassials
6 Coronoid process of lower jaw and zygomatic arch not particularly well developed	6 Strong coronoid process, zygomatic arch and sagittal crest for attachment of powerful jaw muscles
7 Narrow gape	7 Wide gape for gripping prey
8 Relatively long gut harbouring many symbiotic bacteria which secrete cellulase enzymes for the digestion of cellulose	8 Relatively short gut as meat easy to digest.

MAMMALIAN DIGESTION

THE BUCCAL CAVITY

The mouth opens into the buccal cavity, where **mastication** of the food occurs. Mastication involves the teeth, tongue, cheeks, and lower jaw. It increases the surface area of the food for enzyme action, and forms the food into a bolus for swallowing. The food is mixed with saliva, which contains salivary amylase enzyme (ptyalin). This catalyses the hydrolysis of the amylose of cooked starch to maltose. (Amylase is absent from the saliva of carnivores.) The saliva also moistens and lubricates the food for swallowing.

The buccal cavity is lined with stratified non-keratinized squamous epithelium (as is the oesophagus) which resists wear.

THE OESOPHAGUS

After mastication and swallowing the food bolus is passed down the oesophagus. The oesophagus has an outer longitudinal, and an inner circular layer of smooth muscle fibres, which by their coordinated rhythmic wave-like contractions, known as **peristalsis**, force the food bolus down to the stomach. (In man the upper third has voluntary striped muscle fibres.)

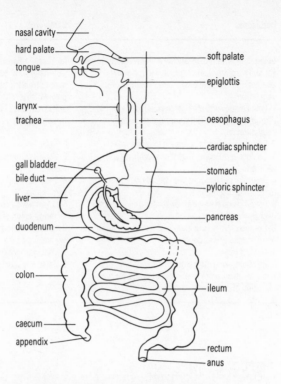

Fig 4.9. Mammalian (human) gut structure.

The walls of the oesophagus have longitudinal folds which reduce the lumen to a small star shape when food is not passing, but allow for expansion to accommodate swallowed food. The circular cardiac sphincter relaxes to allow the food to enter the stomach.

THE STOMACH

The stomach wall has three smooth muscle layers (outer longitudinal, middle circular and inner oblique), and is thrown into folds. It can stretch considerably to accommodate relatively large volumes of food. It is lined with simple columnar epithelium and has three types of glands.

1 cardiac glands secrete mucus
2 pyloric glands secrete mucus
3 fundic glands secrete gastric juice which contains
   (*a*)   mucus – protects gut wall
   (*b*)   hydrochloric acid – kills bacteria, makes calcium and iron salts suitable for absorption in the intestine, provides low pH for optimum pepsin action.
   (*c*)   pepsinogen – activated to pepsin which digests proteins to peptides.
   (*d*)   rennin (chymosin or chymase) – in young mammals which

converts the soluble milk protein into an insoluble form which can be attacked by pepsin.

(*e*)   intrinsic factor – for the absorption of vitamin B_{12}.

Little absorption occurs in the stomach, but some glucose, minerals, water, vitamins, alcohol and drugs are taken up into the blood stream. Contractions of the stomach mix the gastric juice with the food and also aid in its mechanical breakdown, producing a mixture known as **chyme** which is released in small quantities into the small intestine through the pyloric sphincter.

THE SMALL INTESTINE (DUODENUM, JEJUNUM, ILEUM)

This is the main region of digestion and absorption of the soluble end-products of digestion. The outer longitudinal and inner circular layers of smooth muscle in the wall move the food along by peristalsis. It is lined with simple columnar epithelium and the glands in the wall (the crypts of Lieberkühn and the deeper lying glands of Brunner) secrete **succus entericus** or **intestinal juice**.

INTESTINAL JUICE CONTAINS:

1   amylase which converts amylose in starch to maltose
2   maltase which converts maltose to glucose
3   lactase which converts lactose to glucose and galactose
4   sucrase which converts sucrose to glucose and fructose
5   erepsin (a mixture of peptidases) which converts peptides to amino acids
6   lipase which converts fat (emulsified by alkaline bile from the liver) to glycerol and fatty acids
7   enterokinase which activates pancreatic trypsinogen to trypsin which converts proteins and peptides to amino acids, and also activates pancreatic chymotrypsinogen to chymotrypsin which also converts protein and peptides to amino acids
8   mucus which protects the gut lining.

THE PANCREAS

This secretes pancreatic juice into the small intestine via the pancreatic duct. Pancreatic juice contains:

1   dilute solution of alkaline salts to neutralize the acid from the stomach
2   amylase
3   maltase
4   peptidases
5   trypsinogen
6   chymotrypsinogen.

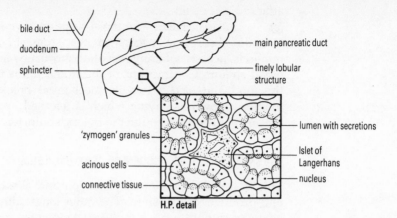

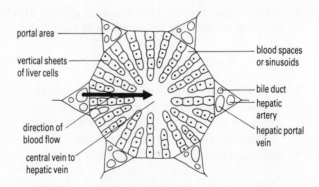

Fig 4.10. *Pancreas structure*. The pancreas has two distinct parts, the endocrine Islets of Langerhans which secrete the hormones insulin and glucagon, and the exocrine part which secretes the pancreatic juice.

Fig 4.11. *Liver structure: HP detail of one liver lobule. Summary of non-digestive functions of the liver.* (a) Destruction of old red blood corpuscles. The iron is stored as ferritin for reuse, the rest of the haemoglobin is broken down into the bile pigments (bilirubin and biliverdin) which pass to the kidney to colour the urine as urobilin or to the gut to colour the faeces as stercobilin. (b) Storage of excess carbohydrates and other carbon-containing compounds as glycogen. (c) Metabolism of fat. (d) Amino acid metabolism, including deamination and urea formation. (e) Synthesis of vitamin A. (f) Storage of vitamins A, D, B. (g) Synthesis of blood proteins. (h) Contributes part of the reticulo-endothelial defence system. (i) Detoxyfication, e.g. the degradation of fat-soluble drugs such as barbiturates, the breakdown of alcohol formed naturally by fermentation in the gut, inactivation in the male of female hormones from the adrenal cortex, and of male hormones in the female. (j) The manufacture of red and white blood cells in the embryo.

THE LIVER

This secretes bile into the small intestine via the bile duct. Bile is a dilute solution of alkaline bile salts which:

1 emulsifies fats
2 activates pancreatic lipase
3 increases activity of carbohydrate and protein digesting enzymes.
4 increases the uptake of vitamins A, D, and K.

The absorption of the end products of digestion (monosaccharides, amino acids, fatty acids, glycerol, minerals and vitamins) takes place over the large surface area of folds and villi. The villi are fingerlike projections (about 1 mm long in man) well supplied with blood capillaries and lacteals of the lymphatic system. (The lacteals absorb fats, fatty acids and glycerol.) The blood capillaries all join to form the **hepatic portal vein** which carries the blood to the liver where various homeostatic adjustments are made.

Fig 4.12. *H.P. detail T.S. duodenum.*

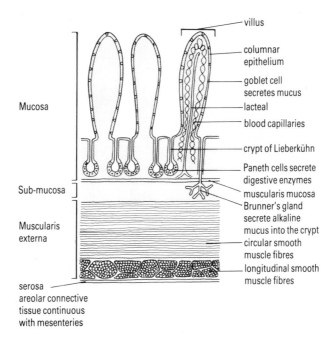

Table 4.4. Summary of digestive enzymes and their action

Secretion	Enzymes	Substrate	Products
Saliva	Amylase (ptyalin)	Amylose	Maltose
Gastric juices	Rennin (only in young) Pepsin Lipase	Caseinogen Proteins Fats	Casein Peptides Fatty acids and glycerol

Secretion	Enzymes	Substrate	Products
Intestinal juice	Amylase	Amylose	Maltose
	Maltase	Maltose	Glucose
	Lactase (induced by regular milk drinking)	Lactose	Glucose and galactose
	Sucrase (invertase)	Sucrose	Glucose and fructose
	Lipase	Fats	Fatty acids and glycerol
	Erepsin (mixture of peptidases)	Peptides	Amino acids
	Enterokinase	Trypsinogen	Trypsin
Pancreatic juice	Amylase	Amylose	Maltose
	Trypsin(ogen)	Proteins	Peptides
	Peptidases	Peptides	Amino acids
	Lipase	Fats	Fatty acids and glycerol
	Chymo-trypsin(ogen)	Proteins	Amino acids
	Nucleases	Nucleic acid	Nucleotides
	Elastase	Elastin	Amino acids

THE LARGE INTESTINE

The small intestine opens into the **caecum** which is well developed in herbivores and which contains symbiotic bacteria which secrete cellulase enzymes to digest the cellulose cell walls of plant material. One end of the caecum continues as the blind-ending **appendix**, and in the other direction it leads into the colon, which is the main region of absorption of water and minerals.

The remains of the food finally enters the **rectum** prior to egestion via the **anus**.

EXERCISE ▶

Exercise 4.6
How may the different constituents in the diets of herbivores and carnivores account for the main differences in structure between the gut of a herbivore and that of a carnivore?

Answer The main differences in the diets are that the vegetable matter of the herbivorous diet consists largely of cellulose which is difficult to digest, and that large volumes must be consumed as vegetable matter is relatively poor in nutrients compared with meat. Thus the herbivore gut is long and often complex, when compared with the shorter and simpler carnivore gut.

EXPERIMENTAL WORK

PLANT NUTRITION

INORGANIC NUTRIENTS OF PLANTS

The inorganic nutrient requirements of plants can be investigated by using a range of culture solutions: one solution which contains all the necessary inorganic nutrients, and a series of further solutions each lacking a particular nutrient.

Seedlings (e.g. oat) are germinated, and when of a suitable size their roots are thoroughly washed in distilled water and one seedling placed in each culture solution and one in distilled water.

Light is excluded from the culture solutions to prevent the growth of algae which would interfere with the results by absorbing some ions and releasing others on their death and decomposition. The solutions are aerated to promote root growth, and topped up as required.

Over a period of time (several weeks) the various deficiency symptoms can be observed (see Table 4.1). The results of such experiments (using either the plants themselves or photographs) may then be presented for examination.

PHOTOSYNTHESIS

Those experiments using fresh water plants such as Canadian pondweed (*Elodea canadensis*) lend themselves better to the study of photosynthesis under varying conditions within a short period of time (i.e. normal practical periods), than do potted plants.

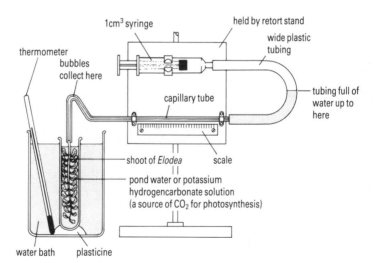

Fig 4.13. Photosynthometer.

1 Set the apparatus up as shown in the diagram (Fig 4.13). Make sure the apparatus contains water and no air bubbles to start with, and that the plunger of the syringe is fully pushed in.

2 Bubbles of gas (mainly oxygen) rise from the cut end of the shoot and from the leaves. The volume of gas evolved in a given time is taken to be directly proportional to the rate of photosynthesis.

3 Note the temperature.

4 Measure the distance of the lamp from the plant.

5 To avoid the problem of uncontrolled light reaching the plant, the experiment should be performed in a darkened room.

6   Expose the plant to the light for a set period of time. If possible take light meter readings close to the plant.

7   At the end of the experimental period draw the gas that has collected in the bend of the capillary tube alongside the measuring scale by pulling the plunger of the syringe out.

8   Read off the measurement carefully. If the scale is in mm, the volume of gas can be calculated from $\pi r^2 \times l$. Where r=radius of capillary bore (usually 1 mm), and l=length of bubble.

9   Draw the bubble further on past the measuring scale until it enters the wide plastic tubing.

10 Push the plunger in fully again for the start of the next experiment.

11 Repeat the experiment with the lamp at different distances from the plant. Remember the light intensity varies inversely as the square of the distance, e.g. the light intensity at 25 mm distance will be four times that at 50 mm.

12 Graph volume of gas produced (vertical axis) against light intensity.

13 Remember that light intensity will only affect the rate of photosynthesis whilst it is the limiting factor.

14 The strength of the hydrogencarbonate solution could be varied e.g. 0.01%, 0.05%, 0.10%, at constant light intensity, and the effect on the rate of photosynthesis investigated.

15 Main source of experimental error is the trapping of bubbles on and under the leaves and stem.

INDICATOR EXPERIMENTS

Another method of measuring the rate of photosynthesis by measuring the rate of oxygen production, is by the use of an indicator solution. For example indigo-carmine solution (0.01 g/l) is normally an inky blue colour. If the dissolved oxygen is removed by the addition of 10% sodium hydrosulphite, the indicator goes yellow (being green near the turning point).

If Canadian pondweed or mares tail (which has been placed in cold, boiled pond water and left in the dark for 48 hours, so as to start the experiment with as little oxygen present as possible), is then placed in a yellow deoxygenated solution of indigo-carmine, in the light, the evolution of oxygen due to photosynthesis is indicated by the colour change to blue.

Photosynthesis in aquatic plants can also be investigated using indicator solutions which change colour with changing pH (acidity/alkalinity). During photosynthesis more carbon dioxide is taken up than is released by respiration. Carbon dioxide is an 'acid' gas and its disappearance from the solution results in a rise in pH (decreasing acidity) and a consequent change in the colour of the indicator solution.

This type of experiment can also be used to investigate the exchange of gases between photosynthesizing plants and respiring animals such as water snails. Tubes can be set up containing plants only, animals only, plants and animals, and no organisms, and these can be studied under varying conditions (comparing any colour changes with colour control tubes).

As in all experiments involving colour change indicators, control tubes of indicator solution in its different colour states should be kept for colour comparison as the experiment proceeds.

In all these experiments the experimental conditions can be varied to study the effect of factors such as light intensity, temperature, carbon dioxide concentration and the colour of the light.

When studying the effect of light intensity, at a given carbon dioxide concentration and temperature, it 'should' be found that the rate of photosynthesis does not continue to increase indefinitely with increasing light intensity, but that it gradually levels off.

It was on the basis of similar findings that Blackman concluded that at least two distinct phases are involved in photosynthesis, the so called **'light'** and **'dark'** stages.

At low intensities the rate of photosynthesis is directly proportional to the light intensity, and temperature has little effect. This is characteristic of a photochemical 'light' stage.

At higher light intensities temperature does have an effect, and this is characteristic of a chemical reaction, that is of a non-light dependent or 'dark' stage.

At low light intensities, the 'dark' stage is receiving only a limited amount of the products that it requires from the 'light' reaction, and is therefore being slowed or limited by it; under these circumstances the light intensity is said to be the **limiting factor**.

As the light intensity increases, a point is reached when the 'dark' stage is working at maximum capacity, and any further increase in light intensity has no effect; under these circumstances light intensity is no longer the limiting factor.

Other factors involved in the 'dark' stage such as temperature and carbon dioxide concentration, become limiting and must be increased if the rate of photosynthesis is to increase any more.

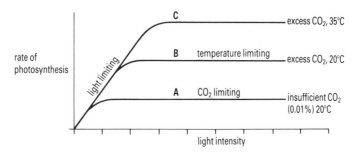

Fig 4.14. *Rate of photosynthesis under varying conditions of light intensity, CO_2 concentration and temperature.* At low light intensities light is the limiting factor. When more than enough CO_2 is supplied at 20°C, temperature is seen to be limiting (curve B). When the temperature is increased to 35°C the rate increases (curve C). Strictly speaking when measuring the rate of photosynthesis, **control** experiments should be set up in the dark, so that allowances may be made for the effects of respiration.

**FORMATION OF STARCH
EXPERIMENT**

Potted plants can also be used. In these, photosynthesis is usually measured by observing the formation of starch in destarched plants which have been kept in the dark for 48 hours.

This is done by:

1 placing leaves in boiling water to kill cells and disrupt membranes
2 placing boiled leaves in hot alcohol to remove chlorophyll
3 testing decolourised leaves for starch with iodine in KI solution.

This technique, however, does not lend itself so easily to quantitative methods such as those described using *Elodea*, where actual rates under varying conditions over relatively short periods of time can be measured.

**ISOTOPIC TRACERS AND
CHROMATOGRAPHY**

Two other techniques, namely the use of **isotopic tracers** and **chromatography**, are widely used in research into metabolic pathways including those of photosynthesis.

Plants are exposed to **isotopes** of elements involved in the processes under investigation. These isotopes are chemically the same as the natural form of the element but have different atomic structure (different numbers of neutrons, giving different mass numbers, e.g. ^{12}C and ^{14}C) which enable their passage through the various metabolic steps to be traced.

Many isotopes are radioactive and in these cases their passage can be traced by detecting the radioactive emissions, for example ^{14}C.

Others are not radioactive and their passage is traced using other techniques (e.g. the mass spectrometer), for example ^{18}O.

For example, in order to determine whether the oxygen released in photosynthesis is derived from the carbon dioxide or from the water, plants are exposed in one case to carbon dioxide labelled with the isotope tracer of oxygen, ^{18}O, and in another case to water labelled with ^{18}O. The ^{18}O only appears in the evolved oxygen in the latter case, demonstrating that the oxygen evolved in photosynthesis is derived from water and not from the carbon dioxide.

In order to trace the path of carbon dioxide through the complex series of steps in the 'dark' reaction of photosynthesis, plants are exposed to carbon dioxide labelled with radioactive isotope ^{14}C for varying amounts of time.

The plants are then killed as rapidly as possible to fix the reactants, which are then extracted and analysed. It is possible to use large plants in this procedure but there are difficulties, due to size, in killing the tissues and fixing all the reactants at the same time throughout the plant. The most accurate work has been done using suspensions of unicellular algae, which can be killed rapidly by the addition of a fixative to the suspending solution. (The ^{14}C is incorporated into bicarbonate ions—$H^{14}CO_3^-$ in the solution.) The experiment is run for a very short time at first, and then for a slightly longer

Fig 4.15

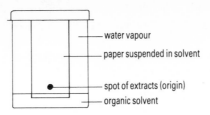

- water vapour
- paper suspended in solvent
- spot of extracts (origin)
- organic solvent

period on each subsequent occasion, so that the sequence of reactions and reactants can be discovered.

Once the cells have been killed, the organic matter is extracted and analysed by the technique of **chromatography**. There are many different chromatography techniques, but the original one (which is still widely used) is that of **paper chromatography**.

A concentrated spot of the extract (initial concentration in plants is very low) is placed near one end of the paper, which is resting in an organic solvent in which all dissolve and the whole is enclosed in a water saturated atmosphere (Fig 4.15). The cellulose fibres in the paper absorb water from the atmosphere which forms the **stationary aqueous phase**. The organic solvent moves by capillary action along the length of the paper. This is known as the **mobile phase**.

The different compounds in the mixture to be analysed are carried along the paper, according to their relative solubility in the organic solvent and in water. As the solvent front moves along the paper the different compounds distribute themselves between the solvent and the water absorbed by the fibres of the paper. Those more soluble in water are carried the shorter distances, and those more soluble in the organic solvent are carried further, within a given time. The distance travelled is given as a so-called R_f value:

$$R_f = \frac{\text{distance compound has moved from its origin}}{\text{distance of the solvent front from the origin}}$$

The R_f value is characteristic and descriptive of a compound (see Fig 4.16).

Fig 4.16

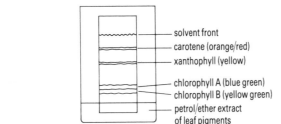

- solvent front
- carotene (orange/red)
- xanthophyll (yellow)
- chlorophyll A (blue green)
- chlorophyll B (yellow green)
- petrol/ether extract of leaf pigments (alternative method)

However, such chromatography in one direction only does not always separate every compound. Therefore **2-dimensional paper chromatography** is employed to further separate closely located substances. Here the process is repeated on the same piece of paper, but using a different solvent at right angles to the first (Fig 4.17). This results in the separation of any overlapping compounds.

Fig 4.17

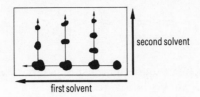

second solvent

first solvent

Since the compounds are usually colourless, the problem of their location and identification remains. When not using radioactive tracers, special sprays are available which locate the different compounds as coloured areas. When using radioactive tracers the paper is exposed to an X-ray sensitive film for a few days, during which time the radioactivity of the tracer is recorded on the film, which is then developed to give an autoradiograph.

The substances can be identified in a variety of ways. If their R_f value is known, and it is clearly distinct from any other, this will identify the compound. The position of the spots can be compared to the position of known compounds run through the same process (Fig 4.18), either on a different piece of paper, or on the same piece of paper. Alternatively, the actual area can be cut out from the original chromatography paper, and the substance extracted by a solvent and analysed.

Fig 4.18

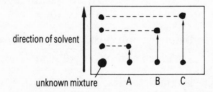

direction of solvent

unknown mixture   A   B   C

Using these methods complex metabolic pathways may be investigated, e.g. the first stable intermediate formed in photosynthesis was identified by such methods as being 3-phosphoglyceric acid (PGA).

The rapidity of photosynthesis reactions is indicated by the fact that 20–30 radioactive compounds can be extracted from algae that have only been exposed to ^{14}C for about 30 s. In fact, all stable intermediates of the Calvin cycle became saturated with ^{14}C within 3–5 minutes.

ANIMAL NUTRITION

Experiments investigating animal feeding mechanisms include those involving the observation of the uptake of microscopic particles, such as yeast, stained with an indicator dye such as Congo Red (blue below pH 3 to red above pH 5.1) or Neutral Red (red at pH 6.8 to yellow at pH 8.0), by animals such as *Paramecium*, and *Daphnia* (Fig 4.19).

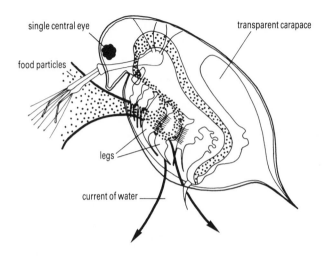

single central eye

transparent carapace

food particles

legs

current of water

Fig 4.19. *Filter feeding in **Daphnia**.* The feeding suspension is prepared by adding yeast to about 10 cm^3 of a 1% aqueous solution (1 g in 100 cm^3) of Congo Red. The thoracic legs have setae which sieve or filter bacteria, algae, and small organic particles. These are then passed to the mouth.

As the particles undergo different phases of digestion at different pH values, the colour change can be observed (although this is extremely difficult with the food vacuoles of *Paramecium* viewed under the microscope).

Most experiments at this level in animal nutrition involve the investigation of digestive (hydrolytic) enzyme activity e.g. amylase converting starch to maltose (a reducing disaccharide). These enzymes may be provided as ready made solutions, or you could be required to extract the enzymes from animal guts, usually invertebrates, e.g. locust or earthworm (the same may be done with plant tissue such as germinating plant seedlings, usually oats). In those experiments requiring the extraction of enzymes from animal guts or from seedlings, some macerating and rough filtering procedure is normally involved.

The testing of these samples for the presence or absence of the expected end-products at the *beginning* of such experiments is extremely important, as with such extracts many substances other than the enzymes will be present. For example a locust gut extract may well contain some reducing sugars.

DIALYSIS EXPERIMENT

Small molecules may be separated from larger ones by placing them within a membrane permeable only to the smaller ones. The smaller ones will diffuse out into the surrounding water.

A mixture of starch solution and amylase is poured into a length of visking tubing already in a glass U-tube containing water, and the apparatus is then placed in a water bath at 37°C.

Visking tubing is differentially permeable and the end products of the digestion of starch diffuse out into the surrounding water, whereas the starch does not.

The reacting mixture and the surrounding water are then tested for both starch and reducing sugars.

Fig 4.20. Dialysis experiment.

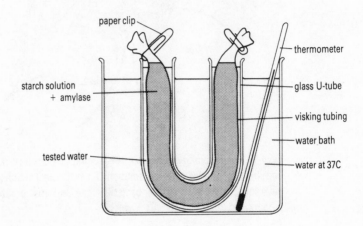

FOOD TESTS

Both plant and animal nutrition experiments can involve food tests. It is often required that various plant materials be investigated for their content of carbohydrate, fat and protein, and many plant and animal enzyme experiments involve digestive enzymes and therefore food tests.

CARBOHYDRATES

(a)   *Simple carbohydrates*
(i) Reducing sugars (monosaccharides and the disaccharides maltose and lactose). These give a yellow-green to red precipitate when boiled with Fehling's solution A and B, or Benedict's solution.
(ii) Non-reducing sugars (disaccharides except maltose and lactose). There is no simple direct test for these, and the following sequence must be employed:
Boil with Benedict's solution to obtain a negative result.
Boil in dilute hydrochloric acid (10% HCl) for a few minutes (this acid hydrolysis splits the non-reducing disaccharide into reducing monosaccharides), neutralise with

sodium carbonate (Na_2CO_3), checking with indicator paper, and then retest by boiling with Benedict's solution which should now prove positive.

(b) *Complex carbohydrates (polysaccharides)*
(i) *Starch*. This gives a blue-black colour with iodine solution.
(ii) *Cellulose*. This stains purple with Schultz's solution, or becomes light blue after soaking in iodine solution and adding 75% sulphuric acid (H_2SO_4).

PROTEINS

These give a brick red colour when boiled with Millon's reagent (which is poisonous as it contains mercury).

The Xanthoproteic test (in which a little concentrated nitric acid (HNO_3) is added, the mixture heated, cooled to cold, and then 880 ammonia added) gives a deep yellow precipitate, if positive.

The Biuret test (in which a little potassium hydroxide (KOH) is added until the test solution clears, and then a drop of copper sulphate ($CuSO_4$) run down the side of the tube) gives a blue/purple/violet ring at the surface if positive.

FATS

These take up the red stain Sudan III. If an oil is shaken up in water with Sudan III, the red-stained oil will separate out.

This also works well if Sudan III is added to milk and shaken up. The fat containing the Sudan III separates out on top.

The emulsion test involves shaking the fat up with ethanol, and pouring it into an equal volume of water, when a white emulsion is formed.

COMMENT ▶

Remember that although the above are practical experimental techniques, questions relating to them also **frequently** occur in theory examinations. One of the criteria used in marking accounts of practical procedures is, 'Will it work as described?' therefore always describe the techniques fully. For example, the statement that 'reducing sugars give a red precipitate with Benedict's solution' is not sufficient. The necessity of boiling must also be mentioned.

QUESTION ▶

Q.   Give a definition and explain the importance of a balanced diet to man (5)
Describe the processes of:
(i) the absorption of glucose (8)
(ii) the assimilation of amino acids (7)

COMMENT ▶

This question requires discussion of a balanced diet, but the mark allocation indicates that no detail is required on the composition or role of individual components, only on the balanced diet as a whole. The description of the processes however do require some detail, as they are more limited topics with a greater mark allocation.

OUTLINE ▶ ANSWER

Balanced diet (5)
Essential for growth development and health;
large amounts of proteins, carbohydrates, fats, roughage and water, small amounts of minerals and traces of vitamins;
must contain essential amino and fatty acids;
composition varies with individual e.g. young, old, amount of activity, male, female, pregnant female;
provides substances for material structure of body (proteins and minerals), and energy (carbohydrates and fats) and general metabolism (vitamins).

(i) Absorption of glucose (7)
Uptake of glucose from lumen of small intestine into plasma of blood in capillaries;
all across large surface area of villi with columnar epithelium with microvilli (brush borders);
brought into close contact with surface of villi by movements of gut wall, peristalsis, segmentation, and villi movements;
absorbed by diffusion from a high concentration in the small intestine down a concentration gradient to a lower concentration in the blood;
also by facilitated diffusion by carrier;
and/or by active transport requiring ATP (energy) which is coupled with sodium ion uptake.

(ii) Assimilation of amino acids (7)
Use of amino acids by the body in metabolism;
synthesis into proteins required by the body;
amino acids can be inter-converted by transamination;
but some not at a rate fast enough to supply the body's needs;
therefore some 'essential' amino acids must be supplied in the diet, from these all others can be inter-converted at a sufficient rate;
protein synthesis under control of mRNA and ribosomes;
amino acids linked by peptide bonds to form proteins;
proteins formed include enzymes, some hormones, antibodies, structural fibres e.g. collagen, muscle, keratin.

1   List the minerals which are known to be essential to green plants, indicating, where possible, why they are needed. Describe how you would show that one mineral nutrient was necessary for the healthy growth of a seedling. State how minerals enter the tissues which require them.   (SU)

2   How would you show, by laboratory experiments, the importance of nitrogen, phosphorus and potassium in plant metabolism? What symptoms would a flowering plant show if it was deficient in these elements?   (SCE)

3   Describe the processes involved in the uptake of water and mineral salts by plant roots.   (W)

4   Bubbles were released from the cut end of the stem of an illuminated shoot of *Elodea*, an aquatic plant. The time taken for the release of 20 bubbles in light of different wavelengths is given below:

Colour of light	Wavelength (in nanometres*)	Time taken for release of 20 bubbles (seconds)
violet	395	58
blue	430	38
blue	450	41
blue-green	485	56
blue-green	500	70
green	550	132
yellow	590	96
red	640	70
red	690	256

(a nanometre is equivalent to a millimicron)

(a)   Construct a graph of wavelength of light against time taken for bubble release.

(b)   Comment on the experiment and the results.

(c)   What would be the effect on bubble release of
    (i) placing the experimental apparatus at varying distances from a white light source.
    (ii) adding sodium hydrogencarbonate at a concentration of 1 mg per cm^3 (ml) to the water in the tube carrying the aquatic plant?

(d)   Suggest a modification of the experiment that would result in bubbles of relatively constant size.   (LOND)

5   Write an account of the process of photosynthesis explaining clearly the meaning of the following: light reaction; dark stage (carbon fixation); photosynthetic phosphorylation; C^4 plant.   (O)

6   (a)   Photosynthesis is composed of two distinct stages, a light dependent stage and a light independent (or dark) stage.
    (i) What are the products of the reactions of the light stage?
    (ii) What is the first product of the dark reaction?
    (iii) What is the main end product of the dark reaction?

(b) What **five** conditions are necessary for photosynthesis to occur?

(c) Describe a simple experiment to establish that the presence of **one** of these factors is necessary for photosynthesis.

(d) Name **four** chloroplast pigments involved in photosynthesis.

(e) Suggest **three** ways in which photosynthesis might be increased in crop plants grown in protected environments such as glasshouses. (W)

7 Three almost identical, healthy geranium plants were removed from their pots and all the soil was carefully washed away from their roots. Each was put in a beaker under a bell jar standing on a greased, glass plate.

Fig 3A

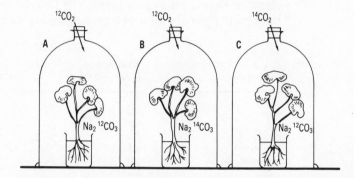

Each beaker contained the same quantity of sodium carbonate solution. In experiment B, radioactively labelled sodium carbonate ($Na_2^{14}CO_3$) was used, while in A and C the beakers contained unlabelled sodium carbonate ($Na_2^{12}CO_3$) solutions. Equal quantities of $^{12}CO_2$ were injected into A and B and the same quantity of radioactive $^{14}CO_2$ was injected into C. After intense illumination for four days, all the leaves were removed and placed, in turn, under the end window of a Geiger-Muller tube. The radioactivity of each leaf was measured over a prolonged, timed period. The results from a large number of experiments are shown below.

Treatment	Average of all readings (counts per minute)
A	43
B	51
C	483

(a) How do you account for the readings produced by the leaves from A?

(b)   By how many times is the radioactivity, resulting from the chemical supplied, greater in the leaves from C than in the leaves from B? Show your calculation.

(c)   What biological processes might account for the large difference between the readings for B and C?

(d)   Suggest **one** reason for the difference in the readings of B and A.

(e)   Give a simple modification of the experiment that you would use to test your suggestion in (d).   (JMB)

8   The graph below shows the relative concentrations of phosphoglyceric acid (PGA) and ribulose diphosphate (RDP or ribulose bisphosphate) in photosynthesising plant material subjected to two different levels of carbon dioxide (CO_2) concentration. Light conditions were optimum throughout the experiment.

Fig 3B

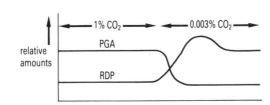

(a)   Explain the changes in the relative amounts of PGA and RDP.

(b)   In the space below construct a diagram to illustrate the principles of the Calvin cycle (the so-called dark stage of photosynthesis). Chemical formulae are not required.   (AEB)

9   An atom of carbon, incorporated in a molecule of carbon dioxide, enters the stoma of a leaf of a higher plant. Sometime later this carbon atom may be located in a molecule of ribulose diphosphate (bisphosphate).

(a)   Outline how this might occur.

(b)   Give any **one** piece of experimental evidence in support of your answer.

(c)   Indicate briefly **three** other possible fates in the plant of the original carbon atom.   (O&C)

10   Which one of the following terms correctly describes the mode of nutrition of an animal which is a scavenger, e.g. *Asellus* (the water louse)?

A   autotrophic
B   parasitic
C   holozoic
D   symbiotic   (CAM)

11   Review the feeding methods in animals other than vertebrates.
                            (LOND)

12   (a)   Briefly describe the mechanical breakdown of cellulose in a *named* herbivorous mammal.

(b)   How are the products of cellulose digestion absorbed?

(c)   Explain how the products of carbohydrate digestion may be utilized by (i) a fungal mycelium, (ii) a germinating seed and (iii) a mammal. (LOND)

13 Describe what you would expect to happen when a suspension of proteins, fats and starch is hydrolysed by activated pancreatic enzymes in a length of Visking (cellulose) tubing suspended in water in a beaker.

To what extent does this experiment represent the structures and functions involved in the processes of digestion and absorption in a mammal? (CAM)

14 What adaptations are used by mammals to enable them to carry out a carnivorous mode of life?

How do the teeth of herbivorous mammals differ from those of carnivores?

Discuss briefly and critically the phrase 'carnivorous plants'. (O&C)

15 With reference to carbohydrates, proteins and nucleic acids, show how monomer molecules are linked to form long chain polymers. (SU)

16 Indicate the importance of each of the following in maintaining good health in man, in each case emphasising its physiological role: amino acids; roughage; a **named** vitamin; sunlight. (O)

17 The digestive secretions of the liver do which of the following
   (1) reduce the surface tension of fat droplets,
   (2) convert fat to fatty acids and glycerol,
   (3) include sodium hydrogen carbonate,
   (4) activate trypsinogen? (JMB)

18 (a) Describe the roles of the liver and the pancreas in
   (i) the digestion of food,
   (ii) the metabolism of absorbed products.
   (b) Account for the fact that a diet of raw liver can alleviate the disease of pernicious anaemia. (JMB)

19 Answer *both* parts **X** and **Y**, which are of equal mark value.
   X Amino acids are described as 'the building blocks' of proteins. Describe *concisely* how and where in the cell this building process takes place. What is the source of amino acids in (a) plants and (b) animals?
   Y Explain carefully, with attention to detail, how you would use *paper chromatography* to determine which amino acids are the building blocks for the protein in *egg albumen*.
   R_f (relative front) is the ratio of the distance moved by a spot to the distance moved by the solvent. If the R_f value for leucine is 0.75 and for alanine 0.38 where would you expect each to be located on your chromatogram if the distance that the solvent moved was 12 cm? (NI)

20 The best separation of substances on a chromatogram would be obtained by
   A drying it, reloading and using the same solvent in the same direction.
   B drying it and using a different solvent in a different direction.

C   drying it, reloading, and using the same solvent in the same direction.

D   running it until the solvent nearly reaches the edge of the paper.   (JMB)

21   R_f values, universally used to describe the movement of a substance in chromatographic studies, are calculated as the quotient of

A $\dfrac{\text{distance moved by solvent front}}{\text{distance moved by substance}}$.

B $\dfrac{\text{distance from origin to the substance}}{\text{distance from the origin to the solvent front}}$.

C $\dfrac{\text{distance moved by substance from solvent surface}}{\text{distance moved by solvent front from solvent surface}}$.

D $\dfrac{\text{distance from the origin to the solvent front}}{\text{distance from the origin to the substance}}$.   (JMB)

22   The autoradiographs illustrated below were developed from a suspension of algae which had been incubated in bright light and whose culture had been injected with ^{14}C bicarbonate solution for different times before a sample was run off and fixed immediately in boiling alcohol.

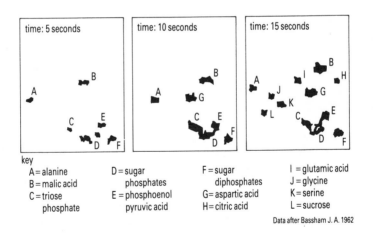

key

A = alanine	D = sugar	F = sugar	I = glutamic acid
B = malic acid	phosphates	diphosphates	J = glycine
C = triose	E = phosphoenol	G = aspartic acid	K = serine
phosphate	pyruvic acid	H = citric acid	L = sucrose

Data after Bassham J. A. 1962

Interpret the results in terms of current ideas on the sequence of reactions involved in carbon fixation in algae during photosynthesis. Your answer should refer only to the products indicated on the autoradiographs.   (AEB)

23   Certain wood-eating termites have a population of flagellates living in their hind-gut. During laboratory investigations the insects can live on pure cellulose and a cellulose-digesting enzyme can be isolated from their hind-gut. If the flagellates are removed, the termites die unless they are fed with glucose.

(a)   Construct a hypothesis, based on the evidence above, to explain the presence of the flagellates.

(b)   Devise a series of experiments to test the validity of your hypothesis.   (AEB)

RESPIRATION

CONTENTS

Respiration is a process carried out in the cytoplasm of all cells, by which chemical energy is transferred from complex organic compounds to the 'energy-carrier' molecules of adenosine triphosphate (ATP). The process of energy transfer from organic compounds to ATP involves many complex enzyme-controlled chemical reactions in which the organic compounds are oxidized to carbon dioxide and water along a variety of pathways.

Anaerobic respiration does not require the presence of oxygen. The complex organic substrates are only partially broken down, resulting in the release of comparatively small amounts of energy and the accumulation of poisonous waste products. Anaerobic respiration is seen in some bacteria and fungi where it is known as **fermentation**.

$$\text{glucose} \rightarrow \text{ethanol} + \text{carbon dioxide} + \text{energy}$$

Anaerobic respiration also occurs in some animal tissues when deprived of oxygen, e.g. exercising muscles.

$$\text{glucose} \rightarrow \text{lactic acid} + \text{energy}$$

In both cases the end products are toxic and if allowed to accumulate, eventually stop the reaction.

Aerobic respiration requires the presence of oxygen. The complex organic substrates are completely broken down to carbon dioxide and water, and comparatively large amounts of energy are released.

$$\text{glucose} + \text{oxygen} \rightarrow \text{carbon dioxide} + \text{water} + \text{energy}$$

Anaerobic and aerobic respiration compared

Anaerobic	Aerobic
No oxygen used	Oxygen used
Incomplete oxidation of substrates and formation of toxic by-products e.g. ethanol and lactic acid which can be further oxidized	Complete oxidation of substrates to CO_2 and H_2O
Low energy yield (68kJ)	Higher energy yield (1292kJ)

The uptake of oxygen and the release of carbon dioxide occurs by means of gaseous exchange with the environment. This gaseous exchange is sometimes referred to as external respiration, as opposed to the internal or tissue respiration occuring in the cells.

INTERNAL OR TISSUE RESPIRATION

Anaerobic respiration occurs in the general cytoplasm or hyaloplasm of the cell, whereas aerobic respiration occurs in the mitochondria. Both processes share common biochemical pathways (Fig 5.1).

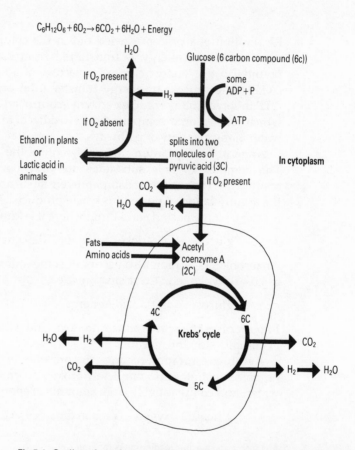

$$C_6H_{12}O_6 + 6O_2 \rightarrow 6CO_2 + 6H_2O + Energy$$

Fig 5.1. *Outline of respiratory pathways.* There are many more steps than those shown, and all steps are catalysed by specific enzymes. Most of the energy released is 'trapped' in ATP as the hydrogen passes down the cytochrome chains to form water.

The production of ethyl alcohol in plants such as yeast under anaerobic conditions is known as fermentation and is exploited commercially in the production of alcohol. The production of lactic acid in animal muscles not receiving sufficient oxygen during strenuous activity leads rapidly to fatigue.

EXERCISE ▶

Exercise 5.1

How many 'turns' of the Krebs' cycle occur in the process of the complete breakdown of a molecule of glucose into carbon dioxide and water?

Answer Two. On the flow chart you will notice that three molecules of CO_2 are given off past the pyruvic acid stage which is a three-carbon compound. Each glucose molecule splits into two pyruvic acid molecules, so the stages from pyruvic acid are all repeated twice for each glucose molecule.

In animals the body movements involved in ventilating a respiratory surface for gaseous exchange are called breathing.

In larger organisms with relatively small surface area to volume ratios, where diffusion alone is insufficient for the transport of oxygen and carbon dioxide between the tissues and the environment, the respiratory gases are carried in circulating body fluids.

COMMENT ▶

The general term 'respiration' can encompass all the aspects mentioned above; namely gaseous exchange, the transport of respiratory gases and the release of energy. The distinction between the meaning of the terms internal or tissue respiration, gaseous exchange or external respiration, and breathing, can be important in the interpretation of examination questions.

ENERGY TRANSFER

In all these processes oxidation of the respiratory substrate is by the removal of hydrogen, which is then oxidized to water in the presence of oxygen. It is during this process of hydrogen and electron transport from substrate to oxygen, along a chain of carriers known as co-enzymes and cytochromes, that the energy transfer occurs.

EFFICIENCY OF RESPIRATION

Not all the energy released in these processes is transferred into ATP: a lot is lost as heat. The efficiency of respiration is calculated by expressing that amount of energy transferred into ATP as a percentage of the total energy available.

For example, the oxidation of one mole of glucose which contains about 2881 kJ mol^{-1} yields 38 moles of ATP, and each mole of ATP traps 33.6kJ. Therefore

$$\text{percentage efficiency} = \frac{38 \times 33.6}{2881} \times 100$$

$$= 44\%$$

RESPIRATORY QUOTIENT

The respiratory quotient (RQ) is the ratio of the amount of carbon dioxide produced to the amount of oxygen taken up during the oxidation of a substrate in unit time. It provides some measure of the main substrate being respired at any given time, for example:

$$\underset{\text{glucose}}{C_6H_{12}O_6} + \underset{\text{oxygen}}{6O_2} \rightarrow \underset{\substack{\text{carbon} \\ \text{dioxide}}}{6CO_2} + \underset{\text{water}}{6H_2O}$$

$$\therefore RQ = \frac{6CO_2}{6O_2} = 1$$

Fats have an RQ of 0.7, but proteins vary so much in composition that estimates for the RQ range between 0.5 and 0.8. Anaerobic respiration will raise the RQ often above 1.0 as there is no oxygen uptake, for example:

$$C_6H_{12}O_6 \rightarrow 2C_2H_5OH + 2CO_2$$

Therefore mixtures of substrates and of aerobic and anaerobic respiration will prevent any simple conclusion being drawn as to the nature of the substrate being used.

EXERCISE ▶

Exercise 5.2
Which of the following would best explain an RQ of just greater than one?
(a)   *Completely anaerobic respiration.*
(b)   *Aerobic respiration of glucose and some fat.*
(c)   *Some anaerobic respiration along with aerobic respiration.*
(d)   *Aerobic respiration of fat.*

GASEOUS EXCHANGE

PLANTS

Small plants with a large surface area to volume ratio, such as many fungi and algae, carry out gaseous exchange by diffusion over their entire surface. Larger plants still tend to have large surface area to volume ratios, due to the form of the structures, for example leaves, and similarly carry out gaseous exchange by diffusion over most of their surface via the stomata.

Considerations of respiratory gaseous exchange in plants are complicated by gaseous exchange that occurs as a result of photosynthesis;

Respiration:

$$C_6H_{12}O_6 + 6O_2 \longrightarrow 6CO_2 + 6H_2O$$

Photosynthesis:

$$6CO_2 + 6H_2O \overset{\underset{\text{light}}{\downarrow}}{\longrightarrow} C_6H_{12}O_6 + 6O_2$$

Thus respiration uses the oxygen released by photosynthesis, and photosynthesis uses the carbon dioxide released by respiration.

At night only respiration proceeds, but as the light intensity increases photosynthesis gradually increases until it equals the rate of respiration. At this point, known as the **compensation point**, there will be no gaseous exchange with the environment.

In full daylight photosynthesis is much faster than respiration, so there is a net uptake of carbon dioxide and release of oxygen.

EXERCISE ➡

Exercise 5.3

Which sequence best illustrates the pathway of carbon dioxide uptake by a leaf?

(a)   *atmosphere → guard cell → sub-stomatal cavity → stoma → inter-cellular spaces in spongy mesophyll → palisade mesophyll → chloroplastid*

(b)   *atmosphere → stoma → sub-stomatal cavity → inter-cellular spaces in spongy mesophyll → palisade mesophyll → chloroplastid*

(c)   *atmosphere → epidermis → palisade mesophyll → chloroplastid*

ANIMALS

Small aquatic animals with a large surface area to volume ratio can utilize their entire body surface for gaseous exchange by diffusion. With increasing size, and therefore decreasing surface area to volume ratio, specialized respiratory surfaces with thin, permeable, large surface areas for gaseous diffusion of oxygen and carbon dioxide are found, richly supplied with capillaries through which blood containing a respiratory pigment is pumped. Such respiratory surfaces are ventilated by breathing movements.

RESPIRATION IN WATER

Most aquatic animals respire through gills, and although of widely different origins, all gills share common features.

Since the gills are supported by water they can have a very large surface area and be very thin without danger of them collapsing, and as there is no danger of desiccation by evaporation they can be well exposed to the external medium which carries the oxygen, namely the water.

Gills are more efficient than the respiratory surfaces of air-breathing animals, and the blood pigments have a greater affinity for oxygen; these features are necessary because of the relatively low concentration of oxygen in water when compared with air.

Fish

Fish gills (Fig 5.2) show all those features mentioned above. In addition the gills have a counter-current blood supply which further aids the uptake of oxygen and the release of carbon dioxide.

Water is pumped over the gills in a continuous through-flow by means of a double pump – the **buccal pump** of the muscles in the floor of the mouth, and the **opercular pump** of the muscles in the operculum (the structure that covers the gills of bony fish).

Thin flaps of skin around the mouth and the edge of the operculum act as valves which ensure a one-way flow over the gills.

The two pumps act alternately so the flow of water over the gills is continuous.

1   With the mouth shut, the floor of the mouth rises and pushes water out over the gills.

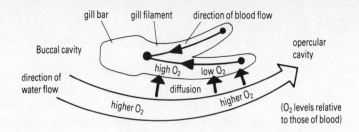

Fig 5.2. *Countercurrent gaseous exchange in fish gills.* The level of oxygen in the water is higher than that of the blood along the whole length of the gill filament, therefore oxygen diffuses in at all times. If the blood flowed in the same direction as the water the level of oxygen in both would soon reach equilibrium and oxygen intake would not occur along the full length of the gill.

2   The mouth opens and the floor of the mouth lowers, drawing more water in through the mouth.

3   At the same time the operculum is shut but bulges out to draw water out over the gills so that even as water is being drawn in through the mouth, it is also being drawn over the gills.

Amphibia

Most amphibia are aquatic or semi-aquatic. The frog has two main respiratory surfaces; the skin and the lungs.

The skin is thin and well vascularized, both oxygen uptake and carbon dioxide excretion by diffusion occur over its surface. The oxygenated blood returning from the skin enters the right auricle and then passes into the single ventricle of the three-chambered heart. From there it can pass along the aorta to the body without all being pumped needlessly through the pulmonary circulation of the lungs.

The lungs are simple with a relatively small surface area, and as there is no thorax they hang in the abdominal cavity. They are ventilated by pumping movements of the floor of the mouth.

EXERCISE ➡

Exercise 5.4

Some amphibia are almost entirely aquatic, and some are almost entirely terrestrial. In which type do you think the lungs are more important in respiration?

Answer Generally the lungs are more important in aquatic types (perhaps rather surprisingly). Water has a low oxygen concentration when compared to air, and in aquatic types uptake oxygen by diffusion over the skin is supplemented by uptake over the lungs.

RESPIRATION IN AIR

Air is much easier to move over a respiratory surface than water, and it has a much higher oxygen content. However, any large, thin, permeable, well vascularized surface exposed to the air will lose water by diffusion and evaporation. To prevent this loss mucus is secreted, but the resulting static layer of water and mucus increases the diffusion distance between the air and the blood, and therefore decreases the efficiency of the surface.

Loss of water by evaporation from respiratory surfaces is a major problem for air-breathing animals.

Insects

The insects are unique in having a gas exchange and transport system separate from the blood system (Fig 5.3). This system of air tubes or trachea gives direct and rapid transport of oxygen in the gaseous state to the respiring tissues, whilst helping to reduce water loss by evaporation.

Fig 5.3. Insect tracheal system.

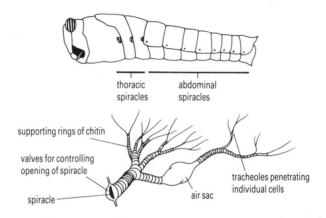

Air is pumped through the system by abdominal movements acting on the thin-walled air sacs. Through flow is achieved by the anterior spiracles opening to allow air to be drawn in as the abdominal volume is increased, and by the posterior spiracles opening to allow air to be forced out as the abdominal volume is decreased.

Carbon dioxide is removed mainly by the blood and is diffused out through the exoskeleton, which although impermeable to water is permeable to gases. Carbon dioxide also combines with nitrogenous wastes to form uric acid in the Malpighian tubules.

Mammals

Mammalian lungs have a large surface area for gaseous exchange by diffusion, being made up of millions of tiny air sacs or alveoli (Fig 5.4). The alveoli have a thin permeable surface of squamous epithelial cells. This large, thin, respiratory surface is richly supplied with capillaries of the pulmonary circulation.

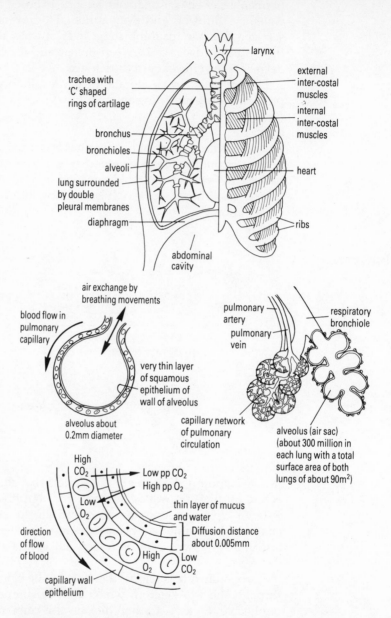

larynx

trachea with 'C' shaped rings of cartilage

external inter-costal muscles

internal inter-costal muscles

bronchus

bronchioles

alveoli

lung surrounded by double pleural membranes

heart

diaphragm

ribs

abdominal cavity

air exchange by breathing movements

blood flow in pulmonary capillary

pulmonary artery

respiratory bronchiole

pulmonary vein

very thin layer of squamous epithelium of wall of alveolus

alveolus about 0.2mm diameter

capillary network of pulmonary circulation

alveolus (air sac) (about 300 million in each lung with a total surface area of both lungs of about 90m^2)

High CO_2

Low pp CO_2

High pp O_2

Low O_2

thin layer of mucus and water

Diffusion distance about 0.005mm

direction of flow of blood

High O_2

Low CO_2

capillary wall epithelium

Fig 5.4. Mammalian (human) thorax and lungs.

The lungs are ventilated as a result of the movements of the diaphragm and the rib cage which make up the walls of the thoracic cavity.

Inspiration and expiration compared

Inspiration	Expiration
1 Muscular diaphragm contracts and moves down	1 Muscular diaphragm relaxes and moves up
2 Inter-costal muscles contract and move ribs up and out	2 Inter-costal muscles relax and ribs move down and in
3 Volume of thorax increased	3 Volume of thorax decreased
4 Internal pressure of thorax decreased below atmospheric pressure	4 Internal pressure of thorax increased above atmospheric pressure
5 Atmospheric pressure forces air into lungs	5 Air forced out of lungs

The in and out flow of air over the same pathway, as seen in the lungs, is known as **tidal flow.** Such tidal flow is less efficient than one-way through-flow (as seen with the flow of water over the gills of fish), as in tidal flow the same air passes over each part of the respiratory surface twice in each breathing cycle. In other words oxygen-depleted air must be breathed out before fresh air can be taken in, whereas in through-flow there is a continuous flow of water of relatively high oxygen concentration over the respiratory surface.

The lungs are held to the internal surface of the wall of the thorax during the breathing movements by the suction effect of the pleural fluid between the double pleural membranes which surround the lungs. The lung tissues are elastic and this enables them to accommodate the changes in size during the breathing movements.

Composition of inspired and expired air

Inspired air	Expired air
21% oxygen	17% oxygen
79% nitrogen	79% nitrogen
0.03% carbon dioxide	4% carbon dioxide
Variable water vapour	Saturated water vapour
Atmospheric temperature	Body temperature
Bacteria	Bacteria

Control
Although voluntary control can be exerted over breathing (essential for speech in man), the basic rhythms are involuntary, being controlled by rhythmic discharges of nerve impulses from the respiratory control centres in the medulla oblongata of the brain. These respiratory control centres respond primarily to the level of blood carbon dioxide, with an increase causing an increase in breathing rate.

EXERCISE ➡

Exercise 5.5
Which of the following best illustrates the sequence of events during inspiration in a mammal?
(a)   diaphragm contracts → diaphragm down → inter-costal muscles contract → ribs move up and out → intra-thoracic pressure decreases → air enters lungs under atmospheric pressure

(b)   *diaphragm down → diaphragm contracts → ribs move up and out → inter-costal muscles contract → intra-thoracic pressure decreases → air enters lungs under atmospheric pressure*
(c)   *inter-costal muscles contract → ribs move up and out→diaphragm contracts → diaphragm down → air enters lungs under atmospheric pressure→intra-thoracic pressure decreases*

TRANSPORT OF RESPIRATORY GASES

Gaseous exchange occurs over the surfaces of the alveoli between the air and the blood, with oxygen diffusing into the blood and carbon dioxide diffusing out.

The oxygen combines with the haemoglobin in the red blood corpuscles (RBC) to form oxyhaemoglobin, in which form it is transported to the tissues (Fig 5.5). This combination of oxygen and haemoglobin is a 'loose' physical association and is easily reversed, releasing oxygen to the tissues. This will occur in areas of low oxygen concentration and high carbon dioxide concentration, namely in the respiring tissues.

Carbon dioxide is carried from the tissues mainly in the form of sodium hydrogencarbonate ($NaHCO_3$) and potassium hydrogen-carbonate ($KHCO_3$) as a result of interaction between the red blood corpuscles and the plasma.

With some in solution in the plasma, as carbon dioxide, and some in combination with the haemoglobin as carbaminohaemoglobin.

When the blood reaches the capillaries of the pulmonary circulation the carbon dioxide is released and diffuses out into the alveoli to be removed by exhalation.

EXERCISE ▶

Exercise 5.6
Which of the alternatives best completes the following statement? 'Oxyhaemoglobin releases its oxygen to respiring tissues **because**:
(a)   *the Bohr shift moves the oxygen from the haemoglobin to the respiring tissues.*
(b)   *the relatively high concentration of CO_2 produced by respiring tissues decreases the affinity of haemoglobin for oxygen.*
(c)   *the relatively high concentration of CO_2 produced by respiring tissues increases the affinity of haemoglobin for oxygen.*

EXPERIMENTAL WORK

Most simple experiments on respiration are concerned with breathing movements in invertebrate animals, or with the measurement of gaseous exchange.

Investigation of breathing movements This usually requires the observation of these movements under varying conditions. For example, an invertebrate such as a locust may be placed in a glass tube and its breathing movements observed under varying conditions of temperature, or carbon dioxide concentration.

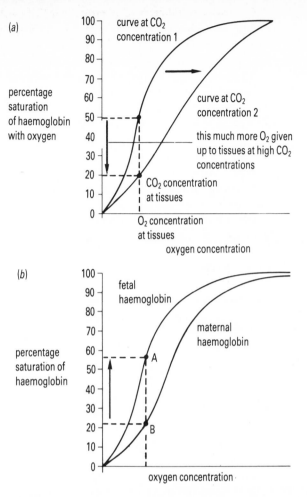

Fig 5.5. *Transport of oxygen by haemoglobin.* (a) *The Bohr shift of mammalian haemoglobin association/dissociation curves.* The curve at CO_2 concentration 2 is shifted to the right of curve 1 by an increased CO_2 concentration. This is known as the Bohr shift and results in the blood releasing oxygen more easily to the tissues at low oxygen concentration.

(b) *Association/dissociation curves of mammalian maternal and fetal haemoglobin.* Fetal haemoglobin loads up higher (A) from lower oxygenated haemoglobin in maternal placental capillaries (B). This is a significant factor in viviparity, as without it the fetus would not be able to 'pick up' enough oxygen from the maternal circulation, since the arteries supplying the placenta arise from the maternal iliac arteries a good distance from the maternal lungs.

In ectothermic animals, increase in temperature up to a certain optimum (usually 30–40 °C) increases the rate of enzyme-catalysed metabolic reactions, and therefore increases the rate of tissue respiration, which in turn results in the need for an increase in the breathing rate.

In most animals the respiratory control centres are sensitive to the carbon dioxide concentration of the body fluids, with an increase in carbon dioxide concentration causing an increase in breathing rate. An increase in the external concentration of carbon dioxide will cause an increase in the carbon dioxide concentration of the body fluids by decreasing the concentration gradient of carbon dioxide between the tissues and the air, and thus slowing down the rate of its diffusion out of the animal. This in turn will stimulate the respiratory control centres to increase the rate of breathing.

When interpreting the results of such experiments it is important to explain them fully in terms of these internal physiological effects.

Investigation of gaseous exchange This usually involves the measurement of volume changes or the detection of pH changes.

In both cases there are problems when working with plant material in relation to the gaseous exchanges of photosynthesis.

Volume changes

Those methods involving the measurement of volume changes require an understanding of the basic equation of respiration:

$$C_6H_{12}O_6 + 6O_2 \longrightarrow 6CO_2 + 6H_2O$$

From this it can be seen that in normal aerobic respiration of carbohydrates the volume of oxygen uptake is equal to the volume of carbon dioxide output.

If the organism is placed in a closed system containing a carbon dioxide absorbent material such as potassium hydroxide (KOH), the resultant decrease in volume will be equal to the volume of carbon dioxide evolved, which in turn is equal to the volume of oxygen uptake.

When carrying out such experiments, great care must be taken to avoid volume changes due to external temperature fluctuations.

The apparatus (respirometer, Fig 5.6) must also be airtight, as any leaks can be another serious source of error; any such leaks will prevent the true decrease in volume due to carbon dioxide absorption from being measured. Results from such respirometer experiments should be given as cm^3 O_2 uptake per gram of body weight per unit time (e.g. per minute).

pH changes

Those experiments involving the detection of pH changes are based on the fact that carbon dioxide is a so-called 'acid gas', producing an acid solution. Therefore the carbon dioxide evolved in respiration can be detected by the use of indicator solutions.

Titration of the solution containing the indicator, both before and after exposure to the respiring organism, would allow the amount of carbon dioxide evolved to be measured; however, in practical examinations simple observation of the change in colour of the indicator solution is all that is required. A measure of the rate of respiration can

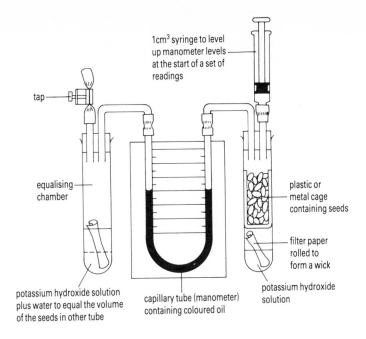

1cm³ syringe to level up manometer levels at the start of a set of readings

tap

equalising chamber

plastic or metal cage containing seeds

filter paper rolled to form a wick

potassium hydroxide solution plus water to equal the volume of the seeds in other tube

capillary tube (manometer) containing coloured oil

potassium hydroxide solution

Fig 5.6. *Simple respirometer.* The wicks serve to increase the surface area of potassium hydroxide exposed to the contents of the tube. The equalizing chamber serves to cancel out any alteration to the readings of the manometer caused by fluctuations in temperature, as any change in volume caused by a temperature change on the right-hand side will be matched by an equal change in volume on the left-hand side. To further reduce changes due to temperature fluctuations the two tubes can be immersed in a water bath (with the manometer outside).

be obtained by recording the time taken for the indicator to change colour.

QUESTION ▶

Q.   Give a concise account of anaerobic respiration (9)
What are cytochromes? (3)
Describe their role in aerobic respiration (8)

COMMENT ▶

This question requires biochemical flow chart diagrams, but only as part of the explanation; and careful selection of material is necessary, especially in the second part where only one aspect of aerobic respiration is required.

**OUTLINE ▶
ANSWER**

Anaerobic respiration (9)
Enzyme catalysed breakdown of glucose in absence of oxygen

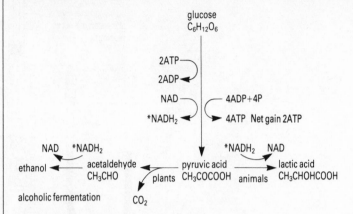

Points required in addition to diagram include;
occurs in cytoplasm not mitochondria;
Krebs' cycle not involved;
animals can 'clear' lactic acid by oxidation pathways if oxygen becomes available;
plants cannot use ethanol;
majority of organisms partial anaerobes, capable of anaerobic respiration for short periods of oxygen lack.

Cytochromes (3)
cell pigments, chromoproteins containing iron;
conjugated proteins with haem group linked to protein;
located within mitochondria;

Role (8)
electron carriers in aerobic respiration;
respiratory substrate is oxidized producing a reduced co-enzyme;
electrons pass from reduced co-enzymes e.g. $NADH_2$, to a sequence of cytochromes and the final reaction with hydrogen and oxygen to form water;
each cytochrome in the chain is alternately reduced and oxidized as the electrons pass along, with the iron changing from the oxidized to the reduced state and back;
this series of oxidations/reductions releases energy and is coupled to ATP formation;

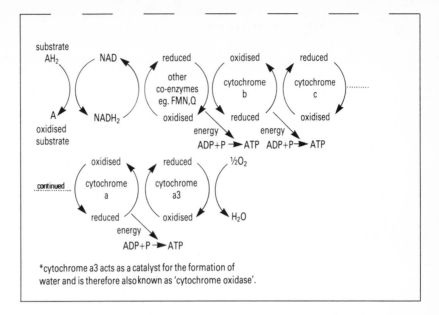

*cytochrome a3 acts as a catalyst for the formation of water and is therefore also known as 'cytochrome oxidase'.

QUESTIONS

1   During respiration, pyruvic acid may be
    (1)   produced during the tricarboxylic acid cycle.
    (2)   decarboxylated to a two-carbon compound.
    (3)   formed only in the presence of oxygen.
    (4)   converted to lactic acid in muscle cells.   (JMB)

2   Compare the biochemical changes, beginning with pyruvic acid, which take place in aerobic and anaerobic respiration. What is the difference in the energy output?   (SU)

3   How is ATP generated in cells? Discuss in detail the relationships between ATP synthesis and the function of **either** mitochondria **or** chloroplasts.   (O)

4   The respiratory quotient of an active person is normally in the range 0.85 to 0.90. If a person is deprived of food for 24 hours the RQ drops to 0.75. This is because
    A   the person becomes less energetic.
    B   the basal metabolic rate changes.
    C   less energy is obtained via the glycolytic pathway.
    D   less carbohydrate is metabolised.   (JMB)

5   (a)   Explain what is meant by Respiratory Quotient (RQ).
    (b)   Write a chemical **equation** to explain why the RQ for the complete oxidation of glucose is 1.0.
    (c)   What is the value of the RQ for the complete oxidation of
            (i) protein,
            (ii) fat?
    (d)   The RQ for a resting human being is approximately 0.85. A man undertook violent exercise for 30 seconds and his RQ was

measured at regular intervals for the following hour. The results are plotted below.

In the period immediately following exercise, lactic acid accumulating in the muscles lowers the pH of the blood. The change in pH stimulates the respiratory centres and increases the rate of breathing.

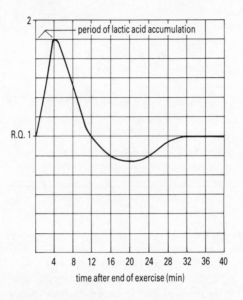

Describe the effect of the increased respiratory rate on the pH of the blood.

(*e*) Explain the rise in RQ during the four minute period following violent exercise.

(*f*) Explain the subsequent fall in RQ.

(*g*) How long does the RQ remain below the normal level?

(*h*) Do you think that RQ measurements are a reliable method of determining which foodstuffs are being metabolised by an animal? Answer 'yes' or 'no', and then explain your answer.   (W)

6   Insects breathe by means of a tracheal system which opens to the exterior of the body via spiracles. The opening and closing of the

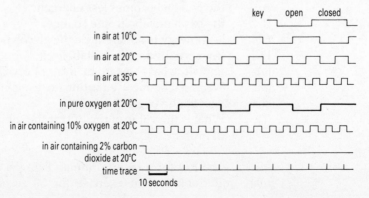

spiracles can be regulated by muscles. The following traces indicate the opening and closing of the spiracles of a flea under different experimental conditions.

(a) Describe the effect of temperature on spiracular activity.

(b) What is the temperature coefficient (Q_{10}) for the interval $10\,°C$ to $20\,°C$?

(c) Suggest why changes in the oxygen concentration result in different spiracular activity.

(d) (i) What is the main effect on spiracular activity of increasing carbon dioxide concentration to 2%?

(ii) What does this suggest about the control of the spiracles?

(AEB)

7 Describe the ways by which oxygen from the environment reaches the respiring tissues in a mammal and in an insect. (SCE)

8 (a) Describe the methods and mechanics of gas exchange in (i) a green plant, (ii) an insect, (iii) a fish, and (iv) a mammal.

(b) Compare the properties of air and water as respiratory media.

(LOND)

9 The graph below illustrates the rates of pulmonary and cutaneous gas exchange at different times of year in *Rana temporaria*, the common frog. Observations were made in the Northern hemisphere.

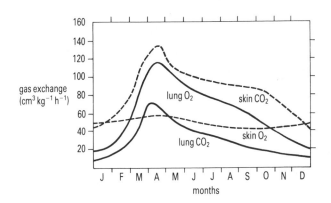

Comment on the conclusions which can be drawn from these data about the structure and physiology of the common frog.

(LOND)

10 Describe inhalation and exhalation in a **named** mammal. Show how inhalation–exhalation cycles are controlled and maintained in the mammal. (O&C)

11   The graph below shows the dissociation curves for human oxy-haemoglobin at three partial pressures of carbon dioxide.

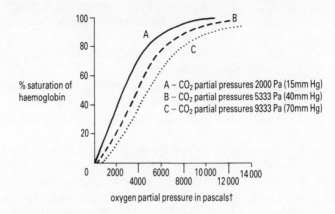

oxygen partial pressure in pascals†

*A pascal (Pa) is a unit of pressure. A pressure of 100 000 pascals is approximately equal to atmospheric pressure (760 mm Hg).

(*a*)   What effect does an increase in the carbon dioxide pressure have on the oxygen-carrying capacity of haemoglobin?

(*b*)   State where in the mammalian body the partial pressure of carbon dioxide is likely to be (i) low, (ii) high.

(*c*)   What effect will variations in the partial pressure of carbon dioxide in different parts of the mammalian body have on the transport of oxygen?

(*d*)   The graph below shows the dissociation curve for myoglobin (the respiratory pigment in muscle) compared with that of haemoglobin in the same animal.

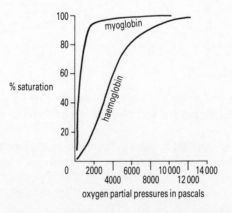

oxygen partial pressures in pascals

State the physiological significance of the relationship between these two pigments.   (LOND)

12   Dissociation curves for a solution of haemoglobin (curve X) and for whole blood (curve Y) are shown below. Points L and T represent the levels of oxygen in the lungs and tissues respectively.

Blood is likely to be a more effective respiratory fluid than a solution of haemoglobin because blood

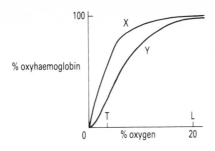

A   picks up less oxygen in the lungs than does haemoglobin.
B   picks up more oxygen in the lungs than does haemoglobin.
C   yields more oxygen to the tissues than does haemoglobin.
D   yields less oxygen to the tissues than does haemoglobin.

(CAM)

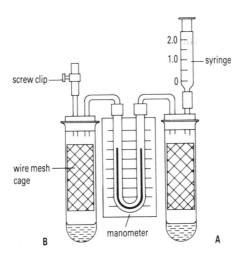

A *respirometer* of constant pressure pattern as shown above, was set up with 1.8 g of fresh dock leaves in tube A and an equivalent mass of paper in tube B. A constant temperature was maintained throughout a series of experiments.

(i) Explain *concisely* how the apparatus is handled to measure volume changes in A relative to B during a known period of time.

In a first experiment tubes A and B were totally covered by foil and a CO_2 absorber was placed in the bottom of each tube. Observation showed a gradual decrease of volume in A.

In a second experiment tube A was uncovered and placed 0.5 m from an artificial light source. A solution of sodium hydrogen carbonate was substituted in the two tubes to maintain a raised CO_2 level. Observation recorded a continual increase of volume in A.

A third experiment was similar to the second except that tube A was only 0.4 m from the same light source. The syringe readings in cm^3, taken at intervals after the start of each experiment, are given in the table below:

		Time in minutes from start					
		0	5	10	15	20	30
Expt. 1	Foil covered	2.0	1.8	1.7	1.5	1.3	1.0
Expt. 2	0.5 m from light	0	0.2	0.5	0.7	0.9	1.4
Expt. 3	0.4 m from light	0	0.4	0.9	1.4	1.8	Off scale

(ii) Why does the volume in tube A *decrease* in the first experiment?

(iii) What is the cause of the *increase* in volume in the second experiment?

(iv) What difference in results might occur if a temperature rise of 10 °C was allowed to occur during the first or second experiments?

(v) Light intensity varies inversely with the square of the distance from a light source $\left(I \infty \dfrac{1}{d^2}\right)$. How intense is the light at 0.4 m? Call the intensity at 0.5 m, 1.0.

(vi) Using the three light intensities (zero for the first experiment, 1.0 for the second and your answer to (v) for the third), plot a simple graph of total gas volume changes in one hour (+ for gas increase and − for gas decrease) against light intensity.

What is the significance of the light intensity where gas volume neither increases or decreases?

(vii) Calculate the *respiratory rate* for the leaf material, expressing your result in cm^3 per gram per hour.

(viii) A similar mass of blowfly larvae was placed in an identical apparatus but the results differed in two respects; (*a*) they caused a much greater reduction of volume in the first experiment, and (*b*) they caused no volume change in the presence of sodium hydrogen carbonate in the second experiment. Explain these observations.

(NI)

14 Myoglobin and haemoglobin are respiratory pigments found in mammals. They share a similar structure in that both are composed of globin (protein) chains each of which bears one haem group. A

haemoglobin molecule is composed of four such globin chains and myoglobin of just one. In which one of the following ways does myoglobin differ from haemoglobin? It

A   has a larger molecular weight.

B   combines with less oxygen per molecule.

C   is incapable of combining with carbon monoxide.

D   is found only in red blood cells.   (JMB)

TRANSPORT

CONTENTS

Small, relatively simple organisms have a large surface area to volume ratio (SA/V), and diffusion is usually a sufficient mechanism for the internal transport of substances, for example for the transport of carbon dioxide, waste products, and oxygen to and from the external surface.

This internal transport by diffusion is further aided by the particular shapes of some organisms and their parts. For example in the Coelenterates with the large enteron filled with the external medium (water); in the flattened shape of the acoelomate Platyhelminthes, and the flattened form of plants such as the gametophytes of liverworts and the leaves of higher plants.

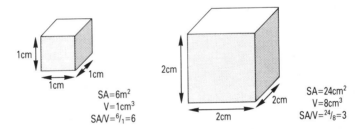

Fig 6.1. The decrease in surface area to volume ratio with increase in size.

With the increase in size and complexity in the coelomate animals, and the consequent decrease in SA/V, there is seen the development of specialized mass transport systems for the rapid and efficient transport of substances to and from the external medium, and between the different tissues and organs.

Such mass flow transport systems have a fluid (blood) circulated by mechanical pumping within a system of blood vessels. Diffusion is still important in transport, as it is by diffusion through large surface areas that substances enter and leave the blood, for example at the lungs and at the surface of the small intestine in mammals.

Higher plants have flattened leaves with large SA/V and diffusion is still important, not only in exchanges with the environment, but also in the subsequent internal transport of substances, for example the uptake of carbon dioxide through the stomata and its transport to the photosynthesizing palisade mesophyll cells via the inter-cellular spaces of the spongy mesophyll.

With the development of the dominant terrestrial sporophyte generation, mass flow systems are necessary between the roots in the soil and the leaves in the air; but in plant transport systems there is no mechanical pumping of the fluids.

EXERCISE ➡

Exercise 6.1

Would it be true to say that size, and in particular surface area to volume ratio (SA/V), is the only determining factor as to whether an animal has a circulatory system?

Answer No. Level of organization is also important. There are many examples of coelomate animals with a circulatory system, which have a larger *SA/V* than acoelomates without a circulatory system. For example some arthropods are smaller than some nematodes.

TRANSPORT IN ANIMALS

Blood vascular systems can be either 'open' or 'closed'.

Open blood system	Closed blood system
1 blood only enclosed in vessels for part of circulation	1 blood is enclosed in vessels for whole circulation except e.g. liver and spleen
2 tissues bathed in blood	2 tissues bathed in tissue fluid
3 blood flow slow	3 blood flows faster
4 blood pressure low	4 blood pressure higher
5 no lymphatic system	5 lymphatic system drains excess tissue fluid.

INSECT OPEN BLOOD VASCULAR SYSTEM

There is a dorsal tubular heart within a pericardial cavity. The heart is expanded by contractions of the alary muscles, and blood is drawn into the heart through the valved ostia (see Fig 6.1). The heart then contracts in a wave-like manner from the posterior to the anterior, forcing blood forwards into the dorsal aorta. From here it flows into the large blood spaces of the body cavity, known as the haemocoel, and bathes the tissues directly.

MAMMALIAN CLOSED BLOOD VASCULAR SYSTEM

There is a muscular compact chambered heart pumping blood around a closed system of vessels (see Fig 6.2). There is a double circulation; the **pulmonary circulation** to the lungs, and the **systemic circulation** to the rest of the body. The blood passes through the heart twice on each complete circulation.

The double circulation allows blood to be pumped to the lungs under a relatively low pressure, which prevents the delicate pulmonary system from being damaged, and also prevents excessive tissue fluid formation which would flood the alveoli.

At the same time it allows blood to be pumped to the systemic or body circulation from the powerful left ventricle of the heart under a relatively high pressure, which causes tissue fluid formation at the tissues, where it is needed to transport substances to and from the tissues.

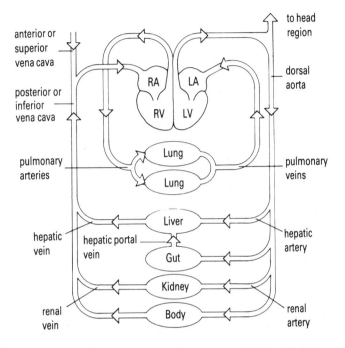

Fig 6.2. *Simplified mammalian circulatory system.* The blood from the gut goes to the liver via the hepatic portal vein.

MAMMALIAN HEART

The structure of the mammalian heart is shown in Fig 6.3.

Cardiac cycle

1 Blood flows into the auricles, pushes open the bicuspid and tricuspid valves and fills both the ventricles and auricles.
2 The auricles then contract (auricular systole) forcing blood into the already full ventricles and causing them to stretch.
3 The ventricles then contract (ventricular systole) forcing the blood up through the semi-lunar or pocket valves at the entrance to the pulmonary arteries and the main aorta, and shutting the bicuspid and tricuspid valves (first heart sound).
4 The ventricles then relax (ventricular-diastole) and the blood falls back, filling and shutting the pocket valves in the pulmonary arteries and the main aorta (second heart-sound).

5   All the valves are now closed and the cycle is repeated. In man at rest the entire cardiac cycle takes about 0.8s.

COMMENT ▶

It must be remembered that the valve movements are passive, being caused by movements of the blood; thus in descriptions of the cycle, the movements must be described in the correct sequence, with blood movements *preceding* valve movements, and not the other way around.

Cardiac muscle

Cardiac muscle is **myogenic**, that is it contracts rhythmically without any nervous stimulation. However the rate of its contraction is controlled by nervous and hormonal stimulation. The sympathetic part of the autonomic nervous system increases the contraction rate, and the parasympathetic part decreases the rate. Nervous impulses are relayed to the heart via the sinu-atrial node or 'pacemaker'.

The hormones adrenaline and thyroxine also increase the rate.

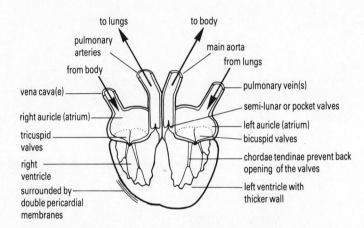

Fig 6.3. *Mammalian heart structure*. The blood passes through the heart twice in each complete circulation of the body. Such double circulation is also found in birds, which also have a high metabolic rate.

BLOOD VESSELS

Arteries

The vessels carrying blood away from the heart are known as arteries, and are of two main types.

Those close to the heart are large **elastic arteries**. These have thick elastic walls, which are stretched by the volume of blood pumped out of the heart by contraction of the ventricles. When the ventricles relax, the recoil of these elastic walls assists in pumping the blood to the tissues.

EXERCISE ▶

Exercise 6.2
What is the relationship between the pulse rate and the heart beat?

Answer The pulse rate follows the heart beat. On each contraction of the left ventricle, about 70 cm³ of blood is forced into the already full elastic arteries, causing a pressure wave to pass along the arterial wall. This is felt as the pulse.

The elastic arteries lead into the **muscular arteries**. These have more smooth muscle fibres than elastic fibres in their walls. The muscle fibres are in a continuous state of contraction or tone. As the muscular arteries divide into finer and finer branches, and eventually into the **arterioles**, this muscular tone is important in resisting the flow of blood and helping to generate the necessary blood pressure. The arterioles lead into the **capillaries**.

Capillaries

Capillaries branch finely in capillary beds throughout all the tissues. Capillary beds can be by-passed by through-vessels which connect arterioles directly with venules. In this way blood can be supplied to some regions when there is high demand (for example the gut during digestion and absorption) and restricted to others where there is less demand or less priority.

Capillaries present a large surface area for the exchange of materials between the blood and the tissues. This exchange is aided by the decreased rate of flow of blood that occurs as the blood passes through the capillaries.

EXERCISE ▶

Exercise 6.3
What is the main reason for the drop in the velocity of the blood in the capillaries?

Answer The velocity of the blood is inversely proportional to the total cross-sectional area of the vessels. Thus the greater the total cross-sectional area, the slower the flow. Although individual capillaries are the narrowest vessels in the circulation, the total cross-sectional area of the capillaries in use is up to one thousand times greater than the cross-section of the aorta. Thus the velocity of blood in the aorta is about 420 mm per second, and in the capillaries about 0.5 mm per second.

The diameter of a capillary is just greater than the diameter of the red blood corpuscles (about 0.8 μm), so that the corpuscles are forced to flow through in single file. This brings them close to the capillary wall through which exchanges occur.

The high systemic blood pressure forces fluid from the plasma through the walls of the capillaries, which are only one cell thick.

Some have pores to assist this process, for example in the endocrine glands, renal glomeruli and villi of the small intestine (all regions of high exchanges).

The fluid that is exuded is known as **tissue fluid**, and carries oxygen, nutrients, antibodies, blood clot enzymes and blood platelets, white blood cells, and hormones to the tissues; and substances such as carbon dioxide and poisonous nitrogenous wastes away from the tissues (see Fig 6.4).

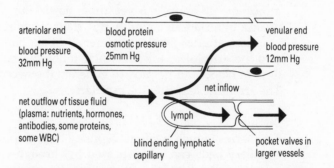

Fig 6.4. *Tissue fluid formation.* The blood pressure falls along the length of the capillary, but the blood osmotic pressure remains fairly constant. Therefore at the venular end water is drawn back into the capillary by osmosis. That which is not drawn back into the capillary, enters the lymphatic capillary (along with a complex of solutes) and becomes known as lymph.

Veins

Capillaries lead into venules, which in turn lead into veins.

Veins are relatively large in cross-section and have thin, non-muscular walls, with pocket valves at intervals. The veins receive blood at very low pressure, and its movement back to the heart is helped by the skeletal muscles massaging the veins and squeezing the venous blood along. The unidirectional pocket valves ensure that the flow is towards the heart.

Arteries and veins compared

Arteries	Veins
1 Thicker wall with muscle and elastic tissue.	1 Thinner wall with less muscle and elastic tissue.
2 Smaller lumen compared to diameter.	2 Larger lumen compared to diameter.
3 No valves (except at entrance to aorta and pulmonary arteries).	3 Pocket valves at intervals.
4 Carry blood under high pressure away from the heart. Pulse.	4 Carry blood under low pressure to the heart. No pulse.

LYMPH AND THE LYMPHATIC SYSTEM

The tissue fluid which is not reabsorbed back into the capillaries enters the blind-ending lymphatic capillaries and becomes **lymph**.

The lymphatic capillaries lead into wider lymph vessels which are similar in structure to the veins, having thin walls and pocket valves.

At intervals in the system there are swellings known as lymph nodes which play an important role in the defence of the body against infection. They contain large fixed phagocytic cells or **macrophages**, which filter out and engulf any foreign bodies.

They also contain T-lymphocytes which circulate in the body fluids and produce antibodies, and B-lymphocytes which differentiate into plasma cells and release antibodies to circulate in the blood.

Lymph is moved within the system by the massaging effect of contracting skeletal muscle, with the pocket valves ensuring a one-way flow back to the venous system in the vena cavae near the heart where it re-enters the blood vascular system.

STRUCTURE AND FUNCTION OF MAMMALIAN BLOOD

Blood is the specialized fluid tissue of the transport system. It consists of fluid plasma and suspended cells.

1 Plasma – 55% blood volume.
2 Erythrocytes (red blood corpuscles) – 45% blood volume.
3 Leucocytes (white blood cells).
4 Platelets.

Plasma

Plasma consists of 90% water and 10% materials in suspension and in solution. There are many such materials, both inorganic and organic, some of which are materials being transported e.g.

1 End products of digestion e.g. amino acids, glucose, fatty acids and glycerol.
2 Waste products e.g. urea, creatine.
3 Carbon dioxide as hydrogencarbonate ions which act as buffers.
4 Oxygen in simple solution.

A major group of substances which are actually part of the plasma are the plasma proteins which are formed in the liver, e.g.

1 Serum globulins
Of which some are antibodies, and some are important in the transport of hormones and vitamins.
2 Fibrinogen
Important in blood clotting.

Erythrocytes or red blood corpuscles (*RBC*)

In man these are small, non-nucleate biconcave discs.

They contain haemoglobin, which combines reversibly with oxygen to form oxyhaemoglobin.

The biconcave shape increases the surface area for gaseous exchange at the lungs and the tissues.

Their average diameter in man is 7–8 micrometres, which, almost being the same as the diameter of the capillaries, ensures that they move through capillaries in single file. This further aids gaseous exchange by bringing all the red blood corpuscles close to the walls of the capillaries.

EXERCISE ▶

Exercise 6.4
Some invertebrates have haemoglobin in solution in the plasma. What advantages are there in vertebrates having haemoglobin in corpuscles?

Answer Vertebrates have true muscular hearts and closed circulatory systems. If the haemoglobin was in solution in the plasma, the viscosity of the blood would be increased, which would make the blood harder to pump. Also the haemoglobin would be lost via pressure filtration by the kidneys.

Leucocytes or white blood corpuscles
Leucocytes are larger nucleated cells important in the body's defence against disease. There are several different types, including

1 **granulocytes** which engulf bacteria and viruses by phagocytosis,
2 **lymphocytes** which form antibodies.

Platelets
Platelets are fragments of large nucleated cells known as megakaryocytes, which originate in the bone marrow. They have an important role in blood clotting.

They aggregate at the site of injury and form plugs, and release substances which cause vascoconstriction, which arrests capillary bleeding.

In blood clotting, damaged cells and platelets release an enzyme, thrombokinase or thromboplastin. This, in the presence of calcium and vitamin K, converts plasma prothrombin into the enzyme thrombin. This in turn converts the soluble plasma protein fibrinogen into insoluble fibrous fibrin. These fibres entangle red blood corpuscles to form the clot. The process normally takes about ten minutes.

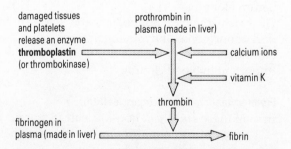

Fig 6.5. Sequence of events in blood clotting.

BLOOD GROUPS

A, B, O System

Erythrocyte membranes bear different antigens.
They may bear antigen A or B, both, or neither.
The plasma contains antibodies.

Blood group	Antigen	Antibody
A	A	b
B	B	a
AB	A & B	none
0	none	a & b

Antigen A is attacked by antibody a.
Antigen B is attacked by antibody b.
The antibodies are ready formed in the plasma, even though it may never have been exposed to the particular antigen.
The antigens do not develop strongly until after birth, and therefore do not cause problems in pregnancy (unlike the Rhesus blood groups).
In blood transfusions the recipient's plasma must be compatible with the donor's erythrocytes, as if they are not a large number of the recipient's antibodies will agglutinate the incoming erythrocytes of the donor, blocking capillaries and disrupting the circulation.
The recipient's erythrocytes are usually unaffected by the smaller amounts of donor antibodies coming in.
Also donor antibodies are absorbed by the recipient's tissues.

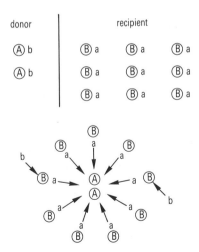

Fig 6.6. *Blood groups in transfusions.* Group AB has no antibodies to attack any incoming antigen and is known as the **universal recipient**. Group O has no antigen to be attacked by any antibodies and is known as the **universal donor**.

Rhesus system

Erythrocytes may also bear an antigen also found in Rhesus monkeys. 85% of the population have the antigen and are Rhesus positive(Rh+). 15% of the population do not have the antigen and are Rhesus negative(Rh−).

Unlike the A,B,O system, antibodies against the Rhesus antigen are not present until a Rh− person is exposed to the Rh antigen.

In transfusions:

Rh− into Rh+ is safe as no antigen is coming in.

Rh+ into Rh− is not safe as foreign antigens are coming in, which will stimulate antibody production.

In pregnancy danger occurs if a Rh− mother carries a Rh+ foetus.

Leakage of foetal Rh+ erythrocytes into the mother stimulates the mother's immune system to produce anti-Rh antibodies.

The first baby is usually born without problems.

However, with a second foetus, the ready formed maternal anti-Rh antibodies invade the foetus and agglutinate its Rh+ erythrocytes.

This may be prevented by injecting the mother with Rh antibodies immediately after the first birth. These destroy any foetal Rh+ cells in the mother, and prevent her immune system being stimulated. The injected antibodies soon break down and disappear.

TRANSPORT IN PLANTS

There are two mass flow transport systems in the flowering plant, one for the transport of water and dissolved minerals from the roots to the leaves; and the other for the transport of organic compounds.

TRANSPORT OF WATER

Water is transported from the roots to the leaves in the xylem tissue. This consists of the elongated tracheids and vessels with their strong, waterproof, lignified walls. They have no living contents and the water moves through the empty tubes. The waterproof nature of lignin keeps the water in the lumen of the elements, and its great strength prevents the tubes from collapsing under the suction of the forces created by the upward flow of water. Pits in the lignified walls of the tracheids and vessels allow water to move laterally between adjacent elements.

WATER UPTAKE

There are two main pathways of water uptake from the soil to the xylem tissue; the cytoplasmic pathway, and the cell wall pathway.

The **cytoplasmic pathway** (Fig 6.7, pathway A) involves water entering the root hair cell by osmosis from the more dilute (hypotonic) soil solution, through the differentially permeable cell membrane, into the more concentrated (hypertonic) cell contents. This cell thus becomes hypotonic to its neighbouring root cortex parenchyma cell, and water moves across the root cortex along this osmotic gradient, through the endodermis to the xylem.

The **cell wall pathway** (Fig 6.7, pathway B) involves water being drawn into the permeable cellulose cell wall of the root hairs, and thence in the cell walls and inter-cellular spaces of the root cortex, through the endodermis and into the xylem, by means of the cohesive pull of the upward movement of water in the transpiration stream.

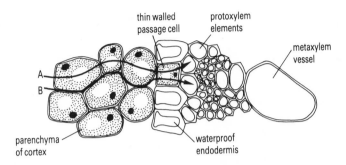

Fig 6.7. *The passage of water across a root of a dicotyledon flowering plant.*
Pathway A. Water is drawn by osmosis from cell to cell and this is the path of highest resistance across the root.
Pathway B. As water is drawn up the plant by the transpiration stream the cohesion of water results in water being drawn across the root cortex through the inter-cellular spaces and the spaces within the cellulose cell walls. Thus the water never crosses a living membrane (except in the thin walled passage cells of the endodermis) and this is the path of least resistance across the root.

EXERCISE ▶

Exercise 6.5
What problem exists with the 'osmotic gradient' theory of water transport across the root, when the water reaches the xylem?

Answer The xylem consists of dead tubular elements (vessels and tracheids) with lignified walls. Water is continually being swept up the plant by the transpiration stream, and it is difficult to see how a sufficiently high concentration of salts could accumulate in the xylem tissue to draw water from the endodermal passage cells by osmosis. It is suggested that one of the roles of the endodermal passage cells could be to actively secrete salts into the xylem, so that water can follow passively by osmosis.

MECHANISM OF UPWARD MOVEMENT OF WATER

Once in the xylem the water is moved up the plant by the cohesive pull of the transpiration stream.

Water evaporates from the surface of the spongy mesophyll cells of the leaf into the sub-stomatal cavity, and from there through the stomata into the atmosphere.

This generates a 'pull' on the continuous column of water in the xylem tissue. This process is known as transpiration.

This column of water is held at the top by the water-holding properties of cellulose, and is supported along its length by surface forces of attraction to the lignified walls of the xylem vessels and tracheids.

In the spring many plants develop a high positive root pressure. For example, de-topped plants will exude xylem sap at a relatively high positive pressure. This may well assist the upward movement of water in the xylem, but the forces involved are not great enough to account for water movement to heights greater than about 10 metres, a height exceeded by many trees.

COMMENT ▶

The transpiration stream from the roots, up the xylem of the stem to the leaves, depends on the cohesion of a continuous column of water. Cohesion is the force holding a liquid together owing to the attraction between its molecules. Should the water column break and air bubbles appear, then the cohesive pull up the plant by the evaporation of water from the leaf would be lost. Although the water column in individual xylem elements does get broken from time to time, there is always a continuous water column in the xylem tissue as a whole.

FACTORS AFFECTING THE RATE OF TRANSPIRATION

Air movements
Water vapour diffuses from the leaves via the stomata, and to a lesser extent through their cuticles, and tends to saturate the air around the leaves. Air movements remove these saturated layers and, by exposing the leaves to drier air, increase the rate of transpiration.

Relative humidity of air
With decreasing relative humidity (drier air), transpiration increases because the water from the leaf can evaporate more easily; and vice versa.

Temperature
An increase in temperature increases the rate of transpiration by increasing the rate at which the water molecules evaporate from the leaf surfaces, and by increasing the amount of water vapour that can be held by a given volume of air, which therefore takes longer to become saturated with water vapour.

Availability of soil water
Any factor that decreases the availability of soil water will decrease the rate of transpiration by limiting water supply. In extreme cases when the rate of transpiration actually exceeds the rate of water supply through the roots, then wilting occurs.

Light intensity
The main effect of light on the rate of transpiration, is by its effect on

the stomata. Light causes them to open (for the uptake of carbon dioxide for photosynthesis) thus increasing the rate of transpiration; they close in the dark, thus decreasing the rate of transpiration.

STOMATA

Stomata are small pores in the leaves of photosynthesizing plants, the opening of which is controlled by guard cells (Fig 6.8). The guard cells are so shaped that when they are flaccid (not distended with water) the stomata are shut, and when they are turgid (distended with water) the stomata are open.

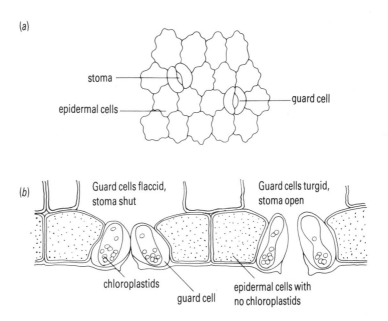

Fig 6.8. (a) *Leaf surface view to show stomata*. (b) *TS epidermis to show stomata*. In dorsiventral leaves there are more stomata on the lower surface. Isobilateral leaves (e.g. daffodil) have equal numbers on both surfaces. Stomata are also found on herbaceous stems and in a reduced form on floral organs. Some submerged aquatic plants have a few vestigial stomata.

The simple explanation of this phenomenon is that in the light the guard cell chloroplastids produce sugars by photosynthesis, and that these sugars increase the concentration within the guard cells so that water is drawn in by osmosis, thus increasing their turgidity and resulting in the opening of the stomata.

In the dark, the sugars would be depleted (by respiration for example), the internal concentration would drop and water would be withdrawn by osmosis to neighbouring cells, thus decreasing the turgidity of the guard cells and resulting in the closing of the stomata.

EXERCISE

Exercise 6.6

Another hypothesis to account for the opening and closing of stomata is that of the starch/sugar balance. Under acid conditions starch production is encouraged, and under less acid conditions sugar production is encouraged. How and when could the necessary changes in acidity occur in the guard cells?

Answer At night there is no photosynthesis, but the guard cells continue to respire and carbon dioxide (an acid gas) is produced. This increases the acidity (lowers the pH) which encourages the conversion of sugars to starch. There is a resultant drop in osmotic concentration, and water is lost by osmosis to adjacent cells which are now hypertonic. The guard cells become flaccid and the stomata shut. (Now attempt to write out the sequence of events that will occur in the light.)

There are usually more stomata on the lower side of dorsi-ventral leaves, and some, for example laurel, have stomata only on the lower side. Isobilateral leaves (for example grasses) tend to have roughly equal numbers on both surfaces.

FUNCTIONS OF TRANSPIRATION

1 Transpiration provides a transport stream bringing water and dissolved minerals to the aerial photosynthetic parts from the soil and the roots.
2 It exerts a cooling effect since the evaporation of water absorbs the latent heat of evaporation from the plant.
3 It recycles water from the soil to the air, which has a significant effect on the climate, and is an important link in the water cycle.

TRANSPORT OF ORGANIC MATERIAL

The transport of organic material in vascular plants occurs mainly in the phloem tissue, from the place of its origin (the 'source') to the place where it is utilized and stored (the 'sink').

This is usually from the leaves and to the roots, fruits, seeds, storage organs and growing points.

However, there is also some upward transport of organic material in the xylem from the roots to the leaves and from storage organs to growing points.

The transport of organic material in the phloem is referred to as **translocation**.

MECHANISM OF FLOW

The way in which organic material is transported in the phloem is not fully understood. However, any explanation must depend on the vital activities of the cytoplasm, since sieve tubes must be living in order to carry out translocation.

The contents of the active phloem are under a high positive pressure (in contrast with the xylem sap), and this may be involved in some way in the transport within the phloem.

Other mechanisms at work may involve cytoplasmic streaming and active **transfer cells** which are found next to the phloem sieve tubes and their companion cells.

Table 6.1. Transport in plants

Material	Source	Sink
Soluble carbohydrates (e.g. glucose, sucrose)	(a) Photosynthesizing cells (b) Any cell converting insoluble starch to soluble sugars (c) Deciduous leaves prior to leaf fall (d) Seed storage tissues when germinating (e) Fruit storage tissues when germination occurs	(i) Any respiring cells with inadequate photosynthesis (e.g. root cells, stem cortex, medullary ray cells, meristems, etc.) (ii) Any storage tissue (e.g. corms, bulbs, rhizomes, fruits, seeds, medullary rays, etc.)
Amino acids	(a) Mainly young leaves (b) Mature rootlets in some cases (c) Deciduous leaves prior to leaf fall (d) Seed storage tissues when germinating (e) Fruit storage tissues when germination occurs	(i) Any cell requiring amino acids for growth, repair or maintenance (e.g. apical and lateral meristems)
Hormones	(a) Apical meristems (b) Developing seeds (c) Leaves	(i) Zones of elongation (ii) Fruits (iii) Flower buds (iv) Lateral buds

EXPERIMENTAL WORK

ANIMAL TRANSPORT

EXPERIMENTS WITH *DAPHNIA*

Most experimental work on animal transport at this level involves the use of small invertebrates in which the functioning heart can be observed easily through the body tissues of the living animals; for example *Daphnia* (the 'water flea', a crustacean).

A drop of water containing one or two *Daphnia* is placed on a cavity slide with some cotton wool fibres or vaseline to restrict their movement and keep them in the field of view of the microscope. The rapidly beating heart can easily be seen towards the dorsal edge of the animal (Fig 6.9).

When observing living organisms under a microscope which uses light from a bench lamp, care must be taken not to overheat the specimens by having the lamp too close. In fact it is better, if possible, to use daylight or the light from the normal laboratory lights.

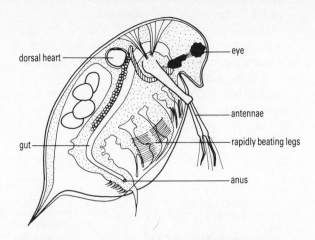

Fig 6.9. *Daphnia, showing the position of the heart*. Daphnia swims by means of its antennae. The rapidly beating legs which can be seen ventrally are used to generate water currents which bring food particles to the mouth and oxygen to the gills. The rapidly beating heart can be seen dorsally through the transparent carapace.

When the animal has settled to its new surroundings, counts of the heart rate can be taken. If very rapid they can be counted by making one dot per beat on a piece of paper. The number of beats per minute can be counted, or the time taken for a certain number of beats.

If using a single animal in an investigation involving studying the effect of changing conditions on the heart rate, it is important to allow the animal to recover completely between different treatments. Otherwise the effect of one treatment may carry over into the next and invalidate the experiment. For example, if studying the effect of alcohol (a depressant) and aspirin (an irritant), it would be necessary to re-establish the normal rate in pond water between the treatments.

DISSECTIONS

In **dissections** of the mammalian circulatory system it is necessary to distinguish between arteries and veins. The veins appear a darker red than the paler arteries. This is due to the muscular walls of the arteries contracting and forcing the blood into the veins, and also to the fact that what blood there is left in the arteries is less visible through the thicker, contracted, muscle walls.

Also, from the ventral aspect (i.e. from the point of view of the dissector), most of the main veins cover or overlap their corresponding arteries, which appear much thinner than the veins.

PLANT TRANSPORT

Stomata may be studied by either direct observation of leaf surfaces with reflected light, epidermal strips or nail varnish films. Epidermal strips can most easily be obtained by folding the leaf so that it breaks on one surface, and then peeling the epidermis off the other side. The epidermal strip is usually thinnest and clearest towards the edge.

Nail varnish films are obtained by painting nail varnish over the surface of the leaf, allowing it to harden for 5–10 minutes, and then peeling the film off under water. They are then mounted in water on a slide under a cover slip; and the pattern of stomatal distribution, the number per unit area, their shape, and their state of opening can all be observed and recorded as required.

Comparisons are often required between upper and lower epidermises, and between Monocotyledon and Dicotyledon leaves.

Transpiration can be measured using a potometer (see Fig 6.10). The potometer is filled by immersing it totally in water, preferably freshly boiled and cooled water which has no air bubbles. The shoot to be used should be cut from the plant under water, to prevent any air bubbles entering the xylem elements.

All joints should be well vaselined to prevent any leaks, which would invalidate the results.

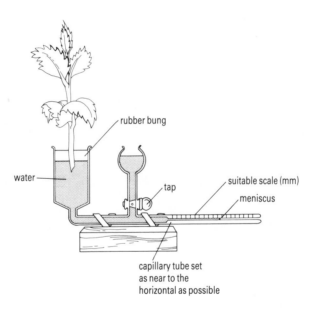

Fig 6.10. Potometer to measure the rate of water uptake.

After setting up, but before allowing air to be drawn into the capillary tube, the apparatus should be allowed to equilibrate (settle down).

As water evaporates from the leaves of the shoot, water is pulled up the shoot by the cohesive pull of the transpiration stream, and air is drawn along the capillary tube at the same rate – thus giving a measure of the rate of transpiration. The time taken for the air bubble to travel a certain distance, or the distance travelled in a certain time, can be recorded.

If the calibration on the capillary tube is in millimetres, and the diameter and hence the radius of the tube is known, then the volume of water taken up can be calculated using the formula:

$$\pi r^2 \times \text{distance travelled by bubble} = \text{volume of water uptake}$$

Sometimes, however, the calibrations are already in units of volume, for example mm^3 or cm^3 (ml).

After it has travelled a certain distance, the bubble is returned to the beaker end by running water in from the reservoir.

Repeat the procedure until some consistent results are obtained. Express the results as either cm^3/minute, cm^3/hour, or cm^3 per hour per cm^2 of leaf area.

The procedure can be repeated under different conditions, for example in an air current produced by a fan, with the shoot in a polythene bag (humid environment), and by sealing the stomata of upper or lower leaf surfaces with vaseline.

The main sources of experimental error are leaks and temperature fluctuations.

Leaks allow air bubbles to be drawn into the apparatus and as a result the rate at which the air bubble in the tube moves towards the shoot will be decreased.

Similarly, any increase in temperature of the surroundings will cause the water in the apparatus to expand and decrease the rate of movement of the bubble towards the shoot.

The potometer actually measures the rate of *water uptake* by the shoot, and this rate of uptake is *assumed* to be directly related to the *rate of transpiration* i.e. the rate of water loss from the leaves.

This can be checked by weighing the potometer at the start and at the end of the experiment, and assuming that 1 cm^3 of water weighs 1g.

In fact the rate of water loss is usually slightly greater than the rate of water uptake, as water uptake by a cut shoot is less effective than a rooted plant.

A measure of the water loss actually at the leaf surface can be obtained using anhydrous cobalt chloride or thiocyanate paper, which is blue when dry and which turns pink in the presence of water.

Small rectangles of blue cobalt chloride paper can be affixed to the surfaces of leaves under glass slides, or under wide sellotape.

The time taken for the colour to change from blue to pink gives a measure of the rate of water loss from the surface of the leaf. (A blue 'standard' paper, the same colour as the anhydrous cobalt chloride paper, can also be attached to provide a reference against which the change to pink can be measured.)

QUESTION ▶

Q. (a) State three functions of water in plants (3)
(b) Explain the way in which two abiotic factors affect water absorption by roots (4)
(c) Explain the significance of the waterproof thickening (Casparian bands) of the endodermis for the passage of water into the xylem (3)
(d) Besides water uptake roots serve other functions; list three of these functions (3)
(e) What is meant by transpiration? How does it;
  (i) resemble, and
  (ii) differ from, sweating in man? (7)

COMMENT ▶

This question requires information about water uptake, transport and loss in plants, that might not have been anticipated; but about which a little careful thought should provide the answers. Also take care in section (b) with the word *abiotic*, this could easily be misread as biotic.

OUTLINE ▶
ANSWER

(a) **Three functions of water (3)**
  (i) As a transport medium for inorganic ions up the stem in the xylem.
  (ii) In providing turgidity in cells, essential for the support of unthickened tissues.
  (iii) As a reactant in chemical reactions of metabolism e.g. photosynthesis (there are many other acceptable points of course)

(b) **Two abiotic factors affecting water absorption (4)**
  (i) Temperature, amount of water entering roots by osmosis is proportional to temperature, very low soil temperatures preventing water uptake.
  (ii) Humidity of air surrounding the leaves, this affects the amount of water vapour lost from the leaves, which in turn affects the amount of water absorption by the roots, e.g. there will be more water uptake by roots on warm dry windy days, than on wet cold still days.

(c) **Effects of Casparian bands (3)**
The waterproof thickening of the cells of the endodermis forces water that is passing from the root cortex into the xylem to pass through the living thin walled passage cells, which exert a controlling effect on the passage of water and ions.

(d) **Three additional functions of roots (3)**
  (i) Anchor plants in the soil.
  (ii) Uptake of inorganic ions from the soil solution.
  (iii) Food storage.

(e) **Transpiration (7)**

This is the loss of water vapour from the aerial parts of terrestrial plants, mainly leaves, mostly through stomata, and to a smaller extent through the cuticle.

(i) Resemblance to sweating

Evaporation of water vapour from the body;

affected by temperature, humidity and air movements;

cooling effect exerted by absorption of latent heat of evaporation.

(ii) Differences from sweating

Does not occur as a result of the activities of special secretory cells in response to temperature control mechanisms;

occurs as a result of having stomata open for carbon dioxide uptake;

water evaporates from surfaces inside the leaf;

not from the surface of the epidermis;

escapes through pores as vapour, not as a fluid.

QUESTIONS

1   What biological problems are associated with large size in organisms? How have these problems been overcome in plants and animals?
(LOND)

2   (a)   What are the specifications for a successful closed circulatory system?
(b)   Describe how the circulatory system of a mammal meets the varying needs of the tissues.   (JMB)

3   (a)   State the similarities and differences between arteries, capillaries and veins.
(b)   Describe the action of the heart of a mammal.
(c)   Explain the effect of fear on the rate of heart beat.
(LOND)

4   The intermittent output of the mammalian heart is converted to a steady blood flow in the capillaries by
A   elastic tissue in the vein walls.
B   muscular tissues in the arterial walls.
C   regular contraction of pre-capillary sphincters.
D   elastic tissue in the arterial walls.   (JMB)

5   Describe briefly the action of the mammalian heart as it pumps blood around the body.
An isolated heart, if kept in an appropriate nutrient fluid, will beat regularly for a long time. How is the heart beat maintained in the absence of outside nervous control?
How does the mammalian heart adjust its rate and output per beat in response to changes in body activity?   (CAM)

6   With reference to a mammal, describe the means by which blood

circulation is maintained and controlled. How is the blood maintained at constant temperature? Review the part played by the blood in conferring immunity from infective disease. (SU)

7 (a) Describe the components of mammalian blood.
   (b) How is blood moved around the body of a mammal?
   (c) Explain how animals such as protozoa and coelenterates are able to survive without a blood system. (LOND)

8 What is lymph and how is it formed and distributed in a mammal?
   What part does the lymphatic system play in a mammal's defence against disease?

   (O&C)

9 In an experiment to compare the rate of transpiration of a runner bean plant with the rate of evaporation of water from a porous pot over a period of 24 hours the following results were obtained:
   The rate of evaporation was measured in millilitres per hour. (ml h^{-1}).
   The rate of transpiration was measured in millilitres per square metre of leaf surface per hour. (ml $m^{-2} h^{-1}$).

Time of day	Rate of evaporation (ml h^{-1})	Rate of transpiration (ml $m^{-2} h^{-1}$)
6–8 a.m.	3.9	93
8–10 a.m.	6.7	163
10–12 noon	8.2	222
12–2 p.m.	9.5	253
2–4 p.m.	9.5	198
4–6 p.m.	9.1	181
6–8 p.m.	6.7	126
8–10 p.m.	3.9	8
10–12 midnight	3.4	19
12–2 a.m.	1.6	19
2–4 a.m.	0.8	14
4–6 a.m.	0.9	24

By using appropriate scales on the same squared paper, plot graphs of the rate of evaporation from the porous pot and the rate of transpiration of the bean plant against time of day.
   Comment on the significance of the shapes of the graphs.

   (O)

10 Explain how the transpiration rate of trees may be affected by the environmental factors experienced by their aerial parts. (SCE)

11 State **one** condition which affects the rate of transpiration of a leafy shoot. How would you measure the effect of this variation?

   (SU)

12 The xylem forms a continuous system of vascular tissue throughout the plant.
   (a) What are the **two** principal conducting cells of the xylem?
   (b) Name **two** other types of cells that occur in the xylem and give their functions.

(c)   Name **two** classes of substances that are transported with water in the xylem.

   Is xylem transport unidirectional or bidirectional?

(d)   For many years there has been general agreement about the mechanism of transport of water in the xylem.

   (i) What is the driving force of the mechanism and where is it located?

   (ii) Is the mechanism active or passive?

   (iii) What theory seeks to explain the mechanism?

(e)   During daylight the rate of water loss by transpiration usually exceeds the rate of uptake by the root system. Explain the significance of this observation in relation to the mechanism of water transport in the xylem.

(f)   Indicate **two** methods to determine the velocity of xylem transport.   (W)

13   Cobalt chloride paper is blue when dry and pink when moist. To show that a leaf loses water from the lower surface, a piece of the dry paper was clipped between the lower surface of the leaf and a glass slide. The most suitable control for this would be

A   a similar arrangement, but using the upper surface of the same leaf.

B   a similar arrangement, but using the lower surface of another leaf.

C   the paper clipped between two glass slides only.

D   the paper exposed freely to the atmosphere.   (JMB)

14   Which one of the following observations indicates that photosynthesis is responsible for the substances present in the sieve tubes of the phloem?

A   Transport of materials in the phloem increases with increasing temperature, reaches a maximum at 25°C, and then falls off.

B   Sieve tube contents are found to vary according to a twenty-four hour cycle.

C   Stems placed in an environment with no oxygen do not transport materials in the phloem.

D   Sugars are transported up and down the plant so that young leaves, roots and developing fruits can utilize these sugars.

                                                                      (C)

OSMOREGULATION AND EXCRETION

CONTENTS

Osmoregulation is the control of the amount of water and dissolved substances (mostly mineral salts) in the cell and in the organism as a whole.

All living cells represent an osmotic system, having a differentially permeable cell membrane (i.e. one more permeable to water than to dissolved solutes) separating two solutions, namely intracellular fluids and extracellular fluids.

If the concentrations of these two fluids differ then osmosis will occur; that is, water will pass from the more dilute (**hypotonic**) solution to the more concentrated (**hypertonic**) solution through the differentially permeable membrane.

This movement of water by osmosis will continue until the two concentrations become equal or **isotonic**, or until an equal and opposing force or pressure develops inside the cell, as in **endosmosis** (water moving into the cell), or until the dehydration of the cell, as in **exosmosis** (water moving out of the cell).

However, cells rarely act as simple osmotic systems. Due to their variable permeabilities and their ability to move solutes actively across their membranes using respiratory energy, considerations of the osmotic movement of water in living cells are complicated. Indeed, the active transport of solutes is one of the main ways in which osmoregulation is achieved by organisms; the salts being moved actively and the water following passively by osmosis. In addition, certain cells have contractile vacuoles by which relatively large volumes of water are actively expelled from the cytoplasm, again using respiratory energy.

EXERCISE ▶

Exercise 7.1

In which direction (if any) will water pass in the following osmotic situations, where the two solutions given are separated by a differentially permeable membrane?

	Solution I	Solution II
(a)	5% sucrose	10% sucrose
(b)	10% glucose	10% sucrose
(c)	10% glucose	10% sodium chloride

Answer

(a) I ⟶ II.

(b) No movement. Osmosis only involves the number of particles in solution, not their chemical nature.

(*c*)   I $\longrightarrow$ II. Sodium chloride (NaCl) dissociates into two ions (Na^+, Cl^-). Therefore, for a given strength of solution, sodium chloride has twice the number of particles as glucose, which does not dissociate.

WATER POTENTIAL

In osmosis water moves as a result of the same forces that cause movements of substances by diffusion. Substances diffuse from regions of their high chemical potential to regions of their low chemical potential down a chemical potential or diffusion gradient.

Water similarly moves from regions of its high chemical potential to regions of its low chemical potential. In Biology the chemical potential of water is referred to as **water potential**.

Pure water at one atmosphere and a specified temperature is used as the standard reference state which is arbitrarily set at zero.

The presence of solutes lowers the water potential i.e. makes it *more negative*. Pressure in excess of one atmosphere raises it, i.e. makes it *less negative* or even positive.

Water will always move from regions of higher water potential to regions of lower water potential.

WATER BALANCE IN DIFFERENT ENVIRONMENTS

If immersed in **hypotonic solutions** the organism is faced with problems of **water gain by osmosis** and **salt loss by diffusion.**

If immersed in **hypertonic solutions** the organism is faced with the problem of **water loss by osmosis** and **salt gain by diffusion.**

If exposed to air in a **terrestrial environment** the organism is faced with the problem of **water loss by evaporation**, but the conservation of water still involves osmotic processes within the organism.

Osmoregulation is essentially a feature of animal cells, as plant cells have the strong cellulose cell wall surrounding the cell membrane. The wall resists over-expansion due to excess water entry from dilute solutions.

Animal cells do not have such a cell wall and are liable to swell and to burst the delicate cell membrane when placed in dilute solutions. They must therefore osmoregulate more actively in these conditions.

The term **excretion** is rather ill-defined. Its simplest definition is the elimination of toxic waste products produced by the body, mainly carbon dioxide and nitrogenous substances.

The carbon dioxide is a product of respiration and it is usually removed by diffusion from the body fluids to the external environment.

The nitrogenous substances are mainly the products of protein and amino acid metabolism, and often require water for their elimination from the body; nitrogenous excretion is therefore often involved with osmoregulation.

COMMENT ▶

Some consider the term excretion to include the elimination of any excess unwanted substance whether it is produced as a result of metabolism or not, or whether it is toxic or not, and therefore would include the elimination of oxygen produced by photosynthesis, and the elimination of excess water and salts, amongst many others. So again care is needed in interpreting examination questions where there might be some ambiguity.

Generally speaking, it is clearer to consider

excretion as the elimination of toxic waste products produced by metabolism

secretion as the output of useful substances, such as sebum from the sebaceous glands in mammalian skin and saliva from the salivary glands; and

osmoregulation as the control of the amount of water and dissolved substances in the cell and in the organism as a whole.

OSMOREGULATION IN ANIMALS

AQUATIC ENVIRONMENT

All animal cells and body fluids are hypertonic to fresh water, therefore in fresh water the problems are of water gain by osmosis and salt loss by diffusion.

Generally the cytoplasm and body fluids of marine invertebrates are roughly isotonic to sea water, so that they are in osmotic equilibrium. The body fluids of marine vertebrates are very hypotonic to sea water, so they have problems of water loss and salt gain. Smaller animals have a greater surface area to volume ratio than larger animals and therefore have greater problems of water and salt exchanges, but the removal of waste products by diffusion is easier.

PROTOZOA

Freshwater protozoa actively osmoregulate by means of the contractile vacuole which expels excess water using respiratory energy. Salt loss is opposed by the active uptake of salts through the plasmalemma.

FISH

Fresh water

(All fresh-water fish are bony fish.) The gills represent a larger surface area of semi-permeable membranes exposed to the water, and much water enters by osmosis. This is eliminated by the kidneys, which produce large volumes of dilute urine.

Special cells on the gills actively take up salts using respiratory energy.

Sea water

The bony fish osmoregulate by drinking sea water and actively taking up salts from the sea water in the gut, as a result of which water follows passively by osmosis. The salts are subsequently eliminated by special cells on the gills, so that there is a net gain of water. To help conserve this water, the kidneys are reduced or even absent, and toxic nitrogenous wastes are excreted from the gills.

The cartilagenous fish overcome the problem of '**physiological drought**' in the oceans in another way. They retain high levels of urea in their body so that their body fluids are hypertonic to the sea water and water can enter over the gills by osmosis. The kidneys are well developed and produce large volumes of dilute urine.

TERRESTRIAL ENVIRONMENT

Terrestrial animals lose water by evaporation from permeable surfaces and by secretion, excretion and egestion.

INVERTEBRATES

Due to their large surface area to volume ratio, invertebrates face great problems of evaporative water loss over their permeable surfaces.

The **insects** have a thin waterproof epicuticle on the outside of their exoskeleton which cuts down water loss, but water loss by evaporation still occurs through the thin flexible articular membranes at the joints.

The trachea or air tubes which penetrate the body open to the exterior by spiracles, the opening and closing of which can be controlled to reduce evaporative water loss. Even so, the greatest water loss still occurs as a result of respiration.

The main organs of osmoregulation and excretion are the Malpighian tubules which arise from the gut. In these, carbon dioxide and nitrogenous wastes combine to form insoluble non-toxic uric acid crystals, which require only the minimum of water for their excretion from the body.

VERTEBRATES

Water loss in terrestrial vertebrates is reduced by the keratinized, waterproof skin,

by having the respiratory surface only opening to the exterior by restricted openings,

by having kidneys which can either produce uric acid as in the reptiles and birds, or which can produce urine hypertonic to the blood as in the mammals.

EXERCISE ▶

Exercise 7.2

Which of the statements best describes the similarities, in terms of problems of water balance, between marine and terrestrial environments?

(a)   In both environments organisms lose water by osmosis.

(b)   In both environments organisms lose water; by osmosis in the sea, and by evaporation on land.

(c)   In both environments organisms lose water to a more concentrated external medium.

KIDNEY FUNCTION

All vertebrate kidneys work on the same principle. Blood under high pressure, due to the pumping action of the heart, undergoes a process of ultra-filtration by which a large proportion of the plasma and its soluble constituents are forced out of the capillaries into the kidney tubules.

As this filtrate passes down the tubules various adjustments to its composition are made by means of reabsorptions, secretions, and excretions; until by the time the filtrate leaves the kidneys it is known as urine.

With regard to osmoregulation it must be remembered that a urine which is hypotonic to the blood represents a loss of water from the body, so that the blood will become more concentrated;

urine which is hypertonic to the blood will mean that the blood will become less concentrated;

an isotonic urine will mean that the blood concentration will be unaltered.

MAMMALIAN KIDNEY

The kidney is a compound tubular organ, being made up of many microscopic kidney tubules or nephrons, and their drainage ducts (Fig 7.1).

Fig 7.1. *LS mammalian kidney.* The kidney is a compound tubular organ composed of many microscopic kidney tubules or nephrons and their drainage ducts which run together to form the larger ducts which lead into the ureter. The average length of a nephron is about 3–4 cm.

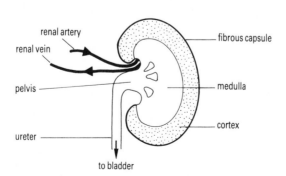

The blood enters the kidneys by the renal artery, which branches into arterioles and finally into the capillary beds or glomeruli which are surrounded by the Bowman's capsules of the kidney tubules (Fig 7.2).

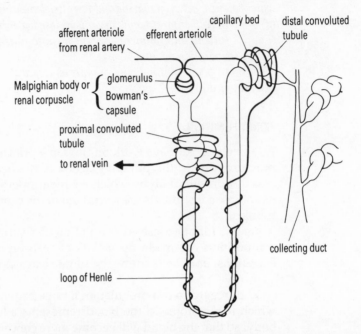

Fig 7.2. *Kidney tubule (nephron) detail.* The Bowman's capsule is usually shown as a simple cup-like swelling, in which the glomerulus 'sits'. In fact the inner wall of the capsule completely surrounds each capillary of the glomerulus in a complex way.

The blood is under a high pressure and a proportion of the plasma is forced out through the walls of the capillaries, through the walls of the Bowman's capsule and into the lumen of the nephron. This process is known as ultra-filtration under pressure (Fig 7.3). The 'push out' due to the blood pressure is opposed by the 'pull-in' due to the osmotic pressure of the blood, so that the effective filtration pressure is the difference between the two forces.

filtration pressure = blood pressure − osmotic pressure

As the filtrate passes through the proximal convoluted tubule, up to 88% of the water, up to 80% of the salts, all of the glucose, and other useful substances are reabsorbed. At the same time unwanted materials are added to the filtrate via the walls of the tubule.

This continuous process of adjustment of the filtrate continues in the Loop of Henlé and the distal convoluted tubule, where the pH of the body fluids is regulated by the excretion of excess acid and the reabsorption of alkaline hydrogencarbonates. The loop is impermeable to water, but salts, mainly sodium chloride, are continually reabsorbed, thus building up a high concentration in this region.

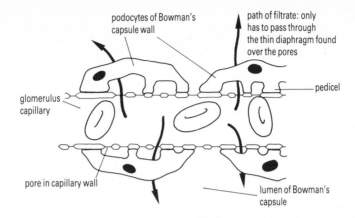

Fig 7.3. *LS glomerulus capillary to show filtration.* The podocytes make up the wall of the Bowman's capsule which completely surrounds all the capillaries. The arrangement of the pedicels and the pores in the walls of the capillaries allows rapid filtration from the blood into the lumen of the Bowman's capsule.

As the collecting duct passes next to this region, water can be reabsorbed from the filtrate in the duct by osmosis (Fig 7.4).

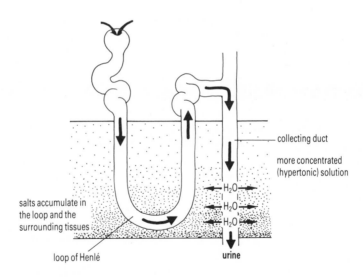

Fig 7.4. *Water reabsorption by the kidney tubule.* The accumulation of salts in the loop and surrounding tissues is an active process requiring energy from respiration. The amount of water reabsorbed in the collecting duct is controlled by the level of anti-diuretic hormone (ADH).

CONTROL OF WATER REABSORPTION

Remember 88% of the water is reabsorbed automatically in the proximal convoluted tubule.

The amount of water reabsorbed is controlled by the anti-diuretic hormone (ADH) which increases the permeability of the collecting duct walls to water.

Osmoreceptors in the carotid arteries in the neck monitor the concentration of the blood, and send information to the hypothalamus of the brain, which in turn sends information to the neurohypophysis (posterior lobe) of the pituitary gland. The secretion of ADH by the pituitary will be regulated according to this information.

If the blood concentration increases, ADH secretion is increased and *more* water is reabsorbed, lowering the blood concentration.

If the blood concentration decreases, ADH secretion is decreased and less water is reabsorbed, raising the blood concentration.

The final fluid leaving the kidney is known as urine.

EXERCISE ▶

Exercise 7.3

What will be the effect on the concentration and volume of urine, if ADH secretion is (a) increased, and (b) decreased.

Answer

(*a*)   The concentration of urine will increase, and the volume will decrease.

(*b*)   The concentration of urine will decrease and the volume will increase.

WATER MOVEMENTS IN PLANT CELLS

The cellulose cell wall of plant cells is permeable to water, but is involved in controlling water entry into the cell by resisting over-expansion of the cell due to water uptake.

In a plant cell the passage of water by osmosis is considered as occurring between the external solution and the vacuolar sap, with the cell membrane, cytoplasm and vacuolar membrane (tonoplast) being considered as a single membrane of negligible thickness.

The force available for water to enter into a plant cell, i.e. the **total waterpotential** of the cell (ψT) is the difference between the force causing the inward movement due to solutes i.e. the osmotic potential (ψs) and the opposing wall pressure (ψp) exerted by the stretched cell wall which opposes the entry of water.

$$\psi T = \underset{\text{Negative}}{\psi S} + \underset{\text{Positive}}{\psi P}$$

When in distilled water, water enters the cell until the stretched cell wall can extend no further and water can no longer enter. When in this state the cell is said to be fully **turgid**. The turgidity of plant cells is very important in the support of plants.

When in a hypertonic solution, water leaves the cell, the contents decrease in volume and the cell becomes less and less turgid or more and more flaccid. The stage at which the cytoplasm just begins to pull away from the cell wall is known as **incipient plasmolysis.**

At this point there is no wall pressure. A solution that just causes this to happen is considered as being isotonic to the cell contents at that point.

$$\psi External = \psi T = \psi S$$

Fig. 7.5. Plasmolysis in a plant cell.

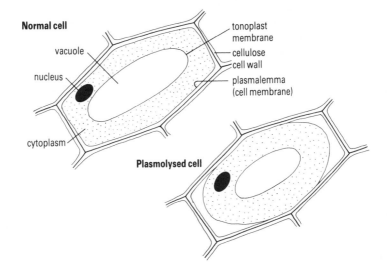

Normal cell

vacuole

nucleus

cytoplasm

tonoplast membrane

cellulose cell wall

plasmalemma (cell membrane)

Plasmolysed cell

WATER CONTROL IN WHOLE PLANTS

Plant life cycles, physiology and structure are all adapted to particular environments, with the availability of water being one of the main factors in determining the nature and distribution of vegetation in the terrestrial environment.

Various terms refer to the main groupings of plants in relation to the amount of water in the environment.

Hydrophytes grow in water or in very wet habitats,

mesophytes grow in habitats with average water supplies, and

xerophytes grow in very dry habitats. Xerophytes have a variety of structural features, known as xeromorphic characters, that enable them to survive in dry habitats. The leaves are often reduced with thick cuticles, stomata are protected in pits and by hairs, or by leaf rolling mechanisms which protect them under dry conditions; the root system can be very extensive; and succulent xerophytes (e.g. cacti) store water in special tissues, on which they can survive dry periods.

EXCRETION

EXCRETION IN ANIMALS

Nitrogenous excretion is essentially a feature of animals rather than of plants. Animals must take up amino acids in their diet and any excess to their needs must be eliminated. Also as a result of general metabolism there is a continual breakdown of proteins, amino acids and other nitrogen-containing compounds. All these activities give rise to toxic nitrogenous wastes.

(Plants, on the other hand, synthesize their own amino acids according to their needs, their metabolic rates are much lower than those of animals, and consequently fewer toxic wastes are produced.)

In animals the unwanted amino acids are **deaminated** by the removal of the nitrogen-containing amino groups, and the non-toxic parts of the molecules are incorporated into the general carbohydrate metabolic pathways.

The amino groups are converted to either ammonia, urea or uric acid; depending upon the amount of water available for their elimination.

Ammonia is very toxic and requires the availability of large amounts of water for its rapid removal by diffusion. It is therefore only found as the main waste product in aquatic animals. Such animals are known as ammonotelic.

Urea is less toxic and requires less water for its removal; it can also be stored for short periods in the body. Animals that have urea as their main waste product are known as ureotelic, e.g. mammals.

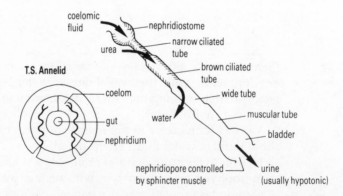

Fig 7.6. *Annelid nephridia.* There is a pair of nephridia in each segment of most annelids. The cilia sweep coelomic fluid from the coelom, down the nephridium. Water and useful salts are reabsorbed, especially through the wall of the wide tube, and the remaining fluid (urine), containing ammonia and urea, passes to the outside.

Uric acid is insoluble and therefore non-toxic and, as it only requires the minimum of water for its removal, uric acid production allows water to be conserved. Being insoluble, uric acid cannot be transported in the blood, and must therefore be formed at the site of excretion.

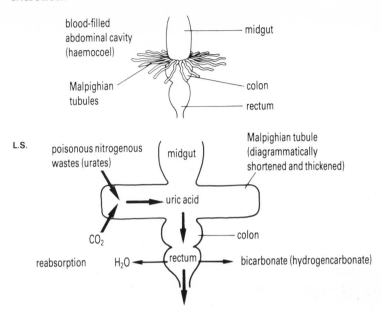

Fig 7.7. *Insect Malpighian tubules.* Nitrogenous waste products (urates) enter the tubules from the blood-filled haemocoel cavity and, as a result of reaction with carbon dioxide, insoluble crystals of uric acid are precipitated. Water and bicarbonate are reabsorbed mainly in the rectum, and the uric acid is eliminated in the faeces.

Animals with uric acid as the main waste product are known as uricotelic, e.g. gastropod molluscs, insects (Fig 7.7), birds and reptiles.

The elimination of these nitrogenous wastes involves the water balance mechanisms of the animals, and can therefore be considered together with osmoregulation.

EXERCISE ➡

Exercise 7.4

Which of the following is the best explanation of the fact that aquatic reptiles produce uric acid as a nitrogenous waste product?

(a)   *Uric acid is toxic and soluble and large amounts of water are needed for its elimination.*

(b)   *Uric acid is insoluble and large amounts of water are needed for its elimination.*

(c)   *Reptiles are primarily a terrestrial group, and typically uric acid is produced to conserve water. Secondarily aquatic reptiles retain this trait.*

EXCRETION IN PLANTS

As previously mentioned, plants do not have the same problems of excretion as animals. Photosynthetic plants excrete carbon dioxide from respiration in the dark, but in the light this carbon dioxide is utilized in photosynthesis and an excess of oxygen is produced. Other waste products are deposited in the heart wood of the xylem in woody perennials, and waste products can be lost during leaf fall in deciduous plants.

COMMENT ▶

Osmoregulation and excretion are most clearly seen in animals. Both processes are closely linked, if not inseparable; although for the purposes of examination questions they may be treated as separate subjects.

The term excretion is variously defined, and care must be taken when answering questions that the most appropriate definition is taken. If in doubt as to the correct interpretation, take the widest view.

EXPERIMENTAL WORK

This **osmoregulation in animals** can be investigated in Protozoa by immersing fresh water species with a contractile vacuole (e.g. *Amoeba*) in solutions of varying concentrations.

Given that all other conditions are at a constant optimum (e.g. temperature), the rate of contraction of the contractile vacuole is proportional to the difference in concentration between the cytoplasm and the external solution.

Thus in increasingly hypotonic solutions the rate of contraction increases to expel the excess water; in isotonic and hypertonic solutions the contractile vacuole disappears.

When investigating the reaction of a single *Amoeba* to a range of solutions, it is important to allow the animal to adjust to each new set of conditions before recording any results.

Larger aquatic animals, such as marine annelids (e.g. *Nereis*) can similarly be immersed in solutions of varying concentrations and any change in weight (due to gain or loss of water) recorded.

However, no change of weight may not necessarily indicate an isotonic solution since many animals actively osmoregulate to maintain a constant water content in the face of external changes.

Plant material is more easily studied, and is widely used in such experiments.

Single cells can be observed for signs of plasmolysis in solutions of different concentrations.

In these experiments care must be taken to make regular observations, as it is possible for a plasmolysed cell to recover from plasmolysis due to penetration of the external solution through the imperfectly differentially permeable membrane. Urea, and glycerol for example, readily penetrates most cell membranes.

Pieces of plant tissue, for example strips of potato tissue about 60 mm long, can be immersed in solutions of different concentrations and changes in weight or length noted.

Such changes are due to water gain or water loss in the individual cells making up that tissue. The optimum shape for such pieces is a long, fairly wide but thin block. Such a shape presents a large surface area over which osmosis can occur; and the long axis ensures measurable changes in length.

It is also important to make sure the entire block is completely immersed in the bathing solution, otherwise evaporative loss could occur.

When weighing such blocks care must be taken to blot excess solution gently off the surfaces; and when measuring changes in length care must be taken to measure between the same points each time, as usually it is difficult to cut the blocks exactly symmetrically.

Percentage changes in weight or length can be plotted against the different external concentrations. The solution that causes no change is taken as being isotonic to the tissue (Fig 7.8).

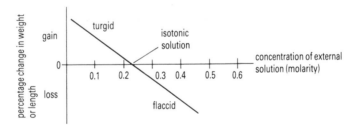

Fig 7.8. *The determination of an isotonic solution using plant tissues.* By plotting the results as shown, the strength of an isotonic solution can be determined, even if it is not one of the solutions actually used.

$$\% \text{ change} = \frac{\text{increase or decrease}}{\text{original value}} \times 100$$

The plant strips may also show differences in turgidity, with those in hypertonic solutions becoming flaccid and those in hypotonic solutions becoming turgid. Changes in turgidity, and thus the relative strength of solutions, can also be investigated using non-woody plant stems cut longitudinally (Fig 7.9).

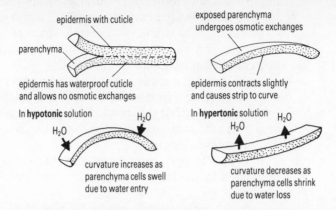

Fig 7.9. *Investigation of the relative strengths of solutions using the curvature of cut stems.* In an isotonic solution the curvature will remain the same since there will be no exchanges.

QUESTION ▶

Q. (i) How does the body of a mammal
(a) lose, (6)
(b) gain water? (3)
(ii) How is the water content of the mammalian body regulated? (8)
(iii) How do terrestrial plants conserve water? (3)

COMMENT ▶

This question requires care in avoiding repetition of material, in parts (i) and (ii), and a bringing together of animal and plant subject matter.

OUTLINE ANSWER ▶

(i)
(a) **Water loss (5)**
By evaporation of water from moist permeable surfaces to a drying atmosphere of lower water potential, including;
evaporation from lung surface with water vapour being exhaled;
secretion of sweat by sweat glands and its evaporation from the skin;
loss of water vapour through incompletely waterproof skin layers;
loss of water from plasma by filtration by kidneys and loss as urine;
loss via secretions including tears, mucus, digestive juices.
(b) **Water gain (3)**
As fluid water in drinking;
as a constituent of food, especially plant food;
absorption of above through gut wall into capillaries of hepatic portal vein;
as 'oxidation water' or 'metabolic water' from cell respiration, especially of fats.

(ii) **Regulation (8)**

Kidneys are organs of osmoregulation;

ultra-filtration under pressure of fluid from glomerulus into kidney tubule;

controlled reabsorption of water through collecting duct wall;

under control of ADH secreted by posterior pituitary;

osmoreceptors in carotid bodies and hypothalamus;

if blood concentration increases, ADH secretion increased, more water reabsorbed, less water lost in urine;

if blood concentration decreases, ADH secretion decreased, less water reabsorbed, more water lost in urine;

balance between water loss and gain (note only one point here as details covered in parts (i)(*a*) and (*b*))

(iii) **Water conservation in plants (3)**

Mechanisms are characteristically passive i.e. by structural adaptations; waterproof cuticle on overground parts e.g. leaf and young stems;

cork on older stems;

stomata protected in pits and grooves and by hairs (closure of stomata to prevent water loss only in severe cases of wilting).

QUESTIONS

1   Define the terms *osmosis* and *osmotic pressure*.

Describe an experiment you have carried out using living material, to demonstrate osmosis. Explain carefully what observations you made and what you concluded.

Discuss the importance of osmosis in **one** vital function in either a *named* animal or plant. (O&C)

2   In an experiment, two species of protozoan were exposed to different dilutions of sea water for one hour and the number of vacuolar contractions counted. The following results were obtained:

	Number of vacuolar contractions per hour	
Concentration of sea water per cent	Species 'A'	Species 'B'
100	0	0
80	0	0
65	0	0
50	6	0
35	20	25
25	42	45
20	56	58
15	64	65
10	63	74
5	20	82
0 (distilled water)	22	90

(*a*)   Explain precisely how you would carry out the above experiment.

(*b*)   Plot the results of the experiment as a graph.

(*c*)   Interpret the results and explain them as fully as you can.

(*d*)   In another experiment small quantities of a mercury compound were added to the 15% concentration of sea water containing the specimens. What results would you expect? Explain your answer.

(LOND)

3   Bony fish have osmoregulatory problems in both marine and freshwater habitats. Outline these problems and describe the mechanisms by which they are overcome.   (SCE)

4   What do you understand by excretion? How does it differ from (*a*) defaecation, (*b*) secretion, (*c*) osmoregulation?

   What are the chief excretory materials of (i) a **named** protozoan, (ii) a mammal, (iii) a flowering plant? For each material, briefly describe its origin and the method by which it is removed from the organism.

(O)

5   Insert the correct word or phrase selected from those listed below so as to complete the sentences which follow.

ammonia	insoluble
uric acid	soluble
urea	in the urine
as a precipitate	by diffusion
water elimination	water conservation

The excretory product of most aquatic animals is _____ which is very _____ in water and is thus able to pass out of the animal _____ . Mammals excrete _____ which passes out _____ but most insects excrete _____ which is _____ and thus aids _____ .   (AEB)

6   Compare and contrast the structure and functions of the excretory system in the earthworm and the cockroach.   (W)

7   Three species of *Littorina* (periwinkle) from the rocky shore excrete the bulk of their nitrogenous waste in different forms. Species A produces mostly ammonia, species B produces mostly urea and species C produces mostly uric acid. Suggest possible reasons for these differences.   (SU)

8   Answer BOTH parts **X** and **Y**, which are of equal mark value.

X   Make a clear labelled diagram to explain the structure of a single uriniferous tubule (a nephron) of a mammal. Explain clearly the function of each region, including an explanation of the terms 'active transport' and 'counterflow'.

Y   (i) *Carcinus* and *Maia* are both marine crabs. When subjected to increasing dilution of sea water the concentration of body fluid is as shown in the diagram below:

   Which of the two species do you consider best suited to life in (*a*) rock pools, and (*b*) estuarine conditions? State your reasons.

   (ii) In most *marine* teleosts (i.e. bony fishes), the body fluids are hypotonic to the surrounding sea water. If uncontrolled this would lead to the loss of essential body fluids. The

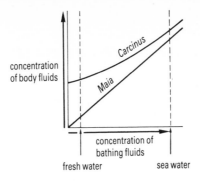

reverse is true of *freshwater* teleost fish where the body fluids are hypertonic to the surrounding water.

How far is the solution of these problems in the two groups related to

(a)   the size, abundance and activity of the glomeruli,
(b)   the length and activity of the uriniferous tubules,
(c)   the volume of urine eliminated,
(d)   the presence of gills, and
(e)   the selective reabsorption or elimination of salts?

(iii) Elasmobranch (cartilaginous) fish are generally able to tolerate high concentrations of urea in the blood. What is the significance of this in osmoregulation?

(iv) In fish, reptiles, birds and mammals the mineral salt concentration of the blood is considerably less than that of sea water. What does this suggest about the condition of the oceans at the time of the establishment of the first vertebrates?   (NI)

9   (a)   From the following list, select the organism which maintains water balance by means of (i) contractile vacuoles and (ii) a high level of urea in the blood.

Man
Starfish
Shark
Paramecium

(b)   The table shows the amounts of substances present in human blood plasma, glomerular filtrate and urine measured in gram per 100 cm^3 of fluid.

Component	Plasma	Filtrate	Urine
glucose	0.10	0.10	nil
amino acids	0.05	0.05	nil
proteins	8.00	nil	nil

Component	Plasma	Filtrate	Urine
inorganic salts	0.72	0.72	1.50
urea	0.03	0.03	2.00
uric acid	0.004	0.004	0.05

(i) Account for the difference in composition between the plasma and filtrate.

(ii) What other fluid present in the human body has a composition similar to that of the filtrate?

(iii) The concentration of inorganic salts in urine is approximately double that present in the filtrate. Why is this so?

(c) The following diagram represents a control system for fluid levels in mammals.

(i) What is the name given to a mechanism such as that represented in the diagram below.

(ii) Identify hormone X.

(iii) Where is the pituitary situated?

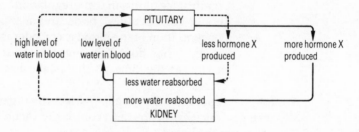

(iv) Give two sources of water loss, other than urine, in a mammal

(d) (i) **Underline** the correct answer.

Synthesis of urea occurs in the

liver

kidney

pancreas

colon.

(ii) Vertebrates from a variety of habitats excrete the nitrogenous substances detailed in the table.

Nitrogenous substance	Toxicity	Solubility in water
ammonia	highly toxic	very soluble
urea	non-toxic	very soluble
uric acid	non-toxic	relatively insoluble

(1)   **Underline** the habitat in the list to make the sentence correct.
The most likely habitat for a vertebrate excreting mainly uric

acid is $\left\{\begin{array}{l}\text{freshwater.}\\\text{swamp}\\\text{desert.}\end{array}\right.$

(2)   Give a reason for your answer to (1).   (SCE)

10 Design an experiment to investigate the following problem, making use of these divisions:

(*a*)   An account of the procedures to be used. You may use simple flow diagrams to illustrate the relationships betwen parts of the experiment.

(*b*)   An explanation of how the results would be presented and analysed.

How would you test the hypothesis that the rigidity of potato tuber tissue is proportional to its water content?   (JMB)

11 Which one of the following statements about the mammalian kidney is true?

A   Urine has a similar composition to that of the glomerular filtrate.

B   Glucose is not found in the proximal tubules.

C   The kidney excretes carbon dioxide in the form of bicarbonate.

D   A low blood pressure does not affect kidney function.
                                        (CAM)

SENSITIVITY AND COORDINATION

CONTENTS

PLANTS

Plants have no nervous system, and sensitivity and coordination are by means of hormones (see also Chapter 9).

PLANT HORMONES

There are three main hormones known to occur naturally and to be essential for the normal development of plants. These are:

1 Auxin
2 Gibberellin
3 Cytokinin

Two other compounds occur naturally as plant growth hormones. These are:

1 Ethene
2 Abscisin

Others that have been suggested include:

1 Florigen (flowering hormone)
2 Traumatin (wound hormone)

AUXIN

Auxin or indoleacetic acid (indole ethanoic acid) (IAA) is synthesized from the amino acid tryptophan in root and shoot tips, buds, expanding leaves and seeds.

Auxin has a wide variety of functions.

It increases cell wall plasticity by loosening the bonding between the cellulose fibres. This decreases the wall pressure, allowing more water to enter, which thus stretches the cell wall and results in cell expansion. This is important in normal growth and tropisms.

Auxin accelerates cell division and may be involved in the division of cambium cells and the formation of callus tissue over wounds. It also accelerates the development of fruit, stimulates root initiation, inhibits lateral bud development and affects flowering.

GIBBERELLIN

Gibberellin was originally isolated from a fungus (*Gibberella fujikuroi*) parasitic on rice, but has now been identified as a plant hormone found in all higher plants.

Gibberellin increases cell elongation. When applied externally to dwarf varieties it causes internode extension of the stem, resulting in the attainment of normal size. When applied to plants like cabbages and lettuces, which in the first part of their life history have short stem internodes, it causes premature extension of these internodes or 'bolting'. (Auxin does not have such strong effects when applied externally.) See Table 8.1.

Table 8.1. Summary of plant hormones and their function

Hormone	Function
Auxin	Increases cell elongation in growth and tropisms. Increases rate of cell division in cambium. Differentiation of vascular tissue. Increases rate of cell division in wounds (traumatin?). Suppresses lateral bud development. Initiates lateral and adventitious root formation. Stimulates development of fruit. Affects flowering: Promotes flowering in long day plants (those normally requiring more than 12 hours light in a day before they can flower) and inhibits flowering in short day plants (those requiring less than 12 hours light in a day to flower (Photoperiodism)).
Gibberellin	Cell elongation. Promotes germination of seeds. Ends dormancy in buds. Affects leaf expansion and shape. Retards leaf abscission. Aids setting of fruit after fertilisation. Removes need for cold treatment in those seeds that normally require a cold period before they germinate (vernalization). Affects flowering (florigen?): promotes flowering in many long day plants.
Cytokinin	Increased rate of cell division. Increased cell enlargement in leaves. Stimulates lateral bud development. Breaks dormancy in some species. Promotes flowering in some species. Stabilizes protein and chlorophyll.
Abscisin	Generally antagonistic to gibberellins and cytokinins. Retards growth. Induces dormancy in buds. Inhibits germination. Hastens abscission.
Ethylene (Ethene)	Promotes ripening of fruit.
'Traumatin'	Heals wounds by callus formation.
'Florigen'	Promotes flowering.

NERVOUS SYSTEMS

In Protozoa the entire cell functions as a sensitive and reactive system, but some (e.g. *Euglena*) also have specialized sensory areas such as 'eye' spots, and possibly specialized strands of sensitive cytoplasm (e.g. the neuronemes in *Paramecium*).

Coelenterates have developed specialized nerve cells which are inter-linked to form nerve nets, and in many there are specialized tracts of nervous tissue where the nerve cells are associated closely together.

Platyhelminthes have concentrations of nerve cells, in which the nerve cell bodies form masses or ganglia, and the fibres form nerve tracts.

The Annelids have their well developed ganglia and nerves arranged into a true central nervous system, with lateral branches forming the peripheral nervous system.

Arthropods, particularly the insects, have nerve concentrations which are sufficiently complex to be called a brain, as well as a system of ganglia and nerves.

Generally Molluscs do not have particularly complex nervous systems, but the cephalopod Molluscs (octopus and squid) have a brain which is comparable in complexity to that of some vertebrates.

Vertebrates have a well developed central nervous system consisting of brain and spinal cord, to and from which lead the cranial and spinal nerves of the peripheral nervous system.

MAMMALIAN BRAIN

In all vertebrates, including the mammals, the brain develops as an anterior enlargement of the dorsal hollow spinal cord. It contains the major integrating association centres, and is closely associated with the major sense organs of the head region.

The basic pattern of its organizaton is into fore, mid and hind brains; but in mammals and in man in particular this is obscured by the tremendous development of special areas, in particular the cerebral hemispheres (Fig 8.1).

The complexity of the functions of the brain depends on the number and complexity of the inter-connections between the neurone cell bodies. These are located in the outer cortex of grey matter of the brain. In the primates and man in particular, the cerebral hemispheres and cerebellum have a much folded surface, which increases their surface area. This in turn increases the grey matter, and hence increases the complexity of the neuronal structure of the brain.

Cerebral hemispheres

The cerebral hemispheres are the centre of consciousness, intelligence, memory and higher mental processes. Although each hemi-

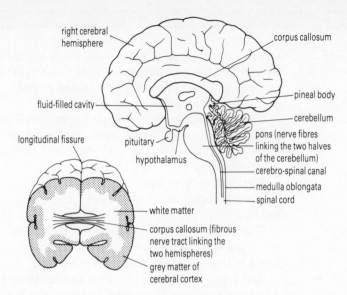

Fig 8.1. Structure of the human brain.

sphere is virtually an independent entity, in man one hemisphere (usually the left) is dominant. Integration between the hemispheres is achieved by a large tract of inter-connecting nerve fibres the **corpus callosum**.

Hypothalamus

The hypothalamus is the major centre for the control of homeostatic reflex mechanisms. This is achieved by its connections with the autonomic nervous system, and the pituitary gland. The hypothalamus produces neurosecretions which pass to the neurohypophysis of the pituitary gland, and which are then subsequently released as hormones into the blood stream.

Cerebellum

The cerebellum is the centre of the coordination of voluntary muscle activity. The stimuli to such activity comes from the cerebral hemispheres and are transmitted to the cerebellum along special direct connections.

Medulla oblongata

The medulla oblongata leads into the spinal cord, and forms part of what is referred to as the brain 'stem'. It contains the control centres of many major reflexes, such as the **cardiac centre** and **vaso-motor centre**.

SPINAL CORD

The spinal cord continues from the medulla oblongata down the neural canal of the vertebral column. It consists of nerve cells and fibres in the form of a hollow tube, with a fine central canal lined with ciliated epithelium which circulates the cerebro-spinal fluid.

Arising from the cord are pairs of segmentally arranged spinal nerves. The cord relays impulses to and from the body and the brain, and is the centre of a large number of spinal reflexes.

PERIPHERAL NERVOUS SYSTEM

Cranial nerves are paired nerves that arise from the brain. Their special segmental origin is obscured by the specialization and cephalization (fusion) of the cranial region in vertebrates (especially in mammals). They include the sensory nerves from the sense organs of the head, the motor nerves to the extrinsic eye muscles that move the eyes and the facial muscles, and the nerves which contribute to the autonomic nervous system.

Spinal nerves arise in pairs from the spinal cord, and consist of sensory and motor nerve cells. Those running to and from those structures that we are conscious of (e.g. voluntary muscle and skin) are known as **somatic nerves**; those running to and from structures that operate subconsciously (e.g. involuntary muscles and various glands) are known as **visceral nerves**.

The **visceral motor nerves** constitute what is known as the autonomic nervous system.

AUTONOMIC NERVOUS SYSTEM

In this system there are always two nerve cells on any pathway from the spinal cord to the effector, which synapse in a ganglion. The pre-ganglionic fibres are medullated or myelinated and the post ganglionic fibres are non-medullated. The system is divided into two parts: the sympathetic and the parasympathetic system.

The **sympathetic system** consists of nerve cells which leave the spinal cord in the thorax and lumbar region, and form chains of sympathetic ganglia on either side of the vertebral column where they synapse with the long post-ganglionic nerve cells which run to the structure supplied (the effector).

The **parasympathetic system** consists of fibres leaving the cranial and sacral regions. In this system there are long preganglionic nerve cells and the ganglia are close to or actually in the effectors.

Many organs and glands are supplied by both systems, which are usually antagonistic in their effects.

Effects of the sympathetic and parasympathetic nervous systems compared

Sympathetic	Parasympathetic
Tends to act as a unified system in preparing the body for emergencies.	Tends to act separately on individual organs in regulating basic functions.
1 Increases heart rate.	1 Decreases heart rate.
2 Dilates bronchioles by relaxing the smooth muscle in their walls.	2 Constricts bronchioles.
3 Decreases blood flow to gut.	3 Increases blood flow to gut.
4 Decreases gut secretions.	4 Increases gut secretions.
5 Dilates pupils by stimulating contraction of radial muscles.	5 Constricts pupils by stimulating contraction of circular muscles.
6 Increases secretion of adrenalin (the effects of which are similar).	6 Decreases secretion of adrenalin.

COMMENT ▶

The autonomic nervous system is of central importance in the regulation of homeostasis in mammals. Although questions tend not to be set specifically on the autonomic nervous system, the information set out here on its structure and function would be relevant to certain questions on homeostasis.

NERVOUS TISSUE

The tissue that makes up the nervous system consists of the actively conducting nerve cells or **neurones**, and the non-conducting packing and support cells or **neuroglia**.

NEURONES

Typically a neurone has a cell body and one or more long fine extensions or fibres (Fig 8.2). There are many types, including sensory and motor neurones.

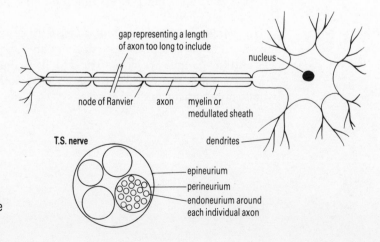

Fig 8.2. Neurone and nerve structure.

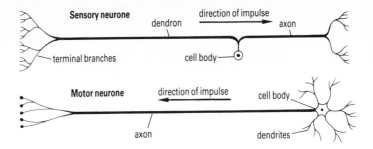

NERVE FUNCTION

The nerve cells or neurones transmit impulses along their length, and from one to another across synapses.

NERVE IMPULSE

A nerve impulse is initiated by the stimulation of the neurone by a sensory terminal, or another neurone. An impulse involves changes in the electrical and chemical state of the neurone.

When at rest the neurone has a **resting potential** of about 50–75 mV across its membrane, being more positively charged outside and more negatively charged inside.

When stimulated, the neurone membrane suddenly becomes permeable to sodium ions, which rush in and make the inside of the neurone positive, in a process known as **depolarization**.

It is the passage of this wave of depolarization along the neurone that constitutes the **impulse**.

The speed of the impulse is proportional to the diameter of the nerve fibre, reaching a maximum of 120 m/s in the largest medullated or myelinated nerve fibres (the myelin sheath restricts the depolarization to the nodes of Ranvier, and the impulse travels much faster in a process known as saltatory or 'jumping' conduction).

Once the impulse has passed, the sodium ions are actively pumped out of the neurone by a process known as the **sodium pump**, and the resting potential is restored ready for the next impulse.

Until the resting potential is restored the neurone cannot be stimulated, and this period is known as the **refractory period**.

Since the action potential does not vary with the nature of the receptor, the type of sensation detected does not depend on the character of the impulse but on the rate or frequency of impulse transmission. The fastest observed rate is about 100 impulses per second.

THE SYNAPSE

Neurones do not usually come into direct contact with each other, but are separated by small gaps or synapses (Fig 8.3).

When an impulse arrives at a synapse it triggers the release of a chemical transmitter substance which diffuses across the gap and stimulates the post-synaptic neurone to initiate an impulse.

The transmitter substance (e.g. acetylcholine) is then rapidly broken down by an enzyme (e.g. cholinesterase), and this clears the synapse for the next transmission.

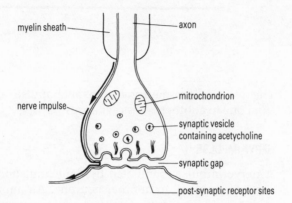

Fig 8.3. The synapse and synaptic transmission.

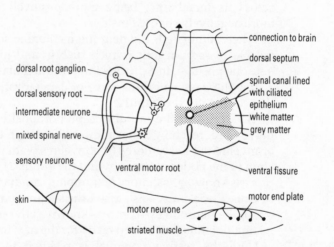

Fig 8.4. *Reflex arc involving three neurones.* Some reflex arcs involve only two neurones (e.g. the knee-jerk reflex) and in these the sensory neurone makes direct contact with the motor neurone. Although the system works reflexly there are connections to the brain.

THE REFLEX ARC

The neurone is the structural unit of the nervous system, but the functional unit, on which the greater part of the activity of the nervous system is based, is the reflex arc (Fig 8.4).

There is a hierarchy of reflex actions from the simplest, based on the spinal cord, to those of the higher centres of the cerebral cortex. All neurones within the system are interlinked and this enables conditioned reflexes to develop, which blend into the higher behavioural patterns of animals.

SENSE ORGANS

All sense organs show certain common characteristics.

1 They respond to some change in the environment known as a stimulus.
2 They change or transduce the energy of the stimulus e.g. light, mechanical etc. into the electrical energy of nerve impulses.
3 The varying nature and intensity of stimuli are translated into different frequencies of transmission of impulses.
4 They are generally specific, with histological and physiological differentiation to deal with a particular type of stimulus.

Sense organs can be classified according to the type of stimulus to which they respond.

Exteroceptors respond to external stimuli, for example photoreceptors (light); mechanoreceptors (sound, touch, and gravity); thermoreceptors (temperature); chemoreceptors (taste and smell), etc.

Interoceptors respond to internal stimuli within the body, for example any change in the internal homeostatic state, such as body temperature, blood glucose, etc.

Proprioceptors detect changes in balance, position and movement. This involves both external stimuli such as gravity and internal stimuli from the muscles and joints of the skeleton.

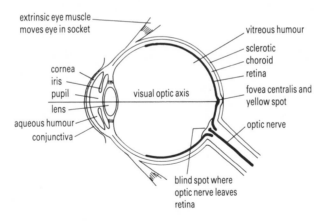

Fig 8.5. Structure of the mammalian eye as seen in horizontal section.

MAMMALIAN SENSE ORGANS

THE EYE

When light passes from one medium, such as air, to another, such as the transparent tissues of the eye, it is bent or refracted. In this way light is focused to form an image of the observed object on the retina. Light-sensitive visual pigments in the rods and cones of the retina undergo photo-chemical bleaching, and as a result nerve impulses are initiated in the optic nerves which travel to the visual cortex of the cerebral hemispheres where the image is perceived.

Focusing

The greatest focusing of light occurs at the air–cornea surface, but the fine focusing is controlled by changes in the shape of the elastic bi-convex lens which produces an inverted image on the retina, in a process known as **accommodation**.

Distant vision

The eye at rest is focused on distant objects. The circular ciliary muscles are relaxed, the suspensory ligaments are taut and pull the lens thinner and flatter, and the image is focused on the retina.

Near vision

When focusing on near objects the ciliary muscles contract and release the tension on the suspensory ligaments, the elastic lens becomes thicker, and the change in curvature of the lens brings the image of the near object to a focus on the retina (Fig 8.6). Also, when focusing on near objects, the eyes converge and the pupils constrict.

Fig 8.6. *Adjustment of the lens during accommodation*. When a circular, ring-like muscle relaxes the ring increases in diameter, and when it contracts the ring decreases in diameter.

A Eye focused on near object
circular ciliary muscle contracted

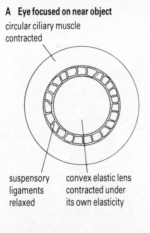

suspensory ligaments relaxed

convex elastic lens contracted under its own elasticity

B Eye focused at a distance
circular ciliary muscle relaxed

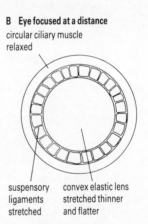

suspensory ligaments stretched

convex elastic lens stretched thinner and flatter

ACCOMMODATION OF THE EYE

Distant vision	Near vision
1 Ciliary muscles relaxed.	1 Ciliary muscles contracted.
2 Ligaments taut.	2 Ligaments slack.
3 Lens thinner.	3 Lens thicker.

CONTROL OF PUPIL SIZE

The pupil is an opening in the iris. The iris is a circular diaphragm of radial and circular smooth muscles which controls the amount of light entering the eye.

CONTROL OF PUPIL SIZE UNDER DIFFERENT CONDITIONS OF LIGHT

Dim light	Bright light
1 Sympathetic stimulation of radial muscles. 2 Pupil dilates.	1 Parasympathetic stimulation of circular muscles. 2 Pupil constricts.

Retina

The retina consists of specialized light-sensitive sensory cells called cones and rods, and many integrating nerve cells.

CONES AND RODS COMPARED

Cones	Rods
1 Sensitive to bright light and colour. 'Daytime vision.' 2 Fovea contains only cones. 3 Each cone a functional unit therefore acuity good.	1 Sensitive to dim light, black and white vision only. 'Twilight vision.' 2 Rods increase towards edge of retina. 3 Many rods connected to single nerve cell, visual acuity poor.

The cones and rods contain photopigments (e.g. rhodopsin or visual purple) which trigger impulses in the optic nerve when bleached by light. Re-synthesis of the pigments occurs, especially in low light intensities, and they become more sensitive in a process of **dark adaptation**.

THE EAR

The ear is an organ of hearing and balance. Its structure is outlined in Fig 8.7.

Hearing

Hearing involves the detection and interpretation of different frequencies of vibration in the air known as sound waves. The sound waves cause the tympanic membrane to vibrate, this in turn sets up a sequence of vibrations through the malleus, incus and stapes to the oval window membrane, and then via the perilymph and endolymph of the inner ear to the basilar membrane and organ of Corti.

The basilar membrane vibrates, and the hair cells of the organ of Corti, which are attached to the basilar membrane at one end and to the stiff tectorial membrane at the other, are stimulated mechanically and transduce this information into nerve impulses.

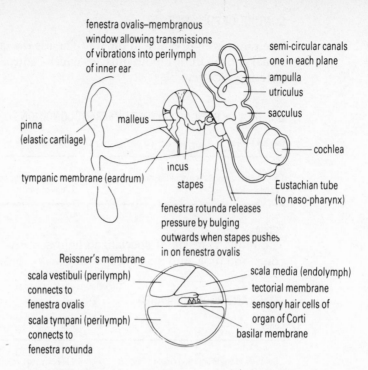

fenestra ovalis–membranous window allowing transmissions of vibrations into perilymph of inner ear

semi-circular canals one in each plane

ampulla

utriculus

sacculus

pinna (elastic cartilage)

malleus

cochlea

incus

tympanic membrane (eardrum)

stapes

Eustachian tube (to naso-pharynx)

fenestra rotunda releases pressure by bulging outwards when stapes pushes in on fenestra ovalis

Reissner's membrane

scala vestibuli (perilymph) connects to fenestra ovalis

scala tympani (perilymph) connects to fenestra rotunda

scala media (endolymph)

tectorial membrane

sensory hair cells of organ of Corti

basilar membrane

Fig 8.7. *Structure of the mammalian ear*. The arrangement of the bones in the middle ear, plus the fact that the eardrum is twenty times larger than the fenestra ovalis, increases the force of vibration so that they can penetrate the perilymph of the inner ear. The eustachian tube is normally closed and only opens during swallowing and yawning, at which times it allows the air pressure to balance on both sides of the delicate eardrum. The inner ear is a labyrinth of membranous tubes containing endolymph enclosed in a system of bony cavities containing perilymph.

The impulses from each ear are transmitted via the auditory nerve and auditory pathways in the brain, equally to the two cerebral hemispheres.

Balance

Each ampulla contains a **crista**, which consists of a small mass of mucus attached to sensory hair cells. During rotatory movements of the head, the endolymph within the canals tends to remain stationary, and the hair cells are bent as the mucus is dragged through the endolymph. This bending is interpreted as a measure of the rotation of the head.

The **maculae** in the utriculus and sacculus are similar, except the mucus contains granules of calcium carbonate and they respond to gravity when the head is tilted.

ANIMAL HORMONES

Hormones are produced by ductless or endocrine glands, and are secreted directly into the blood stream, which carries them to their specific site of action. They are organic compounds of varying chemical composition, and include proteins, polypeptides and steroids. Many hormones have a common name, as well as a more technical name, e.g. growth hormone (somatotrophin).

ENDOCRINE GLANDS AND THEIR HORMONES

Pituitary
The pituitary gland is found below, and connected to, the hypothalamus. The adenohypophysis or anterior lobe is not directly connected to the hypothalamus, but the neurohypophysis or posterior lobe has direct connections along which neurosecretions pass from the hypothalamus.

Adenohypophysis
The adenohypophysis secretes **growth hormone** which promotes growth; **thyroid stimulating hormone** (TSH) which regulates the growth and function of the thyroid; **follicle stimulating hormone** (FSH) which initiates the cyclic changes in the ovaries; **luteinizing hormone** (LH), or **interstitial cell stimulating hormone** (ICSH) which stimulates ovulation; and others (see Table 8.2).

Neurohypophysis
The neurohypophysis secretes **oxytocin** which produces powerful contractions of the uterus, induces lactation, and facilitates the ejection of milk during suckling; and **anti-diuretic hormone** (ADH) which amongst other functions reduces the amount of water lost in the urine.

Thyroid
The thyroid is found in the neck close to the larynx. It secretes thyroxine which stimulates metabolism, and which is involved in most growth and development processes.

Parathyroids
The four parathyroids are small glands embedded in the thyroid. They secrete **parathyroid hormone** or parathyrone and **calcitonin**, which regulate the calcium ion concentration of the plasma and body fluids.

Adrenal glands
The two adrenal glands are found close to each kidney. Each adrenal gland consists of an outer cortex and an inner medulla.

Adrenal cortex

The adrenal cortex secretes **cortisol** (hydrocortisone) which is involved in body fluid balance, the prevention of inflammation, and resistance to stress; **aldosterone** which causes the retention of sodium ions by the kidneys and is thus involved in osmoregulation; male and female sex hormones; and others.

Adrenal medulla

The adrenal medulla secretes **adrenaline** (and the closely related noradrenaline) which increases muscle tone, metabolic rate (particularly the oxidation of blood sugar and fatty acids), heart rate, and rate and depth of breathing. It also dilates the coronary and skeletal muscle blood vessels, and constricts those of the skin and the gut. The sum total of these effects is to prepare the body for response to emergencies.

Table 8.2. Summary of mammalian hormones

Area of function	Hormone	Source	Main effects	Control stimulus
General metabolism and growth	Growth hormone	Adeno-hypophysis	Overall growth	
	Thyroxine	Thyroid	Tissue respiration, basal metabolic rate	Thyrotrophin
	Parathyrone	Parathyroid	Calcium and phosphate metabolism of bones	Blood calcium
	Insulin	Pancreas	Increased glucose use and glycogen storage	Blood glucose
	Glucagon	Pancreas	Antagonistic to insulin	Blood glucose
	Hydro-cortisone	Adrenal cortex	Carbohydrate, protein, and fat metabolism combats stress	ACTH
Circulation	Adrenaline	Adrenal medulla	Increased circulation to muscles	Nervous
	Noradrenaline	Adrenal medulla	Increased blood pressure	Nervous
	Angiotensin	Blood plasma	Increased blood pressure, stimulates secretion of aldosterone	Renin
	Serotonin	Platelets	Increased blood pressure, increased smooth muscle tone	
	Histamine	Tissues	Inflammatory response	Injury
	Vasopressin (ADH)	Neuro-hypophysis	Increased blood pressure	
Osmo-regulation	ADH (vaso-pressin)	Neuro-hypophysis	Increased water reabsorption by kidney	Blood concentration
	Aldosterone	Adrenal cortex	Sodium retention by kidney	Blood concentration
Digestion	Gastrin	Stomach wall	Stimulates secretion of gastric juice	Food in stomach
	Entero-gastrone	Intestine wall	Inhibits secretion of gastrin	Fat in intestine
	Villikinin	Intestine wall	Stumulates 'villus pump'	Food in intestine
	Secretin	Intestine wall	Stimulates flow of watery pancreatic juice	Acid in intestine
	Pancreozymin	Intestine wall	Stimulates secretion of pancreatic enzymes	Peptones in gut
	Cholecys-tokinin	Intestine wall	Causes contraction of gall bladder	Fat in intestine

Area of function	Hormone	Source	Main effects	Control stimulus
Reproduction	Follicle stimulating hormone (FSH)	Adeno-hypophysis	Causes ovary follicles to develop and testis to make spermatozoa	Hypothalamus releasing factor
	Luteinizing hormone (LH) (interstitial cell stimulating hormone (ICSH)	Adeno-hypophysis	Causes release of egg from ovary and follicle to turn into corpus luteum and testis to make testosterone	Hypothalamus releasing factor
	Prolactin (luteotrophic hormone)	Adeno-hypophysis	Affects corpus luteum in pregnancy and milk secretion	Hypothalamus releasing factor
	Oxytocin	Neuro-hypophysis	Stimulates uterine contractions and ejection of milk	Hypothalamus and suckling
	Androgens	Adrenal cortex	Growth of body hair, anabolism	ACTH
	Oestrogens	Ovary	Secondary sexual characteristics. Uterine changes up to ovulation	Ovary development
	Progesterone	Ovary	Uterine changes after ovulation	Ovulation
	Placental hormones	Placenta	Maintain pregnancy	Placental development
	Testosterone	Interstitial cells of testes	Secondary sexual characteristics	LH (ICSH)
Endocrine glands	Thyrotrophic hormone (TH)	Adeno-hypophysis	Stimulates thyroid	Thyroxine levels
	Adreno-corticotrophic hormones (ACTH)	Adeno-hypophysis	Stimulates adrenal cortex	Stress
	Diabetogenic hormone	Adeno-hypophysis	Decreases insulin production and action	Blood sugar
	Hydro-cortisone	Adrenal cortex	Affects entire endocrine system	Stress

Islets of Langerhans

The islets of Langerhans are patches of endocrine tissue scattered throughout the pancreas. They are composed of two types of cell: the cells which secrete glucagon, and the cells which secrete insulin. **Insulin** opposes any increase in blood glucose level by stimulating the liver and muscles to store glucose as glycogen, and by increasing the rate of glucose utilization by the tissues.

Glucagon is antagonistic to insulin, being secreted if the blood glucose level decreases.

Gut mucosa

The wall of the gut secretes several hormones into the blood stream, which contribute to the regulation of digestion.

Reproductive organs

Special endocrine cells in the reproductive organs of both sexes secrete reproductive hormones which are involved in the development and control of the reproductive processes.

QUESTION ▶

Q.   By means of labelled diagrams illustrate the structure of the mammalian brain and spinal cord (8) (5)
Explain what is meant by
         (i) a reflex arc (4)
         (ii) a reflex action (3)

COMMENT ▶

This question requires labelled diagrams as a major feature. Note that even in such a question there are usually not many marks (typically 2 or 3) allocated for the diagrams, and that therefore it is not worthwhile spending too long shading etc.

OUTLINE ▶
ANSWER

Points to be covered include:
Brain – diagram quality with caption (8)
Expected labels might include:
cerebral hemispheres, cerebellum, medulla oblongata, pineal body, hypothalamus, pituitary gland, meninges, corpus callosum, ventricles, pons.
Spinal cord – diagram quality with caption (5)
Expected labels might include:
cerebro-spinal canal, ciliated epithelium, white and grey matter, dorsal root ganglion, dorsal sensory root, ventral motor root, dorsal septum, ventral fissure, membranes.
         (i) **Reflex arc** (4)
         Series of neurones and synapses along which impulses pass to cause a reflex action;
         pathway to include mention of sensory receptor – sensory, intermediate, motor neurones – muscle or gland;
         example: from sensory receptor in skin, via spinal cord, to muscles in the arm.
         (ii) **Reflex action** (3)
         Stimulus causes a rapid automatic response, based upon the reflex arc, impulses passed to brain for information only, e.g. withdrawing hand from hot object.

QUESTIONS

1   Answer part **X** and *either* **Y** *or* **Z**. All parts are of equal mark value.
       X   To determine the effect of the concentration of *auxin* on the growth of shoots and roots of oat seedlings a series of concentrations were applied to their surfaces and the percentage stimulation of

growth relative to a control, whether negative or positive, recorded. The results are set out below.

Concentration (parts per million)	Percentage Stimulation of Growth	
	Root	Shoot
10^{-7}	0	0
10^{-6}	+5	0
10^{-5}	+20	0
10^{-4}	+25	+2
10^{-3}	+20	+15
10^{-2}	−30	+70
10^{-1}	−70	+170
1	−95	+240
10	−100	+200
10^2	−100	+40
10^3	−100	+5

(i) Express these figures *graphically*

(ii) Comment on the relative effect that auxin has on the growth of the root compared with the stem and relate this to its apical origin in the shoot and its passage by diffusion towards the root.

(iii) How far do the conclusions you draw from the data help to explain why when a plant is laid horizontally the shoot bends upwards and the root downwards?

(iv) Explain why when a germinating seedling is fixed horizontally to a klinostat and revolved once a minute no bending is visible, yet when rotated once every two hours the root and shoot assume the shape of a cork screw.

Y One sided illumination of the tip of a shoot causes increased growth in the growth zone lower down the shoot on the opposite side, and hence curvature towards the light.

Two hypotheses could be advanced to explain this:

(*a*) that the one-sided illumination has an inhibitory effect on the cells in the growth zone on that side,

or (*b*) that in its diffusion downward from its site of production the auxin accumulates in greater quantity on the opposite side.

Using the established 'agar block' technique *outline any simple experiment(s)* that would determine which explanation is better.

Z *Gibberellins* like auxins have a profound effect, both normal and abnormal, on the growth of plants. Using a tabular format, *compare their effects* (positive or negative) on

(*a*) cell division
(*b*) cell elongation
(*c*) the bending response of shoots and roots
(*d*) the formation of lateral or adventitious roots
(*e*) internodal growth

The effect of these two hormones on the *growth of the axillary shoots* was studied. Ten plants were included in each group, which were treated as follows, environmental conditions being kept constant.

A – plants left intact
B – apical bud removed,
C – apical bud replaced by auxin on cut end,
D – apical bud replaced by gibberellic acid on cut end.

The mean totals of axillary shoot lengths (mm) were determined. The results are shown on the table below.

Days after start of treatment	Mean total axillary shoot lengths (mm)			
	A	B	C	D
2	3	3	3	3
4	3	10	4	12
6	3	30	4	45
8	3	50	5	90
10	3	78	6	116
13	3	118	30	150

State the conclusions that you *draw from these results*.   (NI)

2 An experiment was carried out with a species of plant which grows initially as a compact rosette. Prior to flowering the shoot 'bolts', elongation of the internodes giving a tall stem with widely separated leaves. Extracts of equal masses of tissue from rosette and bolting plants were incubated in a solution containing IAA. The results are given in the table.

Additions to IAA solution	Percentage of IAA remaining after 2 hours
none	100
boiled extract of rosette shoots	96
boiled extract of bolting shoots	95
fresh extract of rosette shoots	42
fresh extract of bolting shoots	81

The results are compatible with the conclusion or conclusions that
(1)   boiled extracts are unable to decompose IAA.
(2)   fresh extracts decompose IAA largely by enzyme action.
(3)   the activity of IAA-decomposing enzymes increases when the stem bolts.
(4)   the activity of IAA-decomposing enzymes decreases when the stem bolts. (JMB)

3   (*a*)   The following graph shows the apparent relationship between auxin production and fruit drop in the apple.

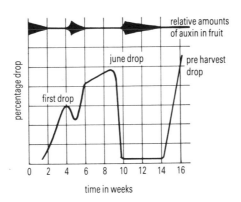

(i) State the relationship between auxin level and fruit drop.
(ii) What might be done to increase the number of apples harvested? (SCE)

4   Distinguish between *hormone, enzyme* and *vitamin*. Describe the origin and mode of action of **one named** animal hormone. Briefly indicate how it differs in nature, origin and mode of action from a **named** plant hormone. (LOND)

5   Fig 1 represents a section of the mammalian brain.
(*a*)   Name the part labelled **Z**.
(*b*)   Indicate by an arrow and the letter **X** on the drawing the area which is responsible for temperature control.

(c)   What is the name of the area you have labelled **X**?

(d)   Name two other functions of this region of the brain.

(e)   Briefly describe two ways in which information about body temperature reaches the brain.   (O)

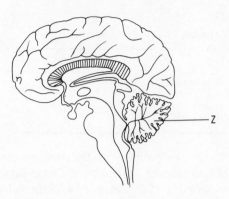

Fig 1

6   The part of the mammalian brain directly associated with the learning process is the

A   cerebellum.

B   pons.

C   cerebrum.

D   medulla.   (CAM)

7   (a)   Make a fully labelled diagram to show the main parts of a mammalian brain.

(b)   Briefly explain the functions of the main parts of the brain in a mammal.

(c)   Give an illustrated account of the way in which nerve impulses are conducted in a mammalian nerve fibre.   (LOND)

8   Describe the structure of

(i) a typical motor neurone of a vertebrate.

(ii) a synapse.

(b)   Compare transmission along a nerve fibre with transmission across a synapse.   (CAM)

9   Which statement most accurately describes a nerve impulse? A nerve impule is

A   the sudden depolarization of the nerve cell membrane.

B   the spread of a wave of electrons down the axon.

C   a self-propagating change in polarity across the membrane.

D   the active removal of sodium ions across a membrane.

          (JMB)

10 Fig X shows what happens when a nerve impulse arrives at the presynaptic membrane.

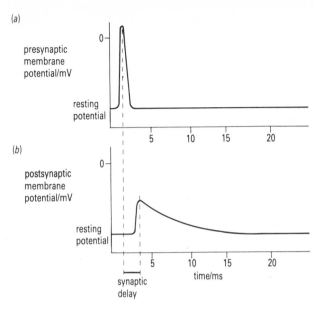

Fig. X

(i) List two important ways in which the postsynaptic potential (**b**) differs from the presynaptic potential (**a**).

(ii) What is released at the presynaptic membrane to bring about the postsynaptic potential?

(iii) What causes the 'synaptic delay'?

(iv) Why does the postsynaptic potential gradually decay?

(v) Why is it important that the postsynaptic potential returns to its resting potential?

11 **Matching pairs question**

In Question 11 a group of questions is accompanied by a set of alternative answers **A, B, C, D** and **E**. Within each group of questions each letter may be used once, more than once, or not at all. Indicate your choice on the answer sheet.

The reflex arc of a vertebrate passes through the following regions, not necessarily in the order shown.

A   white matter of spinal cord
B   grey matter of spinal cord
C   ventral root of spinal nerve
D   dorsal root of spinal nerve
E   dorsal root ganglion

For each item (i) to (v) below, select a letter to represent the region in which you expect the item mainly to occur.

(i) axons of longitudinal neurons connecting different reflex arcs

(ii) axon of the intermediate neuron

(iii) axon of the sensory neuron

    (iv) cell body of the sensory neuron

    (v) axon of the motor neuron   (JMB)

12   **Briefly** indicate the importance of photoreceptors and chemoreceptors to animals.

    Describe how the mammalian eye and ear act as receptors of environmental stimuli.   (SCE)

13   (*a*)   Describe the structure of the mammalian eye (diagrams should be used where appropriate, but their relationship to the intact eye should be explained).

    (*b*)   Discuss **briefly** (i) for formation of the images of near and distant objects on the retina and

    (ii) the function of the rods.   (CAM)

14   Which of the following is a particularly important property of a retina composed of rods?

    A   perception of movement

    B   perception of colour

    C   high visual acuity

    D   high visual sensitivity   (CAM)

15   The graph below shows the number of receptor cells (types A and B) in the human retina along a horizontal line from the nasal side of the eye to the outer side. Distances are expressed as arbitrary units.

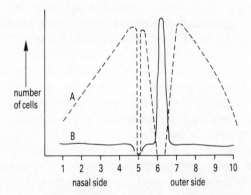

    (*a*)   (i) Identify the types of receptor represented by A and B.

    (ii) Explain why there are no receptor cells at position 5.

    (iii) What is the name of the region of the retina at position 6?

    (iv) Explain why the greatest concentration of receptor cells of type **B** occurs at position 6.

    (*b*)   (i) When a person moves from bright surroundings into a dimly-lit room, objects in the room cannot at first be seen but they gradually become visible. Explain this occurrence.

    (ii) In the dimly-lit room, objects are only visible in black and white. Explain this.

    (*c*)   Describe the particular features of receptor cells which allow objects to be viewed in colour.

    (*d*)   The flowers of three species of cinquefoil, *Potentilla*, are similar in form and all appear to have the same uniformly coloured yellow petals. When photographed in ultraviolet light, each species shows a different pattern on its petals. Using this information, explain in detail how bees are able to distinguish between the flowers of the three species of cinquefoil while man cannot do so.   (AEB)

16 Which one of the following structures is situated immediately beneath the mammalian organ of Corti, adjacent to the scala tympani?

A   tympanum
B   tectorial membrane
C   fenestra rotunda
D   basilar membrane   (CAM)

17 Give an account of
(*a*)   the organ of Corti, and
(*b*)   the retina.
Describe how **either** sound waves reach the organ of Corti **or** light waves are focused on the retina.   (O&C)

18 Discuss the role of the pituitary gland in regulating the functions of the mammalian body.   (W)

19 (*a*)   What is a hormone?
(*b*)   How do mammalian hormones reach their target cells?
(*c*)   Discuss the functions of the pituitary gland.   (O&C)

20 (*a*)   Explain what is meant by (i) chemical coordination, (ii) nervous coordination.
(*b*)   Describe one *named* example of chemical coordination and one *named* example of nervous coordination.   (LOND)

21 An experimental animal, deficient in the production of *parathyroid hormone* was given an injection of this hormone from another source. Both before and after this injection the levels of calcium and phosphorus in the animal's blood plasma were measured in mg cm^{-3} at hourly intervals, the injection being given at the commencement of the second hour. The table below gives the results of the measurements.

↓ Injection

Time (hours)	0	1	2	3	4	5	6	7	8	9
Ca	7.15	7.25	7.15	7.00	7.35	7.75	8.25	9.00	8.75	8.00
P	10.40	10.60	10.40	10.25	9.12	8.00	9.25	9.05	9.15	9.25

(after Albright and Reifenstein)

(i) Plot graphs of Ca and P levels against time on the same set of axes.

(ii) What can be said about changes in plasma levels both of Ca and P (*a*) before and (*b*) after injection?

(iii) How long does it take for the hormone to exert its greatest effect?

(iv) Which foodstuffs are good sources of calcium?

(v) Which vitamin plays a significant role in calcium metabolism?

(vi) In the absence of dietary calcium from where might the plasma derive the necessary calcium?

(vii) What is the importance to the body of phosphate?

(viii) What is the role of calcium in plant metabolism?

(ix) Newly germinated seeds soaked in a solution of gibberellin will show markedly increased growth rates for a time. Devise an experiment that would find out (*a*) that concentration of hormone which could produce a 10% growth increase and (*b*) the time elapsing before the single treatment wears off.   (NI)

22 (*a*)   (i) A man looking into the distance wishes to know the time. Explain how his eye functions to enable him to focus on his watch.

(ii) Explain how the retina is structured to enable small coloured objects to be distinguished in bright light.

(iii) Why are such small objects discriminated less well in poor light conditions?

(*b*)   What is the role of each of the following in the detection of sound?

(i) the ear ossicles

(ii) The differences in area of the tympanic membrane compared with the fenestra ovalis

(iii) the organ of Corti.   (JMB)

MOVEMENT, RESPONSE AND BEHAVIOUR

CONTENTS

Movement of living organisms is normally taken to involve internal forces, often active living processes, rather than purely passive movement as a result of external forces such as wind or water currents. All living things move, but only animals and some of the microscopic algae (e.g. *Chlamydomonas* and *Euglena* with their flagella) carry out locomotion – that is movement from place to place.

Movement and locomotion invariably occur as responses to stimuli. They must therefore involve some sensory system and some effector system capable of responding to the stimuli.

In animals the complexity of the responses are such that the term **behaviour** is used to describe them.

The structure and organization of multicellular plants with their rigid cellulose cell walls is such that movement and response invariably involves growth. Any attempt at dealing with movement and response in plants separately from their growth and development will generate problems, and therefore material described here should be linked to that in Chapter 3.

PLANT MOVEMENT

Plant movements can be classified for convenience as shown below.

MECHANISMS OF PLANT MOVEMENT

1 TURGOR MOVEMENTS

These occur as a result of changes in the turgor of cells. As cells gain water and become turgid, or lose water and become flaccid, they change shape. Many cells are particularly adapted, both in structure and in position to accentuate such changes. Turgor movements allow a rapid response.

Stomatal opening and closing is controlled by movements brought about by changes in turgor of the guard cells;

leaf rolling in the xeromorphic marram grass occurs as a result of changes in turgor of specialised hinge cells;

many fungi have spore dispersal mechanisms dependent upon increasing turgor in the sporangia (e.g. *Mucor*).

2 GROWTH MOVEMENTS

These occur as a result of different growth rates, usually on either side of a structure, such as the bending of stems towards the light. These movements are the slower of the three types.

3 HYGROSCOPIC MOVEMENTS

These usually occur as a result of the drying of differentially thickened dead tissues. As water evaporates from the tissues, unequal shrinking occurs as a result of their special pattern of thickening, which in conjunction with the cohesive forces of the water, result in the movement.

Such movement is seen in the dehiscence of the sporangium wall of ferns, and in the opening and closing of the peristome teeth of the capsules of moss sporophytes; both of which result in the dispersal of spores into air currents.

TYPES OF PLANT MOVEMENT

1 AUTONOMIC MOVEMENTS

These are apparently spontaneous and do not occur as a response to a stimulus.

Included here are the **nutation** movements shown by stem apices, which do not grow straight up but follow a circular or spiral path. This is seen particularly clearly in the stems of climbing plants where it increases the chances of coming into contact with a support of some kind (e.g. Convolvulus).

2 STIMULUS MOVEMENTS

Such movements in response to a stimulus may be of two types. **Nastic** or non-directional, as in the opening and closing of some flowers in response to changes in temperature and light, and leaf rolling in dry air in xerophytes.

Tropic or directional.

Tropic movements

There are a wide variety of stimuli to which plants respond in a directional manner, including photo(light), geo(gravity), hydro (water), rheo(water current), aero(air), thigmo(touch), and chemo (chemical).

The response may be positive (towards the stimulus), or negative (away), or at some angle to the stimulus. The bending of parts of the plant towards or away from a stimulus is caused by an unequal distribution of auxins in the zones of elongation, which results in different growth rates by cell extension on either side.

(i) **Phototropism** Stems are positively phototropic, growing towards the light. Once the stem is pointing towards the light, the response stops as the light is no longer unilateral.

Experiment	Result	Deductions
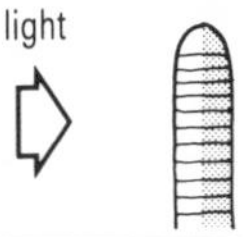 light — shoot marked with parallel lines	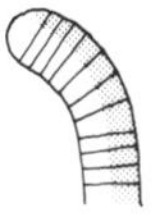 bends towards light	(a) shoots are positively phototropic (b) response occurs in zone of elongation
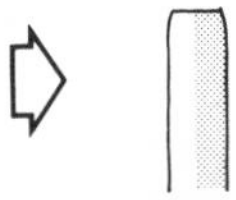 tip removed	 no response	no response without tip
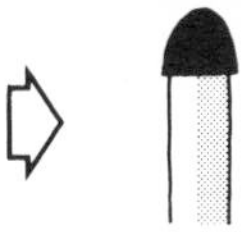 opaque cap over tip	 no response	tip detects the stimulus of unilateral light
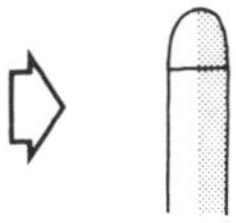 tip cut off and replaced	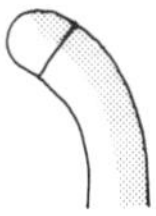 bends towards light	physical continuity is not necessary for the passage of the message from the tip to the zone of elongation indicates a chemical ie hormone
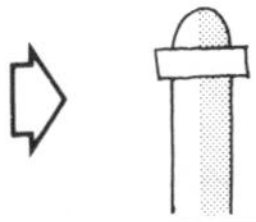 tip cut off and replaced on an agar block	 bends towards light	message is capable of diffusing across a non-living block and still induce bending in zone of elongation ie chemical (hormone)
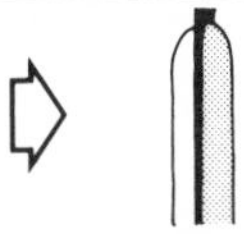 tip divided by thin impermeable layer	 no response	if lateral diffusion from light to dark side is prevented there is no response
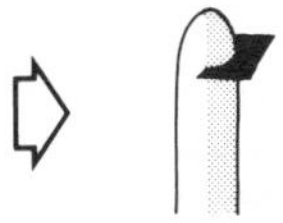 thin impermeable layer on dark side	 no response	if diffusion down the dark side is prevented there is no response
	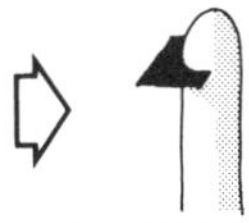  bends towards light	bending towards light occurs as a result of diffusion of a chemical on dark side
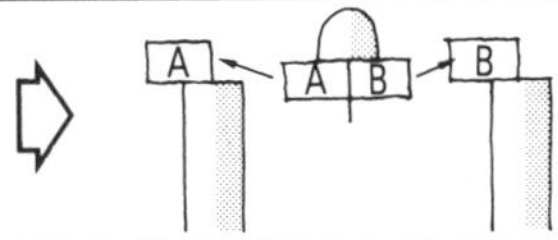 A — A B — B	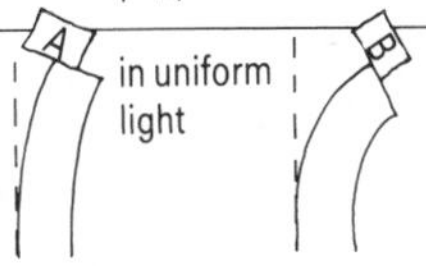 in uniform light	more chemical diffuses down dark side. Degree of curvature is proportional to the concentration of chemical

Fig 9.1. *Summary of some of the experimental evidence relating to the mechanism of phototropism.* Whether the unequal distribution of auxin under unilateral light is the result of decreased auxin synthesis on the light side, increased auxin synthesis on the dark side, destruction of auxin on the light side, or lateral diffusion from the tip to the dark side is still not clear; but lateral diffusion is thought to be the main method.

The stimulus is detected in some way by the stem apex, growth hormones (auxins) pass down to the zone of elongation, and cause greater cell extension on the darker side of the zone of elongation.

This results in a bending growth towards the light. The cause of the unequal distribution of auxin in the zone of elongation (more on the darker side) is still not known (Fig 9.1).

Leaves arrange their laminae at right angles to the incident light for maximum absorption of light for photosynthesis.

Roots show no response to light.

(ii) **Geotropism** Primary roots are positively geotropic.

Lateral roots grow at an angle to gravity.

Tertiary roots are insenstive to gravity.

Main stems are negatively geotropic.

Lateral stems and leaves grow at an angle to gravity (diatropic).

Modified stems such as rhizomes and runners grow at right angles to gravity.

Gravity acts on mass and is detected by some cell inclusions, which become redistributed under gravity. Many geosensitive regions have mobile starch grains which accumulate on the lower side of cells. As a result of the stimulus of gravity, there is an unequal distribution of auxin, with the highest concentration on the lower side of both roots and stems.

This increased concentration on the lower side of roots inhibits cell extension, thus leading to a bending towards gravity. In stems, however, increased concentration increases cell extension and leads to a bending away from gravity. These opposite responses of root tissue and stem tissue to the same concentration of auxin is explained by their differing sensitivities to the hormone (Fig 9.2).

All the tropisms, especially photo, geo and hydro, interact in a complex of ways to result in the overall orientation of the plant in its habitat; for example positive hydrotropism in roots towards water will modify their response to gravity.

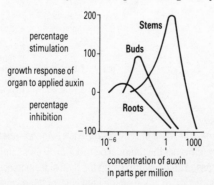

Fig 9.2. *Response of plant parts to different auxin concentrations.* Note the log scale of the auxin concentration.

3 TACTIC MOVEMENTS

These are locomotory movements of whole organisms, and in plants are only found in some of the microscopic algae such as *Chlamydomonas* which can move towards light by means of their flagella.

EXERCISE ➤

Exercise 9.1
Match each of the following types of movement to the appropriate example.
(A) Hygroscopic, (B) Autonomic, (C) Turgor, (D) Nastic, (E) Tropic, (F) Tactic.

(1) Opening of flowers, (2) Bending of roots towards water, (3) Dehiscence of sporangia in the dry, (4) Opening of stomata, (5) Spiral movement of climbing stems, (6) Swimming towards light.

ANIMAL MOVEMENT

There is a range of methods of movement and locomotion to be found in the animal kingdom, including amoeboid, ciliary, flagellate and muscle movement.

AMOEBOID MOVEMENT

Amoeboid movement derives its name from the Protozoan *Amoeba*, but it is also seen in mammalian white blood cells, nematode spermatozoa and slime fungi and bacteria.

It involves the formation of pseudopodia which are formed as a result of the semi-liquid sol endoplasm flowing forwards (Fig 9.3). As with all mechanisms of locomotion it requires energy from respiration and involves contractile proteins in the cytoplasm.

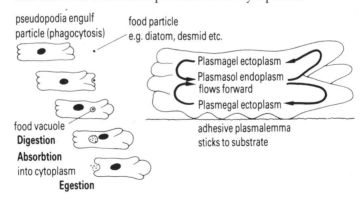

Fig 9.3. *Amoeboid movement.* In this series of drawings the *Amoeba* is moving from left to right.

The pseudopodia are usually also used in feeding, enclosing the food particles in food vacuoles in a process known as **phagocytosis.**

CILIARY MOVEMENT

In small organisms, for example the ciliated protozoa (e.g. *Paramecium*) and the ciliated larvae of many animals, the cilia are used in locomotion and feeding (Fig 9.4 and Fig 9.5).

Fig 9.4. T.S. Cilium.

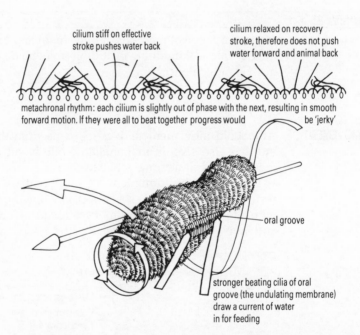

T.S. Cilium (9+2 structure)

one of a pair of central fibrils

membrane

paired outer fibrils (contractile)

0.2μm
(length 5–10μm)

cilium stiff on effective stroke pushes water back

cilium relaxed on recovery stroke, therefore does not push water forward and animal back

metachronal rhythm: each cilium is slightly out of phase with the next, resulting in smooth forward motion. If they were all to beat together progress would be 'jerky'

oral groove

stronger beating cilia of oral groove (the undulating membrane) draw a current of water in for feeding

Fig 9.5. *Ciliary movement in Paramecium.* In *Paramecium* the cilia beat to the right causing the animal to rotate or spin about the longitudinal axis; this prevents the stronger beating oral groove cilia from driving the animal in a circle. The spinning and the tendency to circle resolve into a spiral forward motion.

In larger organisms cilia are used for moving fluids and particles over surfaces; for example the movement of food particles over the gills of lamellibranch molluscs, the movement of wastes in the annelid worms nephridia, the movement of eggs in the mammalian oviducts, and the removal of trapped particles in the air passages of vertebrates.

FLAGELLATE MOVEMENT Flagella are similar in structure to cilia but are much longer (up to 100 μm) and are usually found singly or in pairs.

They are used for locomotion in the flagellate algae (e.g. *Chlamydomonas* and *Euglena*) (Fig 9.6), in many bacteria and in motile male gametes of both plants and animals.

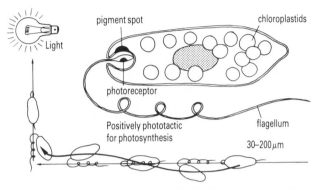

Euglena spins on its own axis and rotates around the flagellum, acting as a sort of inclined plane or propellor pushing water back, thus gaining forward momentum

Fig 9.6. *Flagellate movement in Euglena.* The flagellum waves are actively generated along its length, they are not produced by a simple whiplash effect. Unilateral light is blocked from the photoreceptor by the pigment spot as *Euglena* spins and rotates. This is detected, and the direction interpreted. The *Euglena* then bends towards the light by using its contractile myonemes.

MUSCLE MOVEMENT There are three main types of muscle, unstriated, cardiac and striated.

Unstriated (smooth or involuntary) muscle consists of simple elongated cells (0.5 mm), usually bound together by connective tissue to form sheets.

It is mainly found in the walls of hollow organs and systems, e.g. blood vessels, bladder, gut, lymphatic system, etc., but it is also found attached to hair roots, and in the iris and ciliary body of the eye.

It is innervated by the autonomic nervous system and is not under voluntary control; it is also stimulated to contract by hormones (e.g. adrenaline, histamine, etc.) and in some cases it is capable of contraction without stimulation.

Cardiac muscle consists of unicellular fibres, with cross striations and lateral connections to adjacent fibres. It is only found in the heart.

It is **myogenic**, that is it contracts rhythmically without stimulation, however its intrinsic power of contraction is reinforced and coordinated by the autonomic nervous system, and it is also sensitive to hormones, e.g. adrenaline.

Striated (striped or voluntary) muscle consists of multinucleated fibres bound together into bundles, which form the skeletal muscles (Fig 9.7). These are under voluntary control and contract when stimulated.

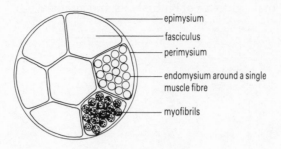

- epimysium
- fasciculus
- perimysium
- endomysium around a single muscle fibre
- myofibrils

Structure of striated muscle as seen in TS.

The myofibrils (muscle fibres) consist of the proteins myosin, actin and tropomyosin, which make up the contractile mechanism (Fig 9.8).

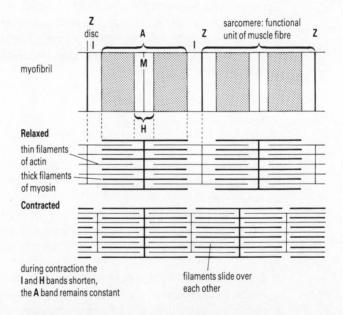

Fig 9.8. *Microscopic structure, and function, of a single striated muscle fibre.* A single muscle fibre may be up to 40 mm long. The striations that are visible under the microscope are interpreted according to the sliding filament theory, as the pattern of banding alters when the fibre contracts. The 'darker' bands have more overlapping filaments than the 'lighter' bands. It is postulated that cross bridges of actomyosin act as a chemical 'ratchet' to move the thick and thin filaments over each other. Contraction of the sarcomeres can produce an overall shortening of fibres of up to 30%.

Myosin molecules have one part which contributes to the physical structure of the muscle, and two chemically active sites, one of which catalyses the breakdown of ATP to release energy for contraction and the other which binds to actin.

Each molecule of actin has a molecule of ATP attached to it, upon which the myosin acts to release energy necessary for contraction.

When stimulated, the actin and myosin interact to form acto-myosin which results in contraction.

The tropomyosin is thought to be important in controlling contractions and possibly sensitizing the contractile proteins to calcium (which is important in contractions).

In striated muscle fibres the smooth endoplasmic reticulum is well developed and forms a complex around each myofibril which is known as the sarcoplasmic reticulum. This conducts the excitatory impulses from the surface of the fibre to each myofibril. The impulse also causes calcium ions to be released into the reticulum, which are necessary for the breakdown of ATP and the release of energy.

EXERCISE ▶

Exercise 9.2

What features are common to amoeboid, ciliate, flagellate, and muscular movement?

Answer Two main features are that they are all based on the activity of contractile proteins, and they all require an energy supply in the form of ATP. Although the motive force behind amoeboid movement is not fully understood, it is suggested that it involves either a 'pulling' forward from the anterior, or a 'squeezing' forward from the posterior; both explanations involve contractile proteins in the cytoplasm.

STIMULATION

Striated muscles are stimulated to contract by:

1 direct motor nerve innervation
2 the muscle spindle reflex.

1 The **direct motor nerve** axon loses its myelin sheath, the nerve fibre forms special motor end plates with the muscle fibre membrane. When an impulse arrives, acetylcholine is released from the nerve and diffuses across to the muscle fibre membrane, which is thus depolarized to form an **end plate potential**. When this reaches a critical level an **action potential** is triggered in the muscle fibre, resulting in contraction.

The **muscle spindles** are sense organs (proprioceptors) found within muscles which detect the degree of contraction or extension. They consist of modified muscle fibres with a special nerve supply (Fig 9.9).

If the muscle is stretched, the spindle is stretched and triggers a reflex contraction of the muscles to oppose the stretching.

In addition, the ends of the spindle fibres are contractile, and by stimulating these to contract with the gamma (γ) motor neurones, the central receptors are stretched and trigger the reflex contraction of the whole muscle via the alpha (α) motor neurones. This mechanism is used in maintaining the muscle tone and in the fine control of muscles.

Direct stimulation of the muscles by the nervous system is found only in sudden and strong contractions.

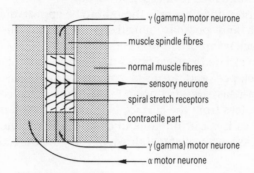

Fig 9.9. Muscle spindle.

SKELETONS

Muscle contraction produces movement and locomotion as the contracting muscles react against each other and against some type of skeleton, of which there are three main types:

1   hydrostatic skeleton,
2   exoskeleton
3   endoskeleton.

HYDROSTATIC SKELETONS

Water is virtually incompressible and therefore body fluids provide a hydrostatic skeleton against which the body muscles can react to produce movement and locomotion.

The soft-bodied invertebrates (e.g. coelenterates, platyhelminthes, nematodes and annelida, etc.) lack any hard skeletal structures, and have only the hydrostatic skeleton provided by the body fluids under pressure from the contracting muscles.

This is most clearly seen in the annelid worms such as the earthworm, which has a fluid-filled body cavity (the coelom) surrounded by longitudinal and circular muscle layers.

The body is metamerically segmented (that is divided into a specific number of segments of basically similar structure), and the fluid-filled coelom is divided into compartments by septa. This restricts the movement of the fluid and allows a coordinated pattern of serial contractions of the muscles to produce locomotion.

At the start of movement, the first few segments become thinner and longer due to the contraction of the circular muscles and the relaxation of the longitudinal muscles.

The chaetae of these segments are protruded and grip the substratum.

The longitudinal muscles of the segments then contract, the segments become shorter, and the posterior segments are pulled forwards.

Successive waves of contraction and relaxation of the circular and longitudinal muscles pass along the length of the animal, to produce an overall movement forward.

Animals with hard skeletal structures (exoskeletons and endoskeletons) usually also have a hydrostatic component in their skeletal systems, provided by muscles acting against fluid-filled body cavities (e.g. the abdominal cavity in vertebrates).

EXOSKELETONS

Exoskeletons are external skeletons, secreted by the epidermal layers of the skin. They are a characteristic feature of the Arthropods.

They are of complex chemical composition and can contain proteins (arthropodin and sclerotin) and complex nitrogen-containing polysaccharides (chitin). The exoskeleton may be pliable or hardened by the deposition of salts such as calcium carbonate (as in the Crustacea).

The insect exoskeleton is rendered waterproof by a thin surface epicuticle of wax or grease.

To allow the necessary flexibility at the joints the exoskeleton is reduced to thin articular membranes. Many of the joints are of the peg and socket type which allow movement in one plane only.

Movement is achieved by the action of opposing or antagonistic pairs of muscles which are attached to internal projections of the exoskeleton known as apodemes.

Fig 9.10. Joint in an exoskeleton.

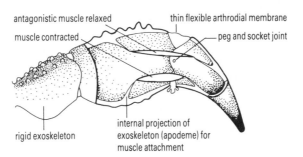

antagonistic muscle relaxed · thin flexible arthrodial membrane
muscle contracted · peg and socket joint
rigid exoskeleton · internal projection of exoskeleton (apodeme) for muscle attachment

ENDOSKELETONS

All vertebrates have internal or endoskeletons, which in the Chondrichthyes (cartilaginous fish, e.g. dogfish, sharks, etc.) is cartilaginous, and which in other groups is a combination of cartilage and bone.

COMMENT ▶ The maximum size of animals with an exoskeleton is limited when compared with those with endoskeletons. The exoskeleton must increase at the same rate as the surface area of the animal during growth. For example, the surface area of a cube of side 1 cm is 6 cm^2. If such a cube were to double to one of side 2 cm, the surface area would be 24 cm^2.

MAMMALIAN SKELETON

A typical mammalian skeleton is shown in Fig 9.11.

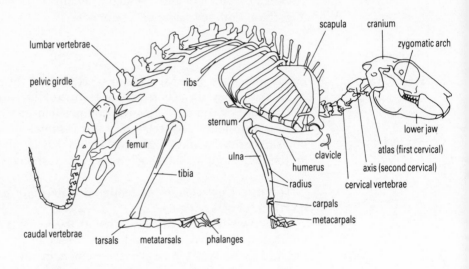

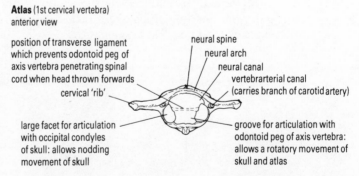

Fig 9.11. A mammalian endoskeleton (rabbit) and detail of vertebrae.

Axis (2nd cervical vertebra)
side view

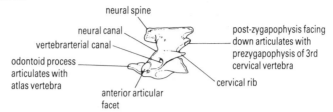

neural spine

neural canal

vertebrarterial canal

odontoid process
articulates with
atlas vertebra

anterior articular
facet

post-zygapophysis facing
down articulates with
prezygapophysis of 3rd
cervical vertebra

cervical rib

Cervical (3rd typical)
anterior view

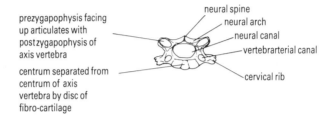

prezygapophysis facing
up articulates with
post zygapophysis of
axis vertebra

centrum separated from
centrum of axis
vertebra by disc of
fibro-cartilage

neural spine

neural arch

neural canal

vertebrarterial canal

cervical rib

Thoracic vertebra
posterior view

neural spine

neural arch

neural canal

tuberculum
of rib

postzygapophysis

facet articulates with
tuberculum of rib

demi-facet articulates
with capitulum of rib

capitulum of rib articulates at the join of two
vertebrae therefore each one has half an
articulating facet (demi-facet)

Lumbar vertebra   lateral view

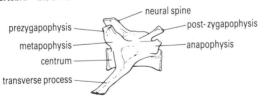

prezygapophysis

metapophysis

centrum

transverse process

neural spine

post- zygapophysis

anapophysis

The skull

The skull consists of the cranium and the facial bones.

The **cranium**, which protects the brain, consists of many bones which grow and fuse by immovable joints or sutures.

At the base of the cranium is the foramen magnum (large hole) through which the spinal cord passes from the brain and down the neural canal of the vertebral column. On either side of the foramen magnum are the paired occipital condyles which articulate with the first cervical or atlas vertebra, and allow for a nodding movement.

The **facial bones** include the nasal bones, those which contribute to the formation of the eye orbits, those which form the zygomatic arch or cheek bone, and the upper and lower jaws. The zygomatic arch, jaw bones and dentition all show special adaptations to particular diets.

The vertebral column

The vertebral column provides for the attachment of muscles used in support, movement and locomotion; and it protects the spinal cord.

There are five main regions: cervical, thoracic, lumbar, sacral and caudal (tail vertebrae – reduced to the coccyx in humans).

Cervical region The first cervical vertebra is modified as the **atlas** for the support of the skull.

The second cervical vertebra or **axis** articulates with the atlas in such a way as to allow a rotatory movement.

Thoracic region In addition to those functions shared with all other vertebrae, the thoracic vertebrae articulate with the ribs. The ribs protect the heart and lungs, and are involved in the breathing movements.

Lumbar region These are the stoutest of the vertebrae. They bear the stresses and strains associated with this region, and the powerful back muscles are attached to them.

Sacral region The vertebrae of this region are fused to form a single structure – the sacrum, which joins with the pelvic girdle, and through which the forces from the hind limbs are transmitted to the vertebral column.

Girdles and limbs

Pectoral girdle This consists of a pair of broad, flat dorsal **scapulae** which provide surfaces for the attachment of muscles, and which articulate with the forelimbs. The scapulae are embedded in muscle and are not directly attached to the vertebral column. This arrangement allows for expansion of the thoracic cavity during breathing, provides a cushioning effect to absorb the shock of landing on the forelimbs during locomotion in tetrapods, and allows mobility of the forelimbs which is important in the Primates.

The ventral elements of the girdle are represented by two relatively small **clavicle** bones which articulate with the scapulae and the sternum, and act as struts stabilizing the scapulae.

Pelvic girdle The left and right halves of the pelvic girdle are joined together, and to the sacrum of the vertebral column, to provide a complete ring of bone in the pelvic region. It provides for the attachment of many powerful muscles and for the articulation of the femurs of the hind limbs.

Limbs All vertebrate tetrapod limbs are based on the **pentadactyl plan.** This basic plan is clearly seen, for example in the rabbit and in man; but in many mammals the basic pattern, and the distal elements (phalanges, metatarsals/metacarpals, tarsals/carpals) particularly, are modified for different functions e.g. horse limb.

TYPES OF JOINT

Joints occur wherever bones come into contact with each other. For convenience they can be classified as shown below, but some categories are not clearly defined.

(*a*)   *Immovable joints*
Allow no movement, bones fused or bound together by connective tissue, e.g. bones of the skull, and sacral vertebrae, etc.

(*b*)   *Slightly movable joints*
Allow limited movement, for example between the centra of vertebrae, the pubic symphysis of the pelvic girdle, the sacro-iliac joints of the sacrum and pelvic girdle, the ribs and sternum, etc.

(*c*)   *Movable joints*
Friction and wear in movable joints is reduced by smooth articular cartilages and by synovial fluid (Fig 9.12).

Fig 9.12. Section through a synovial joint.

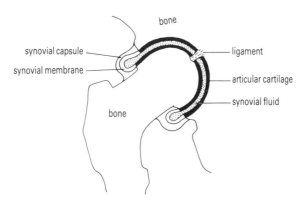

(i) **Ball and socket joints** allow movement in all planes, for example humerus and scapula, femur and pelvic girdle.
(ii) **Hinge joints** allow movement in only one plane, for

example the humerus and radius/ulna, the femur and tibia/fibula.

(iii) **Pivot joints** allow a rotating movement, for example the atlas and axis.

Muscle attachment

Muscles are only effective during contraction and as a result are usually found in **antagonistic pairs**, in which the contraction of the prime mover or agonist is opposed by the antagonist (Fig 9.13). Other muscles are important in steadying the joint during movement.

Muscles are attached to bones by tendons. The end of the muscle attached to the relatively immobile bone in the particular jointing arrangement is known as the **origin**, and the end attached to the bone moved by the contraction of the muscle is known as the **insertion.**

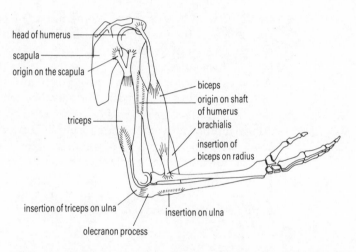

Fig 9.13. *The muscles of the upper arm in man.* The arm is bent by the contraction of the brachialis and the biceps (the flexors), and straightened by the contraction of the triceps (extensor).

BONES AS LEVERS

The bones, joints and muscles are arranged in such a way that in most cases the bones act as levers which work at a mechanical disadvantage, i.e. the effort is greater than the load (Fig 9.14).

However, the arrangement by which the muscle is attached close to the joint (which is the fulcrum of the bone lever) gives a wide arc of movement at the end of the limb for a relatively short distance of muscle contraction.

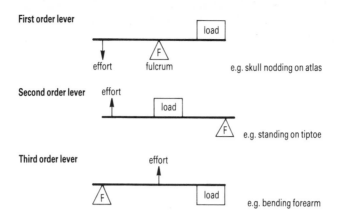

Fig 9.14. Bones as levers.

FUNCTIONS OF THE SKELETON

1　Protection of internal organs.
2　Framework for the attachment of muscles for movement and loco-motion.
3　As a system of levers for movement and locomotion.
4　Mechanism for breathing movements.
5　Framework for support.
6　The production of blood cells in the red bone marrow.
7　As a calcium store for the regulation of blood calcium levels.

BEHAVIOUR

The responses of animals to their environment are described as their behaviour. This behaviour becomes increasingly complex with the increasing complexity of the nervous and hormonal systems of the animals involved.

SIMPLEX PATTERNS OF BEHAVIOUR

TAXES

These are movements, the direction of which is determined by the direction of the stimulus, and include both positive and negative phototaxis (light), chemotaxis (chemicals), and geotaxis (gravity). For example, many invertebrates (e.g. woodlice) show negative photo-taxis as they move away from bright light.

KINESIS

These are non-directional changes in movement as a result of a stimulus, for example woodlice move faster in drier surroundings than they do in damp ones, and *Daphnia* move more vertically under green weed and more horizontally in open water.

EXERCISE ▶

Exercise 9.3

What might the adaptive advantages of these kineses be in (a) the woodlouse, and (b) Daphnia.

ANSWER

(*a*)   Moving more slowly in damp regions will tend to keep the woodlouse in these regions. This will avoid desiccation by the evaporation of water through the permeable exoskeleton (woodlice are Crustacea not insects).

Conversely moving more quickly in dry regions will tend to remove them from these areas.

(*b*)   Daphnia feed on bacteria and other microscopic organisms and particles; and require oxygen for respiration. All these are more abundant around water plants, and the vertical movement will tend to keep the *Daphnia* in these regions. The horizontal movement in open water will help them find patches of green weed.

COMPLEX BEHAVIOUR PATTERNS

INSTINCTIVE BEHAVIOUR

Many behavioural patterns, once elicited by a particular sign-stimulus, go to completion independent of further environmental stimuli. These fixed-action patterns of behaviour are understood as being genetically determined or innate.

The release of such patterns of behaviour by specific sign stimuli is considered as being under the control of an innate releasing mechanism which, when stimulated, releases the **stereotyped** behaviour in its entirety. Such behaviour patterns are typically found in all members of a particular species, and there tends to be very little variation between different individuals.

Instinctive behaviour is generally unaffected by experience, that is learning plays no part in its development; but it is affected by internal factors, for example if an animal is sexually immature and lacks the correct levels of sex hormones in its body, then certain sign stimuli related to courtship will not release the appropriate response. Examples of instinctive behaviour are seen in the courtship of fish and birds.

Table 9.1. Courtship and mating behaviour in the three-spined stickleback

Sign stimulus	Response
Red belly and vertical posture in the male	Aggression in mature male defending territory
Swollen belly of egg-bearing female	Zig-zag dance in mature male
Male zig-zag dance	Female follows to nest
Eggs	Courtship behaviour suppressed in male

LEARNED BEHAVIOUR

This type of behaviour develops as a result of experience and is therefore characteristic of individuals rather than of a species as a whole. Such learning can involve the modification of basic reflexes.

The classic experiments in this field are those of Pavlov's work with dogs. Dogs salivate on the sight of food, and after being taught to associate the sight of food with the sounding of a bell, Pavlov's dogs salivated at the sound of the bell alone.

Thus the reflex of salivation had been conditioned by learning, i.e. a **conditioned reflex** had been established. Conditioned reflexes play a part in the normal behaviour of animals (including man) as they learn to associate certain events and condition their reflex behaviour to fit particular circumstances.

<table>
<tr><td>

EXERCISE ▶

</td><td>

Exercise 9.4

Of which type of behaviour:

(A) Taxis, (B) Kinesis, (C) Reflex, (D) Instinctive, (E) Learned, are the following?

(1) The release of aggressive behaviour in the male stickleback by the colour red.

(2) Woodlice moving more slowly in damp conditions.

(3) The rapid contraction of Hydra when touched.

(4) The movement of Euglena towards light.

(5) The association of an unpleasant experience with a particular set of circumstances.

</td></tr>
</table>

EXPERIMENTAL WORK

PLANTS

Hygroscopic movements These can be demonstrated with fern sporangia. Mature fern sporangia are placed on a slide, which is then warmed at one end. As the heat moves along the slide and reaches the sporangia, they lose water by evaporation. This causes the shrinking of the specially thickened annulus cells, which splits at the thin walled stomium. When the resistance to shrinkage of the annulus cells becomes greater than the cohesive forces of the water, the tension is suddenly released and the spores are flicked out (Fig 9.15).

Whole plant movements and responses These normally involve periods of at least several days. However, the results of such experiments can be presented for interpretation and comment under examination conditions.

Plants can be exposed to unilateral light and the degree of curvature of the stem towards the light (positive phototropic response), which is a function of the colour and intensity and duration of the stimulus, can be observed. (This response is also shown by other structures, for example by the sporangia of Mucor.)

The **klinostat** is a rotating drum to which young growing seedlings

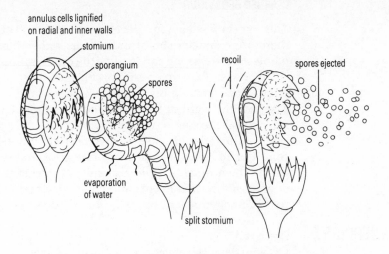

Fig 9.15. Hygroscopic movement in the dehiscence of fern sporangia.

can be attached; as the drum rotates the roots of the seedlings are exposed to the stimulus of gravity on all sides and as a result grow out horizontally.

ANIMALS

The direct investigation of animal movement and behaviour under conditions of the examination is restricted to a study of the invertebrates.

The positive phototaxis of green flagellates (e.g. *Euglena*) can be investigated by the microscopic observation of their migration from a darkened end of a slide into the light.

The negative phototaxes of larger invertebrates such as fly larvae and woodlice can be investigated by observing their movement from light areas to the dark.

Similarly the kinesis of woodlice in response to varying humidity, which usually involves an increase in the speed of movement (orthokinesis) in drier regions, can be investigated using a suitable choice chamber.

In such experiments the interactions between different stimuli, for example light and humidity, must also be taken note of. For example, woodlice will move away from light, and towards areas of high humidity, therefore to study the effect of the variation of one environmental stimulus, other conditions must be standardized.

Similarly, fly larvae are very strongly positively thigmotropic (touch) which leads them to burrow if possible, or to find sheltered positions. Their responses to other stimuli must therefore be investigated when they are on a smooth surface. (If placed on perforated zinc platforms they will push down through the holes which are many times smaller than their body diameter, irrespective of any other stimulus of light or humidity.)

Further, some responses vary with conditions, for example *Daphnia* is positively phototactic only in the presence of a relatively high level of carbon dioxide.

As with all experiments involving living animals, consideration must be given to the effect of the experimental situation on the state of the animal. A long period of acclimatization, in which the animal can adjust to the unusual conditions of the experimental situation, will render the results more reliable.

QUESTION ▶

Q.   Distinguish between locomotion and movement in living organisms. (4)
Give an account (excluding hormonal and nervous control) of the mechanisms of:
(*a*)   forward locomotion of a fish (excluding change in depth). (11)
(*b*)   movement of a plant stem towards unilateral light. (5)

COMMENT ▶

This question requires careful distinction between movement and locomotion which are often confused, and note the exclusion of hormonal and nervous control in parts (a) and (b).

OUTLINE ANSWER ▶

Locomotion and movement (4)
Locomotion is active movement from one place to another as a result of the activities of the organism, typical of animals rather than plants;
active movement of living organisms does not necessarily result in locomotion, e.g. respiratory movements, bending movements of plants.
(*a*)   **Locomotion in fish (11)**
Vertebral column a flexible rod;
blocks of myotome muscles attached along both sides to transverse processes of vertebrae;
sequence of alternating contractions and relaxations of muscle blocks from anterior to posterior;
with the tail showing most side to side movement;
backward force exerted on water resulting in forward movement of the fish through water;
stability of fish maintained by fins, rolling prevented by all fins, side to side yaw prevented by median fins, up and down pitching of head prevented by pelvic and pectoral fins;
steering achieved with pectoral fins and bending of body in that direction.
(*b*)   **Movement in plant stem (5)**
Curvature movement caused by greater cell extension on shaded side;

greater cell extension caused by increased cell wall plasticity;
a lowering of wall pressure;
therefore a lowering of water potential;
therefore more water enters from surrounding cells causing cell extension.

QUESTIONS

1 (a)   Give a comparative account of locomotion in *Paramecium* and the earthworm.
   (b)   Comment briefly on the functions of locomotion in these two animals.   (W)

2 Describe the fine structure of vertebrate skeletal muscle. Give an account of a hypothesis which may explain the mechanism by which a muscle contracts.   (W)

3 Briefly compare the advantages and disadvantages of internal and external skeletons. Describe how mechanical support is achieved in (a) an insect; (b) an earthworm; (c) a herbaceous plant; (d) a tree; (e) a terrestrial mammal.   (O)

4 What is phototropism?
   What can be concluded about the mechanism of phototropism from the experimental evidence you have studied?   (O&C)

5 (a)   Briefly define the following terms and give **one** example of each.
          (i) *Phototaxis*
          (ii) *Photoperiodism*
          (iii) *Vernalization*
   (b)   In a study of the growth of oat coleoptiles experiments were conducted as shown below.

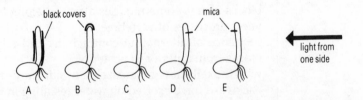

For **each** coleoptile state the result which would be expected after 3 hours and give **one** reason for each statement.   (AEB)

6 (a)   Shoot tips were treated as described in column A below and exposed to unilateral light, as indicated by the arrows. In column B, draw the expected response of the tip to the unidirectional light.

(b)   Give a brief description of each of the experimental results (i) to (v) in (a).   (LOND)

	A	B
(i)	shoot tip intact	
(ii)	shoot tip removed	
(iii)	shoot tip intact: small metal plate XY inserted as shown	
(iv)	shoot tip intact: small metal plate XY inserted as shown	
(v)	shoot tip intact: small metal plate XY inserted as shown	

7 Differentiate between a taxis and a kinesis. Give examples of each type of behaviour and describe how you would demonstrate **one** of these responses experimentally.   (O)

8 Give an example of a sign stimulus and say how the response varies according to the physiological state of the organisms involved.
                                                                                                                              (SU)

9 Male zebra finches show courtship behaviour towards female zebra finches. Experiments were performed in each of which a male zebra finch was caged with

(i) a female zebra finch with a red beak,

(ii) a female zebra finch with a black beak,

(iii) a simple model of a female zebra finch with a grey beak.

The results obtained are expressed in the following histograms.

(a)   Comment on and explain these results as fully as you can.

(*b*)　Explain the significance of the performance by the males of apparently meaningless acts, such as preening, when caged with models of females. Give *one* other example of this form of behaviour.

(*c*)　What are the differences between instinctive and learned behaviour?　　　　　　　　　　　　　　　　　　　　(LOND)

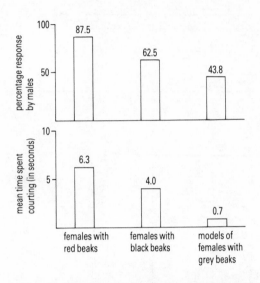

10　Which one of the following is an example of a tactic response?

A　　The brine shrimp swims on its dorsal surface if illuminated from above, but on its ventral surface if the light is placed below the tank.

B　　The average rate of change of direction of a planarian is greater in high light intensity than in low light intensity.

C　　A woodlouse moves more rapidly as the humidity decreases.

D　　A centipede ceases to move when more than 50 per cent of its dorsal surface is in contact with an object.　　　　　(JMB)

11　How can learning modify behaviour of animals?

Referring to Pavlov's work describe what is meant by a conditioned reflex and state the main benefit derived by man from having conditioned reflexes.　　　　　　　　　　　　　　　　　　　(SCE)

HOMEOSTASIS

CONTENTS

Homeostasis is the maintenance of constant internal conditions within an organism, in the face of changes in the external environment, and changes in activity.

The maintenance of constant internal conditions within certain limits provides optimum conditions for the enzyme-catalysed reactions of metabolism necessary for life.

Homeostasis is most perfectly achieved in the higher animals, particularly the homoiotherms ('warm-blooded' animals) where the regulation of body temperature is a good example of homeostasis, enabling them to flourish and survive in a wide range of environmental temperatures.

TEMPERATURE REGULATION IN MAMMALS

Homoiotherms or endotherms generate much internal heat as a result of their body activities, for example digestion, respiration, muscle contraction and general metabolism (especially in the liver).

These processes of heat gain are opposed by those of heat loss, for example expiration, excretion, egestion, secretion, and radiation, conduction and convection to the environment.

Once the correct body temperature is attained, heat gain must equal heat loss if this optimum temperature (about 37°C in man) is to be maintained.

CONTROL OF TEMPERATURE REGULATION

There is a physiological thermostat in the hypothalamus of the brain, which in man is set at about 37°C. The temperature of the blood is maintained at this temperature and any variation from the normal temperature triggers off the reflex homeostatic mechanisms to return the temperature to normal. Such a system is known as **negative feedback** (positive feedback control would accelerate any change, and is thus seldom found in living organisms).

OVERHEATING (HYPERTHERMIA)

If the body is gaining too much heat, then a variety of mechanisms act to prevent this.

Vasodilation of the blood vessels in the dermis of the skin increases the amount of heat lost by radiation, convection and con-duction.

In man **sweating** begins when the body temperature rises by 0.2–0.5°C above normal. As it **evaporates** from the surface of the body, the sweat absorbs its **latent heat of evaporation** (that is the heat required to change it from a liquid to a vapour) from the body, thus lowering the body temperature.

OVERCOOLING (HYPOTHERMIA)

If the body is losing too much heat then a variety of mechanisms act to prevent this loss and to generate more heat.

Vasoconstriction of the blood vessels in the dermis of the skin cuts down heat loss by radiation, convection and conduction.

Also the raising of the hairs traps a thicker layer of insulating air around the body.

Reflex muscle twitches (shivering) also generate more heat.

Small mammals with their large surface area to volume ratios lose more heat per unit of body volume than do larger mammals, and as a result they have relatively high metabolic rates.

EXERCISE ▶

Exercise 10.1

Negative feedback control is typical of homeostatic systems in living organisms because:

(*a*)   *negative feedback reinforces the changes detected.*
(*b*)   *negative feedback opposes the changes detected.*
(*c*)   *negative feedback varies the steady state.*
(*d*)   *negative feedback decreases homeostasis.*

HIBERNATION

In the face of conditions of very low external temperatures and food shortage, certain mammals hibernate. During hibernation they undergo a marked drop in the central or core temperature of the body, with a corresponding reduction in the metabolic rate.

In some ways the hibernating animal is in a state comparable to a poikilotherm (ectothermic or cold blooded); its body temperature is close to that of the environment and rises and falls with it.

However, the nervous system of hibernators remains active at low temperatures, and if the external temperature drops too far, the hibernator increases its basal metabolic rate to prevent a fatal drop in its body temperature. This does not occur in poikilotherms.

Indeed, hibernation is not a passive response to low temperatures, it is a well regulated physiological state.

COMMENT ▶	When discussing homeostasis and homeostatic systems, care should be taken to identify the following. 1 The particular state being held constant. 2 The control centre (e.g. hypothalamus of the brain). 3 The sensory system monitoring the state. 4 The feedback loop. 5 The effector system. In mammals the autonomic nervous system is of central importance in the regulation of homeostasis.

EXERCISE ▶	**Exercise 10.2** *In temperate regions, reptiles 'over-winter' in protected places in a torpid state, in which their body temperature and metabolism drop to a very low level. This is not true hibernation because:* *(a) if the animal depletes its food storage tissues it will emerge to search for food.* *(b) it is dependent upon an internal biorhythm of hormone levels.* *(c) it is simply a passive state, and if the external temperature continued to drop below a certain critical level, the temperature of the organism would also, and it would die.* *(d) it is mainly related to food shortage.*

OTHER METHODS OF SURVIVING ADVERSE CONDITIONS

ANIMALS

Poikilothermic animals (ectothermic or 'cold-blooded' animals) cannot regulate their body temperature, therefore their body temperature equilibrates with the external temperature and shows the same fluctuations. When the external temperature drops, their metabolic rate falls dramatically, and they enter a state of torpor from which they only recover when the external temperature rewarms them.

Aestivation is the term used to describe the state of torpor entered during periods of heat or drought. It is found in many groups including the fish, amphibia, reptiles, and many invertebrates. It is frequently found in fish, amphibia and reptiles that inhabit freshwater habitats which periodically dry up.

Many animals that cannot survive adverse conditions in the larval or adult forms produce special resistant structures. For example many Protozoa produce spores, and some Crustacea, such as *Daphnia* (the 'water flea') produce special resting eggs which can survive extreme adverse conditions, to hatch months or even years later. These resting eggs usually carry the population over winter (a few females may also survive). They hatch (when conditions improve) to give females, which reproduce by parthenogenesis to produce more females. With the onset of adverse conditions again, males are hatched from the unfertilized eggs. When mature, these males fertilize females which subsequently lay fewer, larger, thick-shelled fertilized resting eggs to survive the adverse conditions.

PLANTS

Plants utilize various types of dormancy to survive adverse conditions such as extremes of temperature and drought; for example resistant spores, seeds, fruit, and resting propagules such as winter buds. These dormant stages can also be used to distribute the species over an area, as their dormant state allows time for this to occur.

Some plants have **perennating organs** such as corms, tubers, rhizomes, bulbs and swollen roots which survive underground when the aerial parts die back due to adverse conditions. If division of these organs occurs then they also serve as organs of vegetative reproduction.

Leaf fall allows deciduous plants to survive periods of adverse conditions, such as winter in temperate climates and drought in warmer, drier climates. The abscission of leaves reduces water loss by transpiration (and prevents photosynthesis).

Exercise 10.3
What is the difference between perennation and vegetative reproduction in herbaceous plants?

Answer Perennation refers to the ability of herbaceous plants to survive from one year to the next, usually on the basis of a food storage organ. It does not necessarily result in an increase in numbers. Vegetative reproduction usually involves perennating organs, but results in an increase in the number of individuals.

EXPERIMENTAL WORK

The effect of temperature changes on the metabolism of nonhomeostatic poikilotherms, or ectotherms, can be investigated using small invertebrates in which the functioning heart can be observed easily through the body tissues of the living animal; for example *Daphnia* (the 'water flea'), a crustacean.

When interpreting the results of such experiments, they must be related to the metabolism of the animal. For example, the increase of the heart rate with increase in temperature must be explained in terms of the increase in the rate of the enzyme-catalysed reactions of metabolism, which in turn requires an increase in the rate of supply of oxygen to the tissues. This is achieved by an increase in the heart rate, which results in the more rapid pumping of blood carrying oxygen to the tissues.

QUESTION ▶

Q.   Give a definition of homeostasis (3)
How is the composition of mammalian blood regulated? (14)
To what extent do plants carry out homeostasis? (3)

COMMENT ▶

This question requires a straight definition, a bringing together of many points often studied separately, and a topic possibly not studied before which requires some thought.

**OUTLINE ▶
ANSWER**

Homeostasis (3)
Maintenance of constant optimum internal conditions within narrow limits in the face of changing activities and external conditions;
essential for cell function e.g. enzyme activity;
involves negative feed-back control.

Regulation of human blood (14)
Osmoregulation, water/salt balance monitored by receptors in carotid bodies and hypothalamus of brain, secretion of ADH, control of salt and water loss by the kidneys.
Glucose levels monitored by receptors in hypothalamus, secretion of insulin and/or glucagon from islets of Langerhans, and the inter-conversion of glycogen and glucose in liver and muscles.
Carbon dioxide levels monitored by receptors in carotid bodies and medulla oblongata, breathing rate altered to maintain carbon dioxide and oxygen levels at the optimum.
Oxyhaemoglobin association/dissociation in relation to partial pressure of oxygen and carbon dioxide.
Role of haemoglobin and plasma proteins as buffers regulating blood pH.
Elimination of nitrogenous waste e.g. excess amino acids deaminated with formation of urea in liver and its subsequent excretion by the kidneys.
Intake of nutrients adjusted to regulate blood composition.

Plant homeostasis (3)
Limited extent i.e. lack of nervous and hormonal negative feed-back control systems in whole organism;
control of water content by guard cell movements, and sometimes leaf movements e.g. leaf rolling in xerophytes;
transpiration affords some temperature control.

1   (*a*)   What is homeostasis? Why is it important in a mammal?
    (*b*)   Describe *four* examples of homeostatic regulation in a mammal.   (LOND)

2   What do you understand by (*a*) homeostasis; (*b*) feed-back mechanism? Illustrate your answer by reference to **one** physiological, or one biochemical process occurring in a mammal or a flowering plant.
           (O)

3   Explain what is meant by the term *homeostasis*. What is the importance of homeostasis for an animal?
    Describe the various mechanisms that help to regulate body temperature in mammals and birds.   (CAM)

4   Distinguish between positive and negative feedback systems. Give an example of a biological system which works in one of these ways.
           (SUJB)

5   Briefly show how size bears a mathematical relationship to surface area. Discuss, with named examples, the effect of this relationship on the body temperature of (*a*) amphibia and (*b*) mammals. (SCE)

6   Describe how the skin and nervous system act to regulate body temperature in mammals.   (SCE)

7   Discuss the various ways in which living organisms survive unfavourable conditions.   (O)

EVOLUTION

CONTENTS

The theory of evolution holds that all organisms are related by descent with modifications; that is, after the origin of life, all organisms developed as a result of the accumulation of differences from the ancestral types which adapted them for particular habitats and particular ways of life. Although still a source of some controversy it provides a unifying theme for a wide variety of otherwise apparently unrelated phenomena.

EVIDENCE FOR EVOLUTION

All the so-called evidence for evolution is open to alternative interpretations. However, when taken together, the various pieces of information can be considered as a body of evidence in support of the theory of evolution.

EVIDENCE FROM TAXONOMY

The fact that organisms can be placed in a hierarchical system of classification, from the simple to the complex, on the basis of their structure, suggests that they could be related by descent with modification.

EVIDENCE FROM COMPARATIVE ANATOMY

In classifying organisms, similarities are taken to indicate relationships. Similar structures with similar embryological origin and development are known as **homologous structures**. For example, all tetrapod vertebrate limbs are based on a common pentadactyl or five-digit plan, clearly seen in the human limb.

However, there are a wide variety of modifications to this basic plan, which are taken to have arisen as a result of a process of adaptive radiation, leading to the **divergent evolution** of differently adapted structures.

Analogous structures are those that have the same functions but which are not homologous; for example the eye of a squid (a cephalopod mollusc), and the eye of vertebrates. Such structures are regarded as examples of **convergent evolution**, whereby structures of different origin have become similarly adapted to a common function.

Vestigial structures are those that are considered to have been reduced during evolution to an apparently non-functional remnant, from a once fully functional structure, for example the human appendix.

EXERCISE ➧

Exercise 11.1

Which of the following pairs are examples of (i) analogous structures, (ii) homologous structures or (iii) neither?
(a)   The vertebrate eye and the squid eye.
(b)   The hind limb of a rabbit and the hind limb of a dog.
(c)   The teeth of fish and the teeth of mammals.
(d)   The chaetae of annelids and the hair of mammals.

EVIDENCE FROM PALAEONTOLOGY

Fossil evidence indicates that in most cases simple forms appear before the complex in the fossil record, which is in accord with the theory of evolution.

The fossil record is far from complete, but this would be expected from what is known of the conditions necessary for fossilization, by which the hard parts of organisms become petrified layers of sedimentary rocks. There are also problems in dating the various strata, and therefore in determining the correct sequence of the fossils in the so-called geological column.

EXERCISE ➧

Exercise 11.2

Which of the following does a study of the fossil record most clearly demonstrate?
(a)   The mechanism of evolutionary change.
(b)   The origin of new species.
(c)   The appearance in time of simpler forms before more complex forms.
(d)   The time scale of evolutionary change.

EVIDENCE FROM EMBRYOLOGY

An understanding of homologous structures is particularly derived from embryological studies, where fundamental similarities of structure are observed prior to their divergence in the adult forms. Embryological and larval stages of some animals show striking similarities, and it is suggested that this demonstrates evolutionary relationships. For example, all vertebrate embryos have visceral clefts in the pharynx at some stage of their development.

EVIDENCE FROM LIFE CYCLES

Plant life cycles show an underlying pattern known as the alternation of generations. The remarkable similarity of basic life cycles throughout the plant kingdom is taken as evidence of evolutionary relationship.

EVIDENCE FROM GEOGRAPHICAL DISTRIBUTION

Present day patterns of the distribution of plants and animals in certain parts of the world can indicate the evolutionary process. For example, the marsupial mammals of Australia are considered to have developed as a result of the isolation of the 'primitive' mammalian stock at some time in the past, and their subsequent adaptive radiation to various habitats. In this they show **parallel evolution** to the later more developed placental Eutherian mammals of other parts.

EVIDENCE FROM COMPARATIVE CYTOLOGY AND BIOCHEMISTRY

There are similarities in structure and function of all cells; for example all cells (with very few exceptions) have the same organelles, such as mitochondria, ribosomes, etc., the same biochemical substances such as ATP and many enzymes, and the same DNA/RNA mechanism of inheritance and development. Such similarities are taken as evidence of a common origin at the cellular level.

THE MECHANISM OF EVOLUTION

If it is accepted that evolution has occurred, then it is necessary to attempt to explain how it could have occurred.

Jean-Baptiste de Lamarck (1744–1829) observed that organs varied with use and disuse, and suggested that if they fulfilled a 'need', then such acquired characteristics could be inherited. However, with the discovery of the principles and mechanisms of inheritance Lamarckism has been almost completely rejected; as there would appear to be no major mechanism by which the necessary genetic instructions for the perpetuation of the acquired characteristics could be incorporated into the genetic material so exactly.

Charles Darwin (1809–82), as a result of careful observation of the flora and fauna of all parts of the world, formulated the **'theory of natural selection'** (as did Alfred Russel Wallace (1823–1913) at about the same time).

Darwin noted that a far greater number of offspring are produced by organisms than actually survive, and that there is thus a struggle for existence.

He also observed that the offspring show variations from each other and their parents, and that individuals with certain variations were better fitted to survive.

He thus gave rise to the concept of the **survival of the fittest in the struggle for existence**, that is the concept of **natural selection**.

The better adapted survived to reproduce and pass their favourable variations to their offspring, and this process (it was suggested) led to the accumulation of favourable variations down through the generations, to the extent that new species could arise.

The theory lacked any explanation of the mechanisms by which advantageous variations could arise and be inherited. Such explanations provided by the work of geneticists are incorporated into the modified version of the theory known as **Neo-Darwinism**.

Variations between individuals of a species are now known to occur as a result of gene and chromosomal mutations, and genetic re-combination as a result of sexual reproduction.

In almost all species there are **reproductive isolating mechanisms** separating groups of individuals into breeding communities, which thus act as **'gene-pools'**, in which the genes of the members are intermixed by random breeding.

Examples of such isolating mechanisms include geographical barriers, behavioural differences, differences in timing of the breeding season, and genetic incompatibility mechanisms preventing successful fertilization. Such isolating mechanisms maintain the integrity of the gene pool, ensure the rapid spread of favourable variations throughout that population, and prevent the 'loss' of these genes to other populations. In this way a group of individuals can maintain genetic advantage specific to their local environment. It is suggested that sufficient genetic differences can accumulate in this way to lead to **speciation** – that is the development of new species as a result of the division of a line of descent into two or more new lines of descent.

In contrast **phyletic evolution** is conceived as occurring in a single lineage of descent and results in a particular type of organism becoming better adapted to its environment.

Darwin's observations on the Galapagos Islands are particularly well known. The Galapagos Islands are a widely scattered group of islands (volcanic in origin) about 950 km off the coast of Ecuador. There are many unique species, but the finches in particular attracted his attention. There are many species, and many are unique to specific islands in the group (Fig 11.1) so that Darwin was moved to

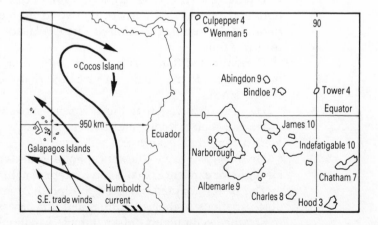

Fig 11.1. *The Galapagos Islands*. The Galapagos Islands are volcanic in origin and about three million years old. Darwin spent five weeks there in 1835, visiting four of the islands. The figures indicate the number of finch species found on each island.

observe that: 'Seeing this gradation and diversity of structure in one small, intimately related group of birds one might really fancy that ... one species had been taken and modified for different ends'.

COMMENT ▶

Although still a controversial area, evolution is a central concept of biology, and is included in all A level biology syllabuses. It is necessary therefore to understand the theory of evolution by natural selection. The essential points to remember are:

1 Variation between individuals occurs in all populations, as a result of chance random mutations.
2 There are more offspring produced than survive.
3 Therefore there is a struggle for existence.
4 The fittest survive as a result of natural selection.
5 The advantageous variations (mutations) increase in frequency in the population.

Table 11.1. Comparison of prevalence of finch species on the Galapagos Islands

	No. of species	Percentages of unique species
Outer islands		
Cocos	1	100
Culpepper	4	75
Wenman	5	75
Hood	3	67
Tower	4	67
Chatham	7	36
Abingdon	9	33
Bindloe	7	33
Central islands		
Charles	8	25
Narborough	9	20
Albermarle	9	20
Barrington	7	14
James	10	5
Indefatigable	10	0

A seed-eating ancestral form is postulated, with wide adaptive radiation due to isolation, adaptation to different conditions, and lack of competition. Flightless or ground-dwelling birds are characteristic of the small islands due to the danger of being blown off and to the lack of predators. (The islands also have unique marine-feeding iguanas, a unique type of flightless cormorant, and one species of penguin which is the only one to be found in the tropics.)

EXERCISE ▶

Exercise 11.3
Which of the following best illustrates the sequence of events suggested by the theory of evolution by natural selection?
(a)   a struggle for existence→ variation between individuals→ the reproduction of the fittest→ the survival of the fittest→ the divergence of new species
(b)   variation between individuals → a struggle for existence → the

survival of the fittest → the reproduction of the fittest → the divergence of new species
(c)   the divergence of new species → the reproduction of the fittest → variation between individuals → a struggle for existence → the survival of the fittest

QUESTION ▶

Q.   Show how evidence from the following has been used to support the theory of evolution:
(*a*)   palaeontology (5)
(*b*)   comparative anatomy (7)
(*c*)   geographical distribution of animals (8)

COMMENT ▶

This question requires a discussion of the value of evidence in support of an argument.

OUTLINE ▶ ANSWER

Points to be covered include:
(*a*)   **Palaeontology (5)**
Study of fossils;
simplest forms in oldest strata;
greater variety of more complex forms in younger strata;
therefore provides evidence for the evolutionary sequence and a time scale for the changes involved;
gaps in fossil record explained on basis of rarity of conditions necessary for fossilization, and on discoveries yet to be made.
(*b*)   **Comparative anatomy (7)**
Similar patterns of structures with similar embryological origins; in different groups i.e. homologous structures, differences related to functions, e.g. pentadactyl limb of tetrapod vertebrates suggests evolution by adaptive radiation from a common ancestor as a result of selective pressures;
vestigial organs, suggest structures being eliminated by selection which were once equally developed in ancestors.
(*c*)   **Geographical distribution of animals (8)**
Genetic differences accumulate in reproductively isolated populations as a result of;
founder effect, pioneer ancestors of different populations had different genotypes;
genetic drift, in small populations alleles may decrease or increase in frequency as a result of chance i.e. whether an individual reproduces or not;
mutation and natural selection, resulting in either parallel evolution if habitats are similar or divergence if habitats are dissimilar.
The result of all these evolutionary forces is seen in the present day geographical distribution of animals, e.g. Marsupials, and Darwin's finches of the Galapagos Islands.

1 Describe how studies in **two** of the following have contributed to our understanding of organic evolution:
comparative anatomy, taxonomy, embryology.   (CAM)

2 Review the evidence that organic evolution has occurred and that it is still taking place. Give a brief account of a theory that explains the mechanism of evolution.   (SU)

3 'It is interesting to observe the result of habit in the peculiar shape and size of the giraffe; this animal, . . . is known to live in the interior of Africa in places where the soil is nearly always arid and barren, so that it is obliged to browse on the leaves of trees and to make constant efforts to reach them. From this habit, long maintained in all its race, it has resulted that the animal's forelegs have become longer than its hind legs, and that its neck is lengthened to such a degree that the giraffe, without standing up on its hind legs, attains a height of 6 metres . . .'

This was Jean Lamarck's celebrated explanation of how the giraffe obtained its long neck and the extract is taken from a translation of his Zoological philosophy published in 1809.

Write out a careful explanation of how Charles Darwin might have explained the development of a long neck and long forelimbs.

Discuss some of the discoveries made since Darwin's time which add support to Darwin's theory.   (AEB)

4 State the theory of evolution put forward by Darwin and cite the evidence he used in formulating this theory. In what ways has this theory been modified by more recent evidence?   (LOND)

5 What contributions to the Theory of Evolution were made by Darwin and Wallace?

In what way did the ideas of Lamarck differ from those of Darwin and Wallace?   (SCE)

6 Answer *both* parts **X** and **Y** which are of *equal* mark value.

X   In his 'On the Origin of Species' Darwin wrote:

'The – Archipelago lies 500–600 miles from the shores of South America. The naturalist looking at the inhabitants of these volcanic islands feels that he is standing on American land. Why should the species which are supposed to have been created in this archipelago, and nowhere else, bear so plainly the stamp of affinity to those created in America? In the conditions of life, in the geological nature of the islands, in their height and climate there is considerable dissimilarity from the South American coast. On the other hand there is considerable resemblance between this and the Cape Verde Archipelago; but the inhabitants of the Cape Verde Islands are related to those of Africa. Such facts admit of no explanation on the view of independent creation.'

Which Archipelago do you think that Darwin refers to? Discuss in more detail the significance of his statement especially in relationship to present day thinking.

Y   Discuss with appropriate examples of your own choice the significance of present and past distribution of plants and animals as evidence of evolution.   (NI)

7   The following data concern the distribution and characteristics of types of Fieldmice (*Apodemus*) on islands off the West Coast of Scotland (after Berry, 1969).

Name	Location	Body length (mm)	Dorsal colour
Apodemus hebridensis hebridensis	Lewis	96	Wood brown
Apodemus hebridensis nesticus	Mingulay	98	Pale brown
Apodemus hebridensis hamiltoni	Rhum	104	Pale brown
Apodemus hebridensis tirae	Tiree	102	Rufous
Apodemus hebridensis tural	Islay	94	Dark rufous
Apodemus hirtensis hirtensis	St Kilda	111	Pepper

Using the data above as the basis for your answer, describe how the process of speciation is thought to occur. It is known that there are different degrees of inter-fertility between the races of fieldmice. What would you predict as the possible long term outcome of this varying degree of inter-fertility?   (O&C)

8   Two morphologically distinct types of the moth *Biston betularia* can be found: the speckled *typica* and the densely pigmented *carbonaria* mutant. In industrial areas *carbonaria* predominates and in rural areas *typica* predominates.

Which **one** of the following *least* satisfactorily explains this distribution?

A   Industrial pollution increases the frequency of mutation of *typica*.

B   *Carbonaria* has a greater survival rate in industrially polluted areas.

C   Changes in the habitat caused by industrial pollution cause selection against *typica*.

D   Changes in the habitat caused by industrial pollution increase the predation on *typica*.   (JMB)

9   The following figure shows the proportion of the melanic morph (*Biston betularia carbonaria*) in the population of the peppered moth along a south-west transect from the centre of Manchester.

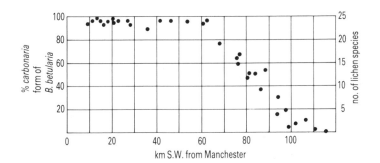

At various points along this transect the numbers of lichen species on tree trunks were counted and the results are shown in the table below.

km south west from centre of Manchester	Number of lichen species
20	2
40	2
60	1
80	10
90	16
100	20
110	25

(*a*)   Plot, on the graph paper above, the numbers of lichen species occurring on tree trunks against the distance from the centre of Manchester.

(*b*)   What is the relationship between the frequency of the melanic morph and the number of lichen species?

(c)   State fully the reasons for the changes in the distribution of moths and lichen species.

(d)   The frequency of the melanic morph of *B. betularia* has recently decreased significantly from 94.8% in 1961 to 89.5% in 1974. Suggest why this reduction may have occurred.

(e)   What is the name of the process which affects the frequency of genes existing in populations of organisms?   (W)

10   The following is an extract from an article on the evolution of species:

'It should be stressed that evolution does not proceed at a constant rate. Its rate depends upon the relative constancy or inconstancy of the environment; the rate of mutation; the size of the breeding population; the intensity of competition; the intensity of selection pressure and the variety of selection pressures. The most slowly evolving organisms are those which inhabit relatively stable environments such as the open sea. The more intense the competition and selection pressure and the higher the rate of mutation, the more rapidly will evolutionary change proceed. Finally, the smaller the breeding population the more rapidly can innovations be tested and either eliminated or fixed in the gene pool of the population.' (N. M. Jessop, Biosphere; A Study of Life).

(a)   In the context of the passage explain briefly by means of theoretical or actual examples the meaning of the following: *gene pool; environment; mutation; competition; selection pressure; population.*

(b)   In what ways can the sea be said to be a more stable environment than most terrestrial environments?   (O)

11   Evolution involves geographical and behavioural isolation. Discuss the ways in which these factors have their possible effects.

(LOND)

ECOLOGY

CONTENTS

Ecology involves the study of organisms in their natural habitats. Such studies can be approached in two main ways: either a single species may be studied throughout its life-history (**autecology**), or entire communities in particular environments may be studied (**synecology**). There is considerable overlap between the two, and the distinction is not as clear as the use of these two terms may imply.

Other more clearly defined terms are as follows:

1 **Ecosystem** – a relatively distinct environment and the system of inter-relationships between the organisms present, and between the organisms and the environment.

2 **Habitat** – a sub-region of an ecosystem (a habitat has been defined as an organism's 'address' within the ecosystem, e.g. the leaf litter in a woodland).

3 **Niche** – an organism's particular position in a habitat in terms of its feeding relationships and other roles in the community, (a niche has been described as an organism's 'occupation' within a habitat e.g. an earthworm acting as a decomposer of leaf litter and a soil conditioner).

INTERACTIONS

The distribution of organisms is affected by the following factors.

1 **Climatic** (light, rainfall, temperature, wind and humidity).

2 **Edaphic** (nature of the soil, its slope and aspect).

3 **Biotic** (competition for light, space, food, shelter etc.)

FEEDING RELATIONSHIPS, FOOD CHAINS AND FOOD WEBS

Within any ecosystem photosynthetic plants are the source of organic nutrients for non-photosynthetic (heterotrophic) organisms. Terms used with respect to feeding relationships are set out below.

1 **Producers** – photosynthetic plants.

2 **Consumers** (or phagotrophs) – animals that feed on plants (herbivores) or on other animals (carnivores).

3 **Food chain** – a sequence of feeding relationships from the producers (first trophic level), to the herbivores (second trophic level), to the carnivores (third trophic level).

4 **Food web** – several food chains interlinking.

5 **Decomposers** (lysotrophs) – heterotrophic organisms living on dead organic matter e.g. fungi and many bacteria.

The organic material consumed by heterotrophic organisms is required for the synthesis of their body matter, for the energy necessary for that synthesis, and for the energy for general metabolism and movement.

Much of the food material remains undigested and passes through the animal to be egested as the faeces. The materials of the faeces and of the nitrogenous excretory products (along with other dead organic matter) are exploited by the decomposers, which render many of the materials (such as nitrates) available again for the photosynthetic plants. Materials are also used up in respiration and much energy is lost as heat.

Thus only a fraction (about 10%) of the biomass of any one trophic level is converted to the biomass of the next highest trophic level. For this reason, the number of trophic levels in a food chain is normally limited to about four. However, food chains with more than four levels can exist, because most carnivores can feed at more than one trophic level and do not rely entirely on the animals immediately before them in the chain to provide all their food requirements.

The loss of materials and energy at each trophic level, and the resultant decrease in biomass up the food chain, gives rise to the concept of a **pyramid of biomass**. This is a more accurate concept than that of the pyramid of numbers, as numbers do not always decrease up the food chain.

EXERCISE ▶

Exercise 12.1
Which of the following is the best example of numbers not decreasing up a food chain?
(a)   Three or four birds feeding on the numerous ectoparasites of a single elephant.
(b)   A pack of ten wolves feeding on a single deer.
(c)   Several thousand insects feeding on a single oak tree.

The materials in an ecosystem are continually recycled, for example in the nitrogen cycle (Fig 12.1) and the carbon cycle (Fig 12.2), but the energy is eventually lost as heat, thus a continuous input of energy is required from the sun, and energy flows through the ecosystem (Fig 12.3).

EXERCISE ▶

Exercise 12.2
The carbon cycle is best illustrated by the sequence:
(a)   carbon dioxide in the air → animal carbon → respiration → plant carbon → photosynthesis → carbon dioxide in the air
(b)   carbon dioxide in the air → photosynthesis → plant carbon → respiration → animal carbon → carbon dioxide in the air
(c)   carbon dioxide in the air → photosynthesis → plant carbon → animal carbon → respiration → carbon dioxide in the air

Fig 12.1. *The nitrogen cycle*. The nitrogen cycle can be represented diagrammatically in many ways. If you find it difficult to remember the one given here, then try constructing a simplified version of your own.

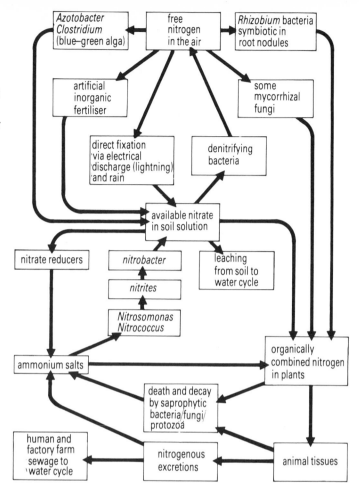

Fig 12.2. *The carbon cycle*. The combustion of fossil fuels is resulting in a steady rise in the level of CO_2 in the air.

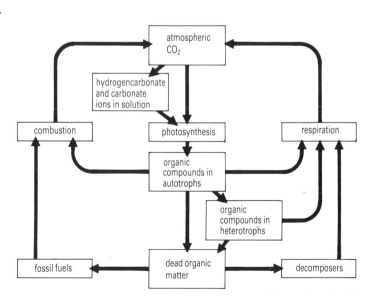

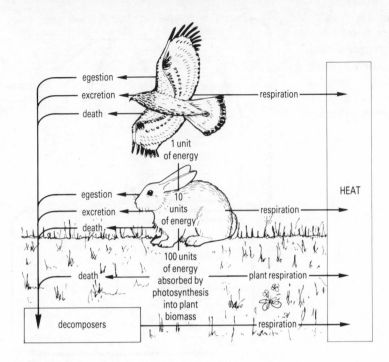

Fig 12.3. Energy flow through an ecosystem

SOIL

The soil is the product of interaction between edaphic (physical characteristics of the soil material), biotic, and climatic factors.

INORGANIC COMPONENT

The inorganic component of the soil is the product of the long-term weathering of the so-called parent rock. This includes the expansion and contraction of the rock as a result of changes of temperature, the expansion of water in cracks on freezing, wind and water erosion, the grinding action of glaciers and the dissolving effects of weakly acidic rain.

The properties of different soils depend to a large extent on the nature of the original parent rock, and the degree of weathering it has undergone.

Differences between sandy soils and clay soils.

Sandy soil	Clay soil
1 Sand particles are relatively large 0.02–2.0mm.	1 Clay particles are relatively small, less than 0.002mm. Colloidal.
2 Sand consists of silica dioxide.	2 Clay very complex chemically.
3 Large air spaces between particles. Good for root growth and respiration.	3 Small air spaces between particles. Poor for root growth and respiration.
4 Drains rapidly, and rapid evaporation of water.	4 Drains slowly, evaporation slow.
5 Dry soil, does not waterlog.	5 Easily waterlogged.
6 Loose soil, easily eroded.	6 Dense soil, easily compacted.
7 Relatively small surface area of particles, no negative charge.	7 Relatively large surface area of particles, negatively charged.
8 Nutrient poor. No cation store. Nutrients easily leached.	8 Nutrient rich due to complex chemicals of particles, and binding of positively charged cations, e.g. K^+, Ca^{++}, MG^{++} to negatively charged large surface area of clay particles (cation store).

ORGANIC COMPONENT

A fertile soil contains large numbers of living organisms, which by their various activities contribute to soil structure and fertility. They can be classified according to size into the Microbiota (micro-organisms such as bacteria, protozoa and fungi), the Mesobiota (nematode roundworms and many arthropods such as soil mites), and the Macrobiota (the large organisms, especially earthworms).

The Microbiota are particularly important decomposers, feeding saprophytically on dead organic matter, and forming a key link in the recycling of materials.

Earthworms are also very important to soil fertility; by their burrowing and feeding they increase aeration and drainage of soils, gradually turn over the soil, break down organic matter, generally conditioning the soil.

The end product of all the activities of the soil flora and fauna on the dead organic matter is a complex of colloidal and fibrous material known as **humus**.

Humus is an essential part of a fertile soil.

1 It is the main source of nutrients in the soil, particularly nitrates and phosphates.
2 It helps bind sand and clay particles together into crumbs, which gives the soil a good structure for plant growth.
3 It retains water, and prevents nutrients being washed away (leached).
4 It releases organic acids that increase the release of nutrients from the soil particles, making them available to plant roots.
5 Its dark colour aids heat absorption from the radiant energy of the sun.

FERTILE LOAM

A cultivated soil combining the best characteristics of a fertile soil is called a loam.

It has roughly the following composition.

Sand 50%
Clay 30%
Humus 20%
Calcium carbonate

SOIL PROFILES

As a result of a complex of factors, including the nature of the parent rock, the climate (particularly rainfall) and the degree of any slope, a soil develops a characteristic sequence of layers known as a **profile**. An example is shown in Fig 12.4.

EXERCISE ▶

Exercise 12.3

What conditions of the nature of the parent material, climate and degree of slope would produce the clearest zonations of horizons in a soil profile?

Answer A sandy soil, which has large air spaces and is rapidly drained. A wet climate, with the rainfall washing or leaching materials downwards as it drained down through the soil. A flat surface with no slope, so that the leaching is vertically downwards, and there is no lateral run-off.

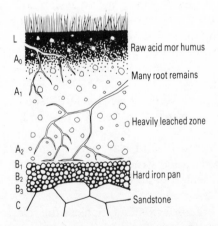

Fig 12.4. *Soil profile – the podzol.* Podzols are acidic soils. There are few bacteria and earthworms present and there is a slow rate of breakdown of the leaf litter which accumulates on the surface as an acidic 'mor-type' humus. Heavy rainfall and rapid drainage result in iron salts and others being washed down (leached) to the *B* horizons where they are precipitated to form a hard 'iron pan'.

Soil profile

Horizon		
	L	Litter – ecological sub-system
A Top soil	A_0	Humus
	A_1	Dark with high organic content
	A_2	Light-coloured leached region low in organic and inorganic content
	A_3	Transitional
B Mineral soil	B_1	Transitional
	B_2	Dark zone of maximum deposition of transported materials
	B_3	Transitional
C Parent material	C	Parent material present if soil formed *in situ* (if soil has been transported by wind, water, etc., it may not overlay its original parent material)

SUCCESSION

When plants have successfully colonized an area, they and their associated fauna interact with the environment and modify the conditions (particularly the soil) so that other plants are able to establish themselves. These new plants compete with the pioneer flora and fauna and, if successful, they in turn can modify the environment for later arrivals. In this way biotic modification of the habitat leads to a succession of plant communities, which in turn leads to a relatively stable climax community, the nature of which is mainly determined by the climate, so that it is referred to as the **climatic climax**.

The succession of communities leading to a climax is called a **sere**.

If the nature of the soil prevents the succession progressing to the climatic climax (for example if it is water-logged and/or poor in nutrients), a local sub-climax community results.

EXERCISE ▶

Exercise 12.4

The typical sub-climax community of sandy podzolized soils is heathland, dominated by Calluna vulgaris *(ling or common heather). What features of this soil do you think would be mainly responsible for this?*

Answer Its acidity, lack of nutrients due to poor parent material and heavy leaching, and hard iron pan act in extreme cases to prevent the natural succession to the climatic climax community of oak or beechwood.

SPECIAL RELATIONSHIPS

MUTUALISM

Association between organisms of different species that is to their mutual advantage, i.e. both derive benefit.

E.g. *Rhizobium* bacteria in root nodules of leguminous plants e.g. beans and peas.

Rhizobium fixes atmospheric nitrogen into compounds which can be used by the plant. The plant produces carbohydrates and other organic substances that can be used by the bacterium.

Other examples are seen in the mycorrhizal association of certain soil fungi with the roots of some higher plants (where the fungi aid water uptake and supply nitrates to the roots, and the roots supply organic compounds to the fungi); the association of algae and fungi in the lichens; and the association between algae and animal cells as seen in the endodermal cells of Coelenterates (where the algae provide the animal with nutrients and oxygen, and the animal cells provide the algae with carbon dioxide).

COMMENSALISM

1   Association between organisms of different species from which one organism benefits, and the other neither benefits nor is harmed e.g. the remora fish has a sucker to attach to sharks, which carry them around; the remora feeds on bits of the shark's meal, but there is no apparent benefit to the shark; and epiphytes e.g. some orchids grow on branches of trees in tropical rain forests.

2   Association between organisms of different species without much mutual influence, e.g. two animals sharing the same burrow.

SYMBIOSIS

1   (broad sense) Any association between organisms of different species i.e.,
   (*a*)   Mutualism
   (*b*)   Commensalism
   (*c*)   Parasitism

2   (narrow sense) Association between organisms of different species to their mutual advantage (i.e. = mutualism).

PARASITISM

A parasitic organism lives on or in another organism of a different species (the host) to the benefit of itself and to the detriment of the host. Parasites can either be ectoparasites or endoparasites.

Ectoparasites live on the surface of their host. The adaptations most commonly seen in animal ectoparasites are those for attachment, such as hooks. They have well developed mouthparts since, being on the outside of the host, feeding is still by biting, sucking or chewing. Transference to new hosts is relatively simple, and therefore their life cycles lack any major modifications and remain similar to their free living relatives.

Examples of ectoparasites include fleas, lice, ticks, fungi (such as those that cause ringworm and athlete's foot), aphids (greenfly and blackfly) and *Dodder* (a non-photosynthetic flowering plant which parasitizes nettles, heather and gorse).

Endoparasites live inside their host, in constant optimum conditions, surrounded by a plentiful supply of readily available food. Therefore structures involved in locomotion, perception and food capture, are correspondingly reduced. Special developments are seen with respect to protection against the host's defensive mechanisms, especially in gut parasites which secrete mucus and anti-enzymes, and often have special organs of attachment. Transference to a new host is a risky business, and there is often an elaboration of the life cycle involving one or more secondary hosts. When the secondary host actively transports the parasite to the primary host, it is known as a **vector**. Resistant stages during the life cycle often occur so that the organism can withstand adverse conditons outside the host.

An example of an endoparasite is the tapeworm, whose life cycle is shown in Fig 12.5.

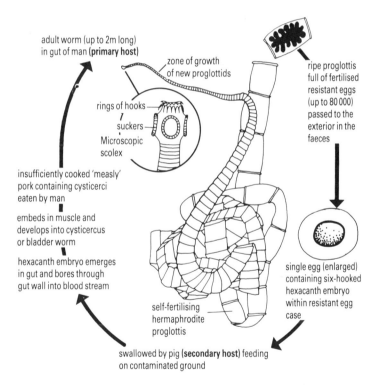

Fig 12.5. *Tapeworm life cycle (Taenia solium, the pork tapeworm)*. There are many different types of tapeworm, and they have a wide variety of primary and secondary hosts, for example, man/cattle, man/fish, dog/sheep, dog/flea, etc. The adult attaches to the wall of the gut of the host by means of the small scolex which is about the size of a pinhead. The adult has poorly developed nervous, sensory, and locomotory systems. It has no gut and it absorbs nutrients from the gut of the host by diffusion over its relatively large surface area.

EXPERIMENTAL WORK

ECOLOGICAL TECHNIQUES

Whichever environment or community is chosen for study it is necessary to obtain as many statistically reliable results as possible. Random sampling methods enable representative samples of a wide area to be taken without bias on the part of the observer, in other words without the investigator being attracted to an interesting but atypical area.

Random quadrat sampling involves throwing a square frame (usually a metre square) at random and the place where it falls is subsequently examined. Within each quadrat the number of individuals of each species can be recorded and the percentage area covered by each species can be estimated. This technique can provide information of plant distribution over a wide area.

A **belt transect** is a non-random or selective form of sampling. This is particularly suitable when studying changes in the vegetation in relation to topographical changes across a habitat, for example down a beach from high water mark to low water mark. In this technique, data is collected from a metre square quadrat which is moved down the chosen line to give a continuous belt of data one metre wide.

The techniques mentioned so far are more successfully employed in studying the vegetation of an area, as the mobility of animals creates difficulties in counting.

ESTIMATION OF ANIMAL POPULATION SIZE

One method of estimating the number of a particular type of animal in a habitat is to count the number in a small area or volume and then multiply up to obtain a figure for the whole area. However this method assumes a uniform distribution, which for most animals with specific requirements would not be true.

Another technique is the capture/recapture method. Here a sample of animals is captured, marked and returned to the population to allow them to mix with the unmarked population, and then a second sample is captured. The total population is estimated using the following relationship:

$$\frac{X}{A} = \frac{B}{C}$$

where:
X = total population (unknown)
A = total number of animals marked in first sample
B = total number of animals in second sample
C = number of marked animals in the second sample.

EXERCISE ▶

Exercise 12.5
Five hundred woodlice were captured from a large, isolated population. They were marked and released. Later, fifty individuals were captured from the

same population, and five of these bore the mark. The nearest assessment of the total size of the population is:
A 1000, B 10 000, C 5000, D 15 000.

QUESTION ▶

Q. Explain the term biomass. (4)
Describe how energy from the sun enters and flows through a simple food chain. (8)
What losses of material and energy occur from this food chain, and how do these losses help explain the concept of the pyramid of biomass? (8)

COMMENT ▶

This question requires a careful explanation of some important ecological concepts that can easily be confused.

OUTLINE ANSWER ▶

Biomass (4)
Total mass (weight) of material in living organisms, usually in an ecosystem;
fresh mass or dry mass if water content complicates the issue;
this biotic material represents the mass of material 'locked' in bodies of organisms at any one time;
is a measure of the productivity in an ecosystem.

Energy flow (8)
Solar energy radiated to earth absorbed by photosynthesic pigments e.g. chlorophyll;
light energy transduced (converted) into energy of chemical bonds by photophosphorylation into ATP;
energy in ATP used to synthesise energy-rich organic compounds e.g. carbohydrates, oils and proteins;
in plants further assimilation uses energy released from these compounds by respiration;
herbivores consume, absorb and assimilate biomass of photosynthetic plants which contains energy
carnivores consume, absorb and assimilate biomass of herbivores which contains energy;
producers (photosynthetic plants) and consumers (herbivores and carnivores) die and provide energy containing food material for decomposers e.g. bacteria and fungi.

Energy loss (8)
Respiration is inefficient, not all the available energy of the respiratory substrate is trapped as ATP, that not trapped is lost as heat;
this loss occurs in all stages of the food chain;
the energy trapped in ATP may in turn be used in metabolic work, e.g. active uptake, muscle contraction, nerve impulses, and therefore be lost;

> consumers only absorb and assimilate a fraction of the biomass eaten and the energy it contains at each trophic level;
>
> thus less and less biomass and its energy is available up the food chain, leading to a pyramid of biomass;
>
> with a large biomass of producers being necessary to support a smaller biomass of consumers.

QUESTIONS

1   (a)   Distinguish between the following ecological concepts:
         (i) ecosystem and trophic level,
         (ii) habitat and niche.

    (b)   Give explanations in ecological terms for the following:
         (i) The pyramid of energy is an essential feature of an ecosystem.
         (ii) The progressive changes in the flora and fauna of a river downstream of a domestic sewage outfall.

                                         (JMB)

2   What is autecology?
Describe and discuss that aspect of your study of the autecology of a plant **or** animal which you found most interesting.   (O&C)

3   Explain carefully what is meant by the term *ecosystem*. Give an example of an ecosystem you have studied and show how the abiotic and biotic factors influence one another. What factors may cause an ecosystem to change over a period of time?

                                         (SU)

4

	productivity (mg/m²/day)	biomass (dry g/m²)	numbers of individuals (m²)
2nd carnivore	0.1	0.1	15
1st carnivore	1.2	0.66	100
Herbivore	26.8	1.25	1.5×10^4
Producer	280	17.7	7.2×10^{10}

The above figures show the community pyramids for an experimental pond. Productivity was estimated from rate of phosphorus uptake. Width of steps for numbers of organisms are on a logarithmic scale.

(a)   Compare the relative merits of the three different methods of representing the community pyramids.

(b)   Explain why the number of steps in the pyramids is usually restricted to four or five.

(c)   Suggest how the three pyramids would differ if they represented an oak wood, or other named deciduous wood. (AEB)

5   Which of the following provides the best description of ecological competition?

A   having the same niche
B   living in the same habitat
C   living in the same territory

D   utilizing the same food supply   (CAM)

6   With particular reference to the same **named** habitat, explain with relevant examples what is meant by (*a*) a food web, (*b*) trophic level, (*c*) competition and (*d*) adaptation to environment.   (W)

7   The diagram below illustrates some of the processes and substances involved in the nitrogen cycle. Answer the questions (i)–(viii) by underlining the correct part (*a*)–(*d*) of each.

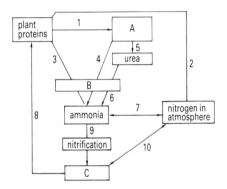

(i) The label required in box **A** is:

(*a*)   animal proteins;
(*b*)   bacterial action;
(*c*)   humus;
(*d*)   roots.

(ii) The label required in box **B** is:

(*a*)   decomposition;
(*b*)   denitrification;
(*c*)   leaching;
(*d*)   nitrogen fixation.

(iii) The process in box **B** is caused by:

(*a*)   amination;
(*b*)   bacterial action;
(*c*)   biochemical reduction;
(*d*)   high energy bonding.

(iv) The label required in box C is:

(*a*) N_2;
(*b*) NH_4^+;
(*c*) NO_3^-;
(*d*)   all of these.

(v) A bacterium which effects nitrification is called:

(*a*)   *Azotobacter;*
(*b*)   *Escherichia;*
(*c*)   *Nitrobacter;*
(*d*)   *Nostoc.*

(vi) What benefit, if any, do nitrifying bacteria themselves derive from the process of nitrification:

(*a*)   a more fertile soil to live in;

(b)　　a supply of oxygen;

(c)　　chemical energy;

(d)　　none, the process occurs for the benefit of green plants?

(vii) Water-logged soils are unfavourable for nitrifying bacteria because:

(a)　　leguminous plants need well-drained soil;

(b)　　nitrification is an oxidation process;

(c)　　the end-products cannot leach out of the soil;

(d)　　the end-products are insoluble.

(viii) Which of the processes shown in the diagram is probably at present of greatest economic value to the farmer:

(a)　　1;

(b)　　4;

(c)　　8;

(d)　　9;　　　　　　　　　　　　　　　　　　　(O)

8　(a)　　What is meant by a soil?

(b)　　Explain why a loam soil is a fertile soil.

(c)　　What are the effects of adding to a soil (i) animal manure, (ii) lime?　　　　　　　　　　　　　　　　　(LOND)

9　Define the term *parasitism*.

Describe the life history of any **one** parasite which you have studied.

Discuss the advantages and disadvantages of a parasitic mode of life.

(O&C)

10　An ecologist, needing to estimate the total population of a species of moth present in a wood of sharply defined boundaries and of an area of about 2500 square metres, captured (using light traps) and marked 50 of these moths and then released them unharmed in the wood. The following night, he collected 120 individuals of which 10 were found to be marked.

(i) Using these figures estimate the total population of this species of moth in the wood.

(ii) If a = the number caught and marked on the first night, and n = the number captured on the second night, of which b = the number found to be marked, state a simple formula for the estimation of the total number (T).

(iii) What factors could complicate the investigation and what precautions would you recommend to minimize any possible errors?　　　　　　　　　　　　　　　　　(NI)

MAN AND THE ENVIRONMENT

CONTENTS

POPULATION

Under suitable conditions with little environmental resistance in the form of shortage of food, predators and competition for space, populations tend to grow exponentially or logarithmically. As the numbers increase, the environmental resistance will increase, and when the birth rate equals the death rate the population will come to an equilibrium at an optimum level for the conditions.

Under certain circumstances, for example the accumulation of poisonous waste products or the over-exploitation of a food supply, there can be a catastrophic collapse of the population, until a new equilibrium is reached at a lower level. Such patterns of growth are seen in all populations, including human populations.

At present the human population is undergoing an exponential increase. Between 1950 and 1960 the growth rate of the world's population was 2.14%, giving a doubling time of about 33 years. This is almost certainly the fastest growth rate the world will ever see.

There are difficulties when considering human populations; but as environmental resistance increases, particularly in the form of short-

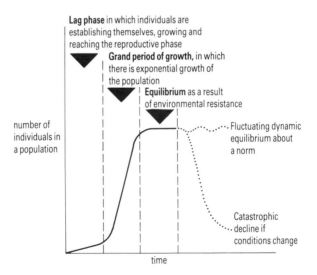

Fig 13.1. *Population growth curve.* The dotted lines represent alternative fates of such a population, depending on the particular conditions.

age of food and material resources, human populations must come into some sort of equilibrium with the environment.

The human population explosion is thought to be mainly due to the decrease in infant mortality and to the increase in life expectancy, owing to improvements in hygiene, the prevention of infectious diseases and nutrition. Whether this situation will persist in the face of increasing environmental resistance remains to be seen.

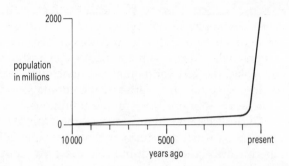

Fig 13.2. *Human population growth*. Projections (*not* predictions) made on the basis of present figures vary, but the world population is expected to have doubled by sometime around the year 2000 to an estimated 6000 million. The annual increase is between 60–70 million.

EXERCISE ▶

Exercise 13.1

In the 'S' shaped curve representing the growth of a population under initially optimum conditions, the steepest (exponential or logarithmic) part of the curve showing maximum growth rate is due to:
(a)　*an increase in the number of offspring for each parent.*
(b)　*an increase in the age of individuals.*
(c)　*an increase in the mortality rate.*
(d)　*an increase in the number of parents.*

FOOD PRODUCTION

FISHERIES

The same considerations of population dynamics apply to fish populations, but exploitation by man introduces a new dimension.

As has been seen, when a population attains such a size that the carrying capacity of the environment is reached, it tends to level off at this optimum size. It should then show a fairly constant structure with the proportion of the different ages tending to remain constant, and with the surviving young replacing those that die.

The aim of good fisheries practice is to exploit such a population so that it will continue to provide the largest catch possible. Indeed with strict control of breeding grounds, fishing seasons and fishing practice – particularly the mesh size of nets, fishing can actually result in the increase and improvement of fish stocks.

When adult fish dominate a population they compete with the young, and the food they consume does not increase the biomass of fish. If the adults are removed by fishing, there is an increase in the survival of the young and a greater gain in biomass for the same amount of food consumed by the population.

In this way, as long as fishing does not exceed a certain point, production in fishing areas will be higher than in unfished water, and the **maximum sustainable yield** will be obtained. However, this has very rarely been achieved, usually due to the difficulties of getting international co-operation on fishing.

The first sign of overfishing is a decrease in the size of the largest fish caught, and subsequently greater and greater efforts have to be made for smaller and smaller catches. If fishing then continues unchecked the fish population will eventually collapse, as few fish will reach maturity. This collapse of the fish stock will have repercussions throughout the ecosystem which will vary according to the trophic level of the particular fish in the food chains and webs. Thus there will be an increase in those organisms at lower trophic levels, and a decrease in those at higher trophic levels.

EXERCISE ▶

Exercise 13.2

Under controlled conditions fishing can actually increase the productivity of a particular stock. Which of the alternatives below is the best explanation of this?

(a)   *Smaller mesh-size nets catch more fish.*

(b)   *The young fish are removed to allow the adults more food.*

(c)   *Removal of a quota of the adults leaves more food for the young, which then have a faster growth rate.*

(d)   *Removal of fish allows their food sources to develop.*

AGRICULTURE

To support the growing human population, modern agricultural practice must continually make advances, again in the face of increasing environmental resistance. The development and introduction of new, high yield varieties of cereal crops, especially rice and wheat, has had such an impact on food production that it has been referred to as the Green Revolution. For example, in Colombia new dwarf varieties of rice doubled the yield per hectare between 1961 to 1975. However, these new varieties require irrigation, and high fertilizer and pesticide inputs which are becoming increasingly expensive.

The breeding of disease resistance into crop plants (usually from wild relatives) has been achieved with great success, but such is the mutation rate of many plant parasites (particularly the fungi) that the use of pesticides, herbicides and fungicides remains a major feature of modern agriculture.

PESTS AND PEST CONTROL

PESTS

In natural ecosystems an intricate system of checks and balances normally prevents the sudden population explosion of individual species. The simpler the ecosystem the less stable it is, thus the typical 'monoculture' of modern agriculture, in which vast areas are covered by a single crop plant, present ideal conditions for the population explosion of pests that attack such crops. The danger is even greater when a potential pest is introduced into a country where there are no natural predators or parasites to prevent its rapid spread through massive monocultures.

Insect pests with their tremendous powers of reproduction, mobility and variability by which strains resistant to pesticides can rapidly arise, are of tremendous economic importance. As well as inflicting direct mechanical damage with their biting, chewing or sucking mouthparts, they act as vectors of virus and fungal diseases which cause even more damage.

For example, aphids (greenfly and blackfly) feed by piercing the plant tissues with sharp mouthparts and sucking the contents from the phloem tissue. During this process, if the plant is diseased, viruses, bacteria, or fungi can be picked up and subsequently transferred to the next plant that the aphid feeds on.

Fungi are responsible for many economically important diseases of crops. Examples include *Phytophthora infestans* (potato blight) and *Puccinia graminis* (wheat rust).

Phytophthora infestans (a Phycomycete) is an obligate parasite which invades the tissues of the potato plant, with intercellular hyphae which have processes or haustoria which penetrate the host cells and absorb nutrients from them. Eventually, branched sporangiophores which bear sporangia are protruded through the stomata of the stems and leaves. The sporangia are dispersed intact, either by direct contact with nearby leaves or by splash droplets. The sporangia release biflagellate zoospores which swim in any surface moisture before settling and producing a germ tube which penetrates the tissues of the new host.

EXERCISE ▶

Exercise 13.3

Virus-free stocks of seed potato are maintained in areas of low temperature, high humidity and windy conditions. Which of the alternatives below would be the best explanation of this?

(a)   The conditions discourage the proliferation of the virus.
(b)   The conditions discourage aphids, and thus remove the vector of the virus disease.
(c)   The conditions are those which best suit the growth of potatoes.
(d)   The conditions are necessary for the pollination of the potato plants.

PEST CONTROL

This can involve chemical control, biological control; or a mixture of both methods.

Chemical control involves the use of a wide variety of chemicals collectively known as pesticides. Pesticides should be highly specific, only killing the target pest, but some 'broad spectrum' pesticides are toxic to such a wide variety of organisms that the term biocide would be more appropriate.

Many pesticides are persistent in the environment, causing pollution. Broad spectrum persistent pesticides can destroy the soil microflora and fauna and cause outbreaks of other pests as a result of the destruction of predators. In addition, resistant strains of pests soon emerge as a result of selection, by which those few individuals that have a natural resistance to the poison survive to reproduce and increase in number.

Biological control or ecological methods of control avoid the dangers inherent in the use of chemicals.

If a foreign pest has invaded an area, an attempt is made to re-assemble the natural enemies of the pest in the new area. If successful, a permanent, balanced equilibrium results between the pest and the controlling organism.

Control by natural predators can be even more effective if the predator also feeds on non-pest species. In these cases the predator is maintained at high numbers all the time, without dropping down when the number of pests decreases.

Another method is the 'sterile male' technique in which large numbers of sterilized males are released into the environment to compete with the normal males on mating. The result is many failed matings and a consequent drop in the population of the pest insect.

POLLUTION

Pollutants vary in their persistence in the environment: some are broken down relatively quickly into harmless substances, whilst others persist indefinitely. The persistent pollutants are particularly dangerous, as they undergo biological concentration up food chains to poison top carnivores and omnivores (including man).

Table 13.1. Biological concentrations of DDT residues up a food chain

	DDT (ppm)	Increase on previous level
Sea water	0.000 05	–
Zooplankton	0.040	×800
Shrimp	0.16	×4
Fish	1.33	×8
Gannet	75.5	×57
Total		×1 459 200

Also there is always the problem of the **synergistic effect**, where interactions between different pollutants and with living organisms can result in an increased toxicity.

WATER POLLUTION

PHYSIOLOGICALLY TOXIC SUBSTANCES

The persistent pesticides eventually get leached into rivers, lakes and oceans, where they become serious water pollutants. The chlorinated hydrocarbons, DDT, BHC, Dieldrin and Aldrin, and the organophosphorus compounds Parathion and Malathion, have all entered aquatic ecosystems and caused wild-life catastrophes, especially among sea birds.

Persistent herbicides, such as 2,4,5–T (which can contain traces of dioxin as an impurity) and fungicides containing copper or mercury, can similarly pollute water, and by their effect on the plants, can disrupt natural ecosystems.

POLLUTANTS THAT REDUCE DISSOLVED OXYGEN

These consist mainly of organic matter such as domestic sewage, animal excreta from intensive farming units; and organic effluent from paper mills, food processing factories, dairies, breweries, silage, etc. This is broken down by aerobic saprophytic bacteria, which reduce the oxygen content of the water as they do so. The reduction of the oxygen content of the water can lead to the death of aquatic animals and a disruption of the aquatic ecosystem.

This problem is compounded by thermal (heat) pollution which is invariably associated with such organic effluents, as an increase in temperature decreases the solubility of oxygen in water, as well as increasing the metabolic rate of organisms so that the animal population requires more oxygen.

EXCESS NUTRIENTS THAT CAUSE EUTROPHICATION

Eutrophication occurs when water becomes loaded with organic and inorganic nutrients. This can occur naturally, but man's contribution in the form of human and animal excreta, waste vegetable matter, phosphate-containing detergents and leached inorganic fertilizers containing phosphates and nitrates, give rapid artificial eutrophication.

One of the ecological results of artificial eutrophication is a sudden increase in algal growth, known as an algal 'bloom', which continues exponentially as the algae utilize the rich supply of nutrients. The algae eventually die and their decomposition by aerobic bacteria uses up all the available oxygen and gives rise to anaerobic conditions. The complex aquatic ecosystem breaks down, and only anaerobic organisms can survive.

EXERCISE ▶

Exercise 13.4

The events resulting from eutrophication are best illustrated by:

(*a*)　*increase in algal growth → depletion of key minerals → death of algae → decomposition by aerobic bacteria → depletion of oxygen in water → anaerobic conditions*

(*b*)　*increase in algal growth → depletion of oxygen → death of algae → decomposition by anaerobic bacteria → anaerobic conditions → death of algae → depletion of nutrients*

(*c*)　*decrease in oxygen → anaerobic conditions → death of algae → decomposition by anaerobic bacteria → increase in nutrients*

AIR POLLUTION

Although air pollution in Britain has been greatly reduced since the 1956 Clean Air Act, many problems remain.

The two main sources of air pollution are the burning of coal and oil (external combustion) and the burning of petrol and oil (internal combustion). Combustion also depletes atmospheric oxygen and increases the level of atmospheric carbon dioxide.

EXTERNAL COMBUSTION

The main pollutants from external combustion are sulphur dioxide (SO_2), carbon dioxide (CO_2), smoke and dust.

Sulphur dioxide emissions in Britain are about 6 million tonnes per year. It is relatively short-lived in the air, with about half being removed within a few days by combining with ammonia to form non-toxic ammonium sulphate, and about a fifth being washed out of the air as sulphuric acid.

The acidification of soil and water by acid rain is being recognized as a major ecological problem. It causes the collapse of aquatic ecosystems (as seen in the lakes of Scandinavia), and damage to land plants, including the disruption of photosynthesis. One of its effects is to increase the solubility of various substances in the rocks and the soil, such as iron, magnesium and aluminium salts, often to toxic levels.

Carbon dioxide levels in the air are calculated to have risen by about 15% since 1900. Increased carbon dioxide aids photosynthesis in the light, but if the atmospheric level is increasing, then it must mean that the increase in carbon dioxide is greater than that which can be absorbed by photosynthesizing plants.

Smoke and dust consist of small particles of the incompletely combusted fuel (especially coal). The particles can be abrasive and coated with carcinogenic tar hydrocarbons, causing damage to the delicate tissues lining the respiratory tract.

Dust, which consists of larger particles than those in smoke, settles out of the air more rapidly, and can coat the leaves of plants, thus reducing the amount of light and blocking the stomata. This interferes with photosynthesis and transpiration.

INTERNAL COMBUSTION

The main pollutants from internal combustion are carbon monoxide, lead, various hydrocarbons, nitrogen oxides and aldehydes.

Carbon monoxide combines very readily and irreversibly with the haemoglobin in the red blood corpuscles to form stable carboxy-haemoglobin. This prevents the reversible combination with oxygen to form oxyhaemoglobin, and its subsequent transport and release to the tissues. Carbon monoxide persists in the atmosphere for several years before being converted to carbon dioxide.

Lead in the form of tetra-ethyl lead is added to petrol for reasons which remain controversial. As a result 'aerosol' lead is emitted in the car exhaust. Lead is a persistent pollutant in the environment, and can find its way into the body via the air, food and water. Lead poisoning is cumulative and essentially permanent, causing damage to the central nervous system, to which children are particularly susceptible.

COMMENT ▶

All air pollutants can find their way either directly or indirectly into rivers, lakes or seas, thus becoming water pollutants. Therefore, if answering a question on water pollution do not forget this connection with air pollution.

EXERCISE ▶

Exercise 13.5
What is the order of persistence in the environment of the following substances, starting with the least persistent?
(a) lead (b) carbon monoxide (c) sulphur dioxide

WATER PURIFICATION

Water supplies are obtained from lakes, deep wells and rivers.

Lakes (often man-made) are generally used to supply cities at some distance. The catchment area must be kept free from pollutants such as animal and human wastes, nitrate fertilizers and persistent pesticides.

Deep wells which exploit underground water-bearing layers of rock (aquifers) are usually a source of pure water. This is a result of the natural filtration and purification effect of percolation through layers of soil and rock. However, these aquifers are now threatened by the leaching of nitrates and pesticides from the surface layers.

Rivers are the major water source in Britain, and the water usually requires extensive purification.

Straining through a series of graded screens removes the larger suspended materials.

Storage of the water in a reservoir allows suspended solids that pass through the screens to settle. Whilst in the reservoir, the water is exposed to ultra-violet light which destroys many pathogenic bacteria, and natural purification processes due to bacteria, fungi, protozoa and algae take place.

Filtration through gravity filter beds of about 1 metre of sand and gravel, grading from sand at the top to gravel at the bottom, completes the main purification of the water. A film of algae in the surface layers acts as a very fine filter, and deeper in the filter beds saprophytic bacteria and fungi break down any organic matter.

Sterilization with chlorine or ozone destroys any remaining bacteria.

SEWAGE TREATMENT

Sewage contains human waste and rain water which drains from hard covered surfaces of built up areas.

Screening removes the larger suspended material: any such organic matter is ground up and returned to the sewage flow.

Grit removal is achieved by passing the sewage slowly through long channels or grit pits, which allow the grit to settle. This is reclaimed for various uses. The sewage then passes to sedimentation tanks.

Sedimentation of much of the organic matter occurs to form sludge, which undergoes a separate treatment from the liquid effluent.

Biological oxidation, which breaks down any remaining organic matter in the effluent, exploits the purifying activities of micro-organisms, such as bacteria, protozoa and fungi. These are mostly aerobic and thus require a supply of oxygen, and there are two methods of effluent treatment which provide adequate supplies.

In the **percolating filter method**, effluent is trickled down from slowly rotating arms, through about 2 metres of graded coke or stones, with the finer grades at the top. These particles provide a large surface area for the attachment of the micro-organisms, and the spaces between them allow the penetration of air containing oxygen. As the effluent trickles down, the organic matter is broken down by the micro-organisms, and a relatively pure effluent emerges.

In the **activated sludge method** the same principles apply, but the micro-organisms are suspended in the effluent which is agitated to raise the level of dissolved oxygen.

Humus tanks receive the effluent after biological oxidation, and any remaining organic matter settles out as a milder form of sludge or humus.

Sludge treatment varies, but the commonest method involves anaerobic sludge digestion. In this process anaerobic bacteria digest the sludge, producing methane which is used as a fuel, and destroying any pathogenic micro-organisms present. The digested sludge is dried and either dumped or (if suitable) used as an organic fertilizer.

EXERCISE ➡

Exercise 13.6

The order of the major processes in sewage treatment is best illustrated by the sequence:

(a)   sedimentation of sludge → screening → sedimentation of humus → biological oxidation → pure effluent

(b)   screening → sedimentation of sludge → biological oxidation → sedimentation of humus → pure effluent

(c)   screening → biological oxidation → sedimentation of humus → sedimentation of sludge → pure effluent

INFECTIOUS DISEASES

Infectious diseases (those that can be passed from one individual to another) are caused by Viruses, and parasitic members of the Bacteria, Fungi, Protozoa, Nematoda, Platyhelminthes and Arthropoda.

Infectious diseases can be spread by a variety of means. The minute droplets of moisture exhaled during breathing, talking, coughing and sneezing provide ideal conditions of warmth and moisture for the transference of various micro-organisms.

Some are readily spread by contact, and these are called **contagious diseases**. The contact need not be direct, but can be via contaminated objects, which are collectively known as fomites.

Some are spread in contaminated food and water, for example many bacteria and parasitic worms; whilst others are spread by animals such as insects.

Such spread by insects may be indirect or direct.

An example of the indirect spread of disease by insects is the spread of infectious micro-organisms and worm eggs by houseflies from dog faeces on the street to food and objects in the home.

This contrasts with direct spread, by which, for example, biting and blood-sucking insects actively transfer infectious agents directly from host to host; such insects are known as **vectors**. Examples of insect vectors are the *Anopheles* mosquito which carries the Protozoan blood parasite *Plasmodium* which causes malaria; and the tsetse fly which spreads the Protozoan blood parasite *Trypanosomas* which causes sleeping sickness.

The prevention of infection is achieved by high standards of personal and community hygiene (including sewage treatment and water purification, and the hygienic storage and preparation of food); and the breaking of the cycle of infection, which requires a knowledge of the life-cycle of both the infectious organism and any vector.

DEFENCES OF THE BODY AGAINST INFECTIOUS DISEASE (IN MAN)

1. PHYSICAL DEFENCES

(a)   The **skin** has an impermeable surface layer of dead keratinized skin scales: these are waterproof and play an important part in the prevention of water loss by evaporation, but they also serve as a barrier against infection.

(b)   The **enamel** of the teeth forms a hard covering that resists bacterial attack which results in tooth decay, and which would in turn lay the body open for further invasion.

(c)   **Mucus** is secreted by many glandular epithelial cells which line tracts that are open to the exterior; for example the trachea of the mammalian respiratory system, where the mucus protects the surface and traps unwanted particles.

(d)   **Ciliated epithelia** trap and remove unwanted particles by their rhythmic one-way beating.

(e)   **Blood clotting** prevents infection when the skin and underlying blood capillaries are broken.

2. ANTIMICROBIAL SECRETIONS

A number of body secretions, for example sebum, sweat, tears and saliva, contain bacteriocidal substances which can destroy bacteria. Also the hydrochloric acid secreted in the stomach destroys most micro-organisms that enter with the food.

3. RETICULAR-ENDOTHELIAL OR MACROPHAGE SYSTEM

This consists of fixed phagocytic macrophage cells found lining the lymph nodes, the spleen, the connective tissue (especially beneath the skin), the liver sinusoids and the bone marrow. They respond as a system to any infection. The macrophage cells engulf any foreign bodies present by surrounding them with pseudopodia in a process known as phagocytosis.

4. BLOOD AND LYMPHATIC SYSTEM

The white blood cells called granulocytes and monocytes are phagocytic, whilst the lymphocytes form and secrete antibodies which neutralize any foreign substance or antigen.

IMMUNITY

This is the ability of organisms to resist infectious diseases, and concerns mainly the antigen-antibody reaction. Immunity can be active or passive.

Active immunity occurs as a result of the body's defence systems being stimulated by the presence of the infecting agent.

Passive immunity occurs when the body's defence systems are not directly stimulated.

There are a variety of ways in which each of these can occur.

1. Inherited immunity occurs passively as a result of the inheritance of some genetically determined resistance to particular diseases, for example some people have such an immunity to TB and some to polio.

2. Naturally acquired immunity can be active or passive.

(*a*)   The **active type** occurs as a result of natural exposure to the infectious agent, sometimes in amounts too small to cause the disease.

(*b*)   The **passive type** occurs as a result of the transfer of antibodies from the mother to the offspring, either across the placenta or in the first secretions (colostrum) of the mammary glands.

3. Artificially acquired immunity can also be active or passive.

(*a*)   The **active type** occurs as a result of **vaccination**, whereby a non-disease-producing dose of a disease organism or its toxin is introduced into the body to stimulate the body's defences, so that any subsequent invasion by the disease can be better resisted.

Vaccines can be prepared from preparations of the infective agent that have been attenuated or diluted below the concentration needed to produce the disease, this is the case for vaccines of rabies, polio, TB, German measles and measles.

They also can be prepared from dead organisms or their deteriorated toxins, which although no longer toxic, are still **antigenic** (i.e. they stimulate **antibody production**); this is the case for the vaccines of whooping cough, cholera, influenza, diphtheria, tetanus.

(*b*)   **Passive** artificially acquired immunity takes place when ready-made antibodies are injected into the body. This can be done if the body is infected with a disease that is too dangerous to leave until the body's natural defences are activated, or as a preventive measure to guard against such an infection.

QUESTION ▶

Q   Make an outline diagram of the Nitrogen cycle. (12)
What is the significance of the cycle in nature? (2)
In what ways can Man's activities encourage the activity of beneficial nitrogen cycle bacteria in the soil? (6)

COMMENT ▶

This question requires a simple flow chart diagram without further explanation, and a bringing together of material from a variety of sources in a way that may not have been anticipated.

OUTLINE ▶ ANSWER

Nitrogen cycle (12)
see Fig 12.1 (design a simplified version of your own for the question)

Significance (2)

Available nitrate is a limiting factor in the productivity of the biosphere;

most atmospheric nitrogen not available as nitrogen fixation is limited to certain organisms;

therefore organic and inorganic nitrogen containing compounds need to be continually recycled.

Man's activities (6)

Aeration of soil e.g. by digging, ploughing and draining encourages the activities of the nitrifying bacteria, whereas anaerobic and/or waterlogged soils encourage the activities of denitrifying bacteria;

liming where necessary raises the soil pH, acid conditions discourage activities of decay and nitrifying organisms;

addition of organic matter (manure) increases humus in the soil, which is a source of organic nitrogen for the nitrifying organisms;

crop rotation with legumes and ploughing in of this 'green manure' increases the organic nitrogen content of the soil.

QUESTIONS

1 The following graph shows the growth curve of a population of yeast in nutrient broth.

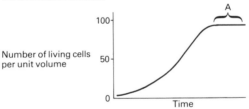

(i) At A, what is the relationship between rates of multiplication and of death?

(ii) Assuming a constant temperature, name two factors which could be responsible for the levelling off of the graph at A.

(iii) Alter the graph to show the growth curve if population increase was unchecked. (SCE)

2 What are the causes of the human population explosion which is at present occurring in various parts of the world? Give a detailed description of the more important biological effects of this explosion and suggest any methods which might be taken to mitigate them.

(O)

3 Discuss the ways by which the size of animal populations may be regulated.

Indicate why these considerations do not necessarily apply to human populations. (O&C)

4 An insecticide was used in a lake to kill an insect whose larvae developed in the mud on the floor of the lake. The insecticide was sprayed annually in concentrations known to be harmless to all other forms of life in the lake. After a number of years large numbers of predaceous water birds living on the lake died. The most likely explanation of this is that

A at this point the water birds became sensitive to the insecticide.

B the concentration of the insecticide in the water built up over the years.

C the insecticide killed the fish in the lake.

D the birds were at the top of a food chain involving the insect larvae. (CAM)

5 Give an example of adverse effects caused by man's use of biochemically active substances in the environment on a natural population of organisms. Suggest ways in which the damage done may be repaired. (SU)

6 The effect of prolonged exposure to an antibiotic was examined in *Phytophthora infestans*, the causal organism of late blight of potato. The antibiotic was added at a concentration of $50 \mu g \, cm^{-3}$ to a nutrient agar on which the fungus was grown for a period of three months. After this time discs of mycelium were taken from the culture and transferred to petri dishes containing concentrations of the same antibiotic. The growth of a control culture (i.e. one **not** previously exposed to antibiotic) was also followed under the same conditions.

The table below presents the mean results of the experiment in units of millimetres of growth per day.

Antibiotic concentration $\mu g \, cm^{-3}$	0	100	200	500
Control culture, mm per day	12.3	1.5	1.0	0.5
Culture previously grown with antibiotic, mm per day	13.0	10.4	9.8	8.8

(a) Describe the effect of the antibiotic on the growth of the
(i) control culture,
(ii) culture previously grown with antibiotic.

(b) Explain in evolutionary terms the differences between (i) and (ii) above.

(c) Suggest a mechanism that could account for the response of the antibiotic-treated culture to high levels of antibiotic.

(d) Assuming that other micro-organisms show a similar response to antibiotics, what is the probable long term effect of the excessive use of antibiotics in medicine? (W)

7 The following information was obtained by analysis of the breast muscles of a number of species of birds for organochlorine insecticide.

	Species	Insecticide residue (parts per million)	Diet
Terrestrial birds	sparrowhawk	3.7	mainly flesh
	owl	1.6	mainly flesh
	thrush	0.7	omnivorous
	wood pigeon	0.4	mainly plant
Aquatic birds	heron	13.8	mainly fish
	duck	6.0	omnivorous
	moorhen	0.2	mainly plant

What is the significance of this information for the survival of these species? Briefly indicate why the use of organochlorine insecticides may be biologically unwise. (SCE)

8 In the biological control of insect pests, when parasites or predators of the pest species are introduced to areas where the pest is a problem, it is often found that the most successful control organisms have the following characteristics:
(a) their life cycle is of the same duration as that of the pest,
(b) they originate from areas of approximately the same latitude as the pest,
(c) they attack only the pest species,
(d) they attack late, rather than early, life cycle stages of the parasite.

Explain why you think that these features are desirable in a biological control agent.

Even though a parasite or predator with these characteristics may prevent excessive outbreaks of the pest it will be unable to prevent periodic rises in pest density. Why is this and what features would you look for in seeking a second control organism to supplement the first? (AEB)

9 Biological control of insect pests is sometimes achieved by sterilizing males of the pest species and releasing them into the pest population. This method of control *could* be successful provided that
A mating occurred only once in the female's lifetime.
B parthenogenesis could occur.
C males of this species mate with more than one female.
D a small number of males was released into the population.
(JMB)

10 (a) List the chief characteristics of insects.
(b) Give an account of the various ways in which insects may affect man. What methods may be used to control insect pests?
(LOND)

11 Consider the following information.

Lichens are slow-growing plants which live on a variety of surfaces. Lichen vegetation in urban areas can be divided into zones in that the occurrence of any one species appears to be associated with different environmental levels of sulphur dioxide, one of the most common aerial pollutants. Examples of five species of lichen and the associated levels of sulphur dioxide are given in the table below.

Lichen	Mean winter sulphur dioxide (μgm^{-3})
Lecanora	150–160
Xanthoria	125
Parmelia	100
Evernia	40–60
Usnea	35

(*a*) By referring to the information given above explain why a lichen can be called an 'indicator species'.

(*b*) Only a limited number of plants or animals can be used as indicator species. Suggest characteristics which would make an organism especially suitable as an indicator species.

(*c*) Suggest ways in which an aerial pollutant such as sulphur dioxide may affect the physiology of lichens. Give detailed instructions for a series of tests which could be carried out to verify any **one** of your suggestions. (AEB)

12 (*a*) Explain what is meant by the statement 'Water is essential for life'.

(*b*) State briefly how river water may be made fit for human consumption. (LOND)

13 What do you understand by a safe water supply and what tests are used to demonstrate that water is suitable for drinking? Describe the chief processes involved in the conversion of polluted river water, coming from an industrial town, into water fit for domestic use.

(O)

14 What is sewage? Discuss **two** different methods by which sewage is purified and rendered harmless. What recycling processes are involved in these methods? (O)

15 Discuss the impact of man's agricultural activity on the biosphere.

(LOND)

16 Write an essay on **one** of the following:

'The Green Revolution'; Food from the Sea; Recycling (O)

17 With reference to EITHER fisheries OR agriculture, say how scientific study has increased the production of acceptable food. (SU)

18 In a book entitled *The Famine Business*, Colin Tudge (1977) writes:

'Not so long ago the United Nations dubbed the world food problem as "the greatest crisis mankind has faced". Of the world population of 3.7 billion, something like one in eight are ill-fed and probably a further one in six hover on the brink of malnutrition. More importantly, in many developing countries making up a quarter of the globe, food production is not increasing as rapidly as the population.' Discuss what is meant by (*a*) famine, (*b*) malnutrition. Explain how biologists could alleviate the effects of (*a*) and (*b*) by developing new sources of food and improving the production of existing ones.

(O)

19   Explain the importance of *two* of the following:
    (*a*)   Atmospheric pollution;
    (*b*)   Overfishing;
    (*c*)   Pesticides;
    (*d*)   Plant monoculture.   (LOND)

20   Describe the main methods for the control of human diseases and comment on the problems which may arise when such control measures are applied.   (LOND)

21   Cases of diphtheria decreased from 60000 in 1930 to 10000 in 1950. How is this reduction explained? What would you expect to find if lung cancer were investigated in the same way? Say why the histories of the two diseases are different.   (SU)

22   Outline the main steps which are taken to reduce the incidence and spread of disease in urban communities.   (O)

VARIETY OF LIFE

CONTENTS

The variety of life is overwhelming in its complexity, and it is only through the development and use of systems of classification, that a frame work for understanding can be established. The study of the classification of organisms is known as **taxonomy.**

The classification of organisms is based mainly on similarities in structure, that is on comparative morphology and comparative anatomy. Such a system is assumed to reflect evolutionary relationships, as there is a hierarchy of increasing complexity of organization. Other evidence for relationships between members of the various groups comes from the study of fossils (palaeontology); the study of similarities in cell structures, functions, and biochemistry; and genetics, for example, investigating the ability of organisms of different taxonomic groupings to interbreed.

There is no single, universally recognized, authoritative body on classification; and as a result there is no single, universally recognized system of classification.

The basic taxonomic grouping of all systems is the **species.** However there is no simple definition of a species; a species is characterized rather than defined.

With regard to structure, members of a species generally do not differ from one another more than the offspring of a single pair of sexually reproducing individuals may do, and they are usually distinctly different from members of another species (there usually being no intermediate forms). Thus a species is the smallest taxonomic unit commonly used.

Another characteristic is that members of a species are capable of interbreeding and producing fertile offspring, but are not capable of interbreeding with members of another species to produce fertile offspring.

However, some species are polymorphic, that is they have forms that differ considerably from their parents and each other, and show no intermediate forms. For example, some species of butterfly have members which mimic other species, and other members which do not; also social insects can have different castes specialized for particular duties which differ dramatically from each other.

Cross-breeding or hybridization between species can sometimes also produce fertile offspring. Furthermore, the concept of the species as a breeding unit cannot apply to organisms where sexual reproduction is not strongly developed, nor to fossil species.

Above the level of the species, there are increasing problems relating to the status and size of the various categories.

The Swedish botanist Linnaeus (1707–78) initiated the **Binomial System of Nomenclature** in 1753. Each organism is given a two-word name, the specific name describing the species, and the generic name describing the next highest grouping, namely the genus, to which similar species belong. The name of the genus is always written with a capital initial letter, and the name of the species with a small initial letter; for example:

Fagus sylvatica (beech tree)
and *Lumbricus terrestris* (earthworm)

Genera that appear to be closely related are grouped together in **families**, groups of related families are placed in the same **order**, groups of related orders in the same **class**, and related classes into the same **phylum**.

Traditionally the phyla are placed into one of two kingdoms, the plant kingdom or the animal kingdom.

In addition to all these groupings there can also be various sub-groups, such as the sub-phylum, the sub-class, and the sub-order; and various larger groupings such as the super-family and the super-order.

An outline classification of the plant and animal kingdom is included here to act as a framework of reference for the rest of the course. An alternative system of classification is outlined at the end of this chapter, both to provide an alternative and to highlight the problems inherent in designing such systems.

EXERCISE

Exercise 14.1
Arrange the following taxonomic categories into the correct sequence from smallest grouping to largest.
A Genus, B Family, C Order, D Species, E Phylum, F Kingdom, G Class.

PLANT KINGDOM

COMMENT ▶ There are problems in including the bacteria, and the blue-green 'algae', the motile pigmented unicellular organisms, and even the fungi within the Plant Kingdom; other systems are designed to overcome these problems.

Generally the term Division is used in the Plant Kingdom as an equivalent to that of Phylum in the Animal Kingdom.

DIVISION SCHIZOPHYTA
Unicellular or colonial; reproduce by fission; no true nucleus (pro-karyotic or akaryotic); if photosynthetic pigment present it is not enclosed in a special organelle; cell wall structure different from that of other plants.

CLASS SCHIZOMYCETES

The bacteria. The photosynthetic autotrophic types do not evolve oxygen as a result of photosynthesis. (Fig 14.1.)

CLASS CYANOPHYCEAE

The 'blue-green algae' (can in fact be classified as algae), found in all environments from hot springs to bare rock. Photosynthetic and evolve oxygen; unicellular and filamentous; non-motile; many are symbiotic partners to fungi in lichens; several genera have species which fix atmospheric nitrogen, and are important in soil fertility.

THALLOPHYTA

An 'older' grouping including both the Algae and the Fungi. Have true nuclei (eukaryotic); plant body a simple thallus showing no differentiation into root, stem, and leaves; little if any tissue differen-tiation; sex organs and spore-producing structures usually unicellular haploid and diploid phases can alternate with each other, in absence of alternation the thallus is usually haploid.

ALGAE

COMMENT ▶

The algae are mainly aquatic, and are a very large and varied group of photosynthetic plants, all containing chlorophyll a and β-carotene. The marine types are the well-known seaweeds. They were once considered as belonging to a single Division (the Phycophyta), but are now more generally considered as belonging to several distinct Divisions. There is a marked difference between the Divisions, based on morphological and biochemical criteria, such as differences in the type, position, and number of flagella in motile cells; differences in the types of pigments; the nature of the reserve food material; and the composition of the cell wall.

DIVISION CHLOROPHYTA

CLASS CHLOROPHYCEAE

The green algae. Pyrenoids usually present in chloroplasts, have starch as the storage product; asexual reproductive cells and male gametes motile, with two apical flagella; adult stage haploid, sometimes alternation of generation between haploid and diploid phases of identical form (isomorphic).

The largest group of algae with a tremendous range of size and structure, of which only some Orders are described here.

Order Volvocales

Freshwater plankton. Flagellate, unicellular or colonial forms; asexual reproduction by motile zoospores or daughter colonies; e.g. *Chlamydomonas Volvox*.

Order Chlorococcales

Mainly freshwater plankton, also found on moist soil, tree bark, fencing, etc. Unicellular or aggregates; non-motile vegetative cells; cytoplasm divides into many motile zoospores; some are symbiotic partners in lichens, and in some invertebrate animals (e.g. *Hydra*); e.g. *Chlorella*.

Order Conjugales

Almost entirely freshwater. Unicellular or unbranched filamentous chains of cells; sexual reproduction by amoeboid gametes; includes the planktonic **Desmids** which have a great variety of shapes and a cell wall of two sculptured equal halves, and *Spirogyra* (Fig 14.1).

DIVISION PHAEOPHYTA

CLASS PHAEOPHYCEAE

The brown algae. Marine, the brown 'seaweeds', some rare freshwater species. Range in structure from minute, simple, branched filaments to massive complex pseudoparenchymatous thalli many metres long; contain chlorophyll, but it is masked by the brown pigment fucoxanthin. Both asexual zoospores and gametes are motile with two unequal flagella; some show isomorphic and some heteromorphic alternation of generations, with a haploid gametophyte and diploid sporophyte which is usually dominant.

Order Laminariales

Sporophytes can be very large, e.g. up to 100 m long, and can show quite complex morphological and anatomical differentiation. The large complex sporophytes alternate with microscopic female and male gametophytes which grow in felt-like masses; e.g. *Laminaria*.

Order Fucales

The commonest inter-tidal algae (along with some of the Laminariales) of the colder seas. Have no clear alternation of generation; no asexual reproduction; diploid thallus produces haploid gametes in special structures known as conceptacles; e.g. *Fucus* (Fig 14.1) *Ascophyllum, Sargassum (S. muticum* or Japanese seaweed is a recent unwanted introduction into British waters).

DIVISION RHODOPHYTA

CLASS RHODOPHYCEAE

The red algae. Mainly marine, some occur in freshwater, but vast majority are the red 'seaweeds'; can be found at depth of 200 m where only the blue light penetrates. The chlorophyll is 'masked' by the red pigment phycoerythrin; some are the best source of agar.

One family, the Corallinaceae, are calcified and are important members of coral reefs, e.g. *Porphyra, Lithothamnium* (reef builder).

DIVISION EUGLENOPHYTA

CLASS EUGLENOPHYCEAE

Freshwater, especially in stagnant water rich in nutrients. Photosynthetic, with chlorophyll a and b, and a unique xanthophyll; motile with one long and one short flagellum, but with only one visible externally; lack firm wall, surrounded by flexible, non-cellulose, polysaccharide pellicle. Often classified as flagellate protozoa; e.g. *Euglena*.

DIVISION PYRROPHYTA

CLASS PYRROPHYCEAE

The dinoflagellates. Few freshwater, most marine. Important members of the phytoplankton.

DIVISION CHRYSOPHYTA

CLASS CHRYSOPHYCEAE

The golden algae. Mainly freshwater and marine. Important members of the phytoplankton; unicellular; golden-brown due to various xanthophylls; includes the **diatoms** (Diatomales or Bacillariales) with characteristic two silicified 'box and lid' type walls inside the cell membrane, of which there are more than 10 000 species.

Fig 14.1

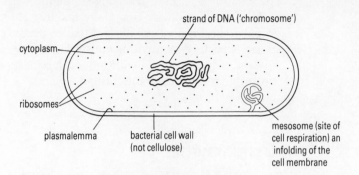

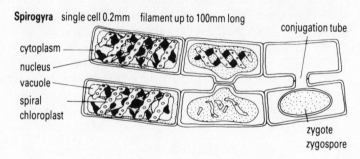

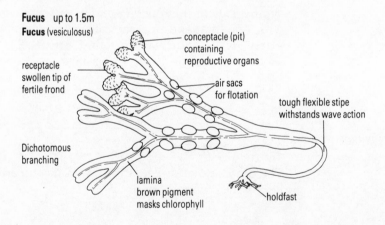

FUNGI

The fungi are freshwater or terrestrial, rarely marine. Usually colourless, non-photosynthetic pigments can occur particularly in the spore-bearing fructifications of the higher fungi; heterotrophic, being either saprophytic or parasitic; cell walls not usually cellulose, but chitinous; vegetative body typically composed of filamentous hyphae known collectively as a mycelium; reproduction mainly asexual via spores of various kinds. The fungi are generally divided into two Divisions, the **Myxomycophyta** or slime moulds, and the **Eumycophyta** or true fungi.

DIVISION EUMYCOPHYTA

CLASS PHYCOMYCETES

The 'true fungi'. Range in form from microscopic uninucleate unicells to large branched filamentous, tubular, non-septate (coenocytic) multinucleate hyphae which form an extensive mycelium.

Order Zygomycetales
Mainly terrestrial, saprophytic moulds, cell walls predominantly chitin; reproduction adapted to terrestrial conditions with multinucleate non-motile spores, with walls resistant to desiccation, being produced in sporangia; in sexual reproduction they never produce gametes, but two multinucleate gametangia fuse forming a zygote; e.g. *Mucor mucedo* (pin mould) (Fig 14.2), *Rhizopus* (black bread-mould).

Order Oomycetales
Cell walls have cellulose but no chitin; reproduction adapted to terrestrial conditions by entire sporangium being detached when ripe, giving rise to biflagellate zoospores when it germinates; both male and female gametes non-motile with the male gamete being carried to the egg by a tube. Two main families.

Family Peronosporaceae
Mainly parasitic on higher plants, some of great economic importance; e.g. *Pythium*, *Phytophthora infestans* (potato blight).

CLASS BASIDIOMYCETES

Mycelium of branched septate mycelium with pores in the crosswalls; there are no special sex organs but fusion of uninucleate hyphae of opposite strains results in binucleate or dikaryotic 'fruiting' or secondary mycelia; fructifications or spore producing bodies are composed of compacted pseudo-parenchymatous hyphae. They have a fertile layer known as the hymenium bearing special cells, the basidia, in which nuclear fusion and subsequent meiotic division occurs to give characteristically four basidiospores. Include the well-known mushrooms (*Psalliota*, Fig 14.2), toadstools, bracket fungi, and puffballs; and the important parasites of cereal crops, the rusts, smuts, and bunts.

CLASS ASCOMYCETES

Mainly terrestrial, some aquatic. Widely varied group, but long-recognized as a natural class mainly on the basis of the produce of four or eight characteristic ascospores by meiosis on a specialized structure known as an ascus; the asci are usually borne on or in special structures such as closed, flask-shaped perithecia or disc-shaped apothecia; can have specialized hyphae known as conidiophores which cut off asexual conidiospores at their tips.

Order Saccharomycetales
Much reduced forms; e.g. *Saccharomyces* (yeast).

Order Plectascales
Asexual reproduction usually by bluish-green conidia; e.g. *Penicillium*.

Order Sphaeriales
Very large group of saprophytes and parasites; e.g. *Ceratocystis ulmi* (Dutch elm disease), *Gibberella* (source of gibberellins, parasitic on rice), *Neurospora* (widely used in biochemical genetics), *Sordaria* (widely used in biochemical genetics).

Fig 14.2

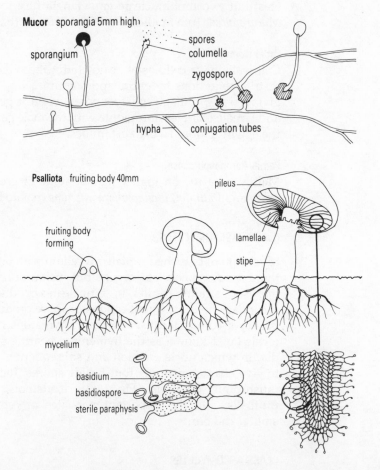

DIVISION BRYOPHYTA　　Well-developed heteromorphic alternation of generations with the haploid gametophyte dominant and forming the persistent vegetative body with rhizoids, and sometimes with stem and leaf-like structures. The gametophyte thallus has a delicate waterproof cuticle; typically shows dichotomous branching; bears multicellular sex organs, the male antheridia and the female archegonia; fertilization is achieved by biflagellate male gametes or spermatozoids swimming in a film of water to the female oosphere in the archegonium (zoidogamous fertilization); fertilized diploid zygote grows into the diploid sporophyte generation consisting of a sporogonium of foot, stalk, and capsule, which is completely or partially dependent on the gametophyte generation; produces haploid spores by meiosis; spores are all of one type (homosporous); spores of some form characteristic filamentous protonema before forming gametophyte thallus; vegetative reproduction of gametophyte well developed.

CLASS HEPATICAE

The liverworts. Great variety of gametophyte structure, some flattened and thallose, others leafy or 'foliose'; cells of most contain unique oil-bodies; have unicellular rhizoids; dichotomous branching; sporophyte simple, spore mother cells produce both spores and sterile cells called elaters which aid in spore dispersal by hygroscopic movements.

Archegonia formed behind growing tip, sporogonium arises from dorsal surface with its base covered by a flap of gametophyte tissue the involucre; e.g. *Pellia* (Fig 14.3).

CLASS MUSCI

The mosses. Gametophyte well-developed with spirally arranged leaves arising from a stem; multicellular rhizoids; sex organs in groups at tips of lateral branches of main stem; strong powers of vegetative reproduction either by fragmentation of thallus or gemmae; well-developed sporophyte with photosynthetic tissue and air pores (stomata); some show beginnings of heterospory with two different types of spore giving rise to two separate types of male and female gametophyte; complex dehiscence of capsule with 'teeth' but no elaters; spores always produce well-developed protonema.

SUB-CLASS SPHAGNIDAE

The 'bog-mosses'. Contains only one genus, *Sphagnum*; grows in wet, acid areas forming deep accumulative peat forming bogs; spores only germinate in the presence of mycorrhizal fungus.

SUB-CLASS BRYIDAE

Largest group with widest variety of form and highest level of differentiation; e.g. *Funaria* (Fig 14.3), *Bryum* (800 species), *Mnium*, *Polytrichum*.

Fig 14.3

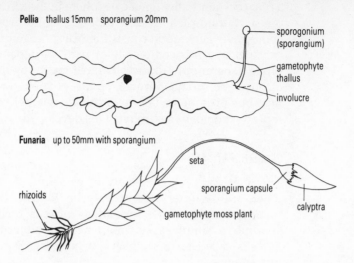

Pellia thallus 15mm sporangium 20mm

- sporogonium (sporangium)
- gametophyte thallus
- involucre

Funaria up to 50mm with sporangium

- rhizoids
- seta
- sporangium capsule
- gametophyte moss plant
- calyptra

TRACHEOPHYTA

All plants above the Bryophytes have a dominant conspicuous sporophyte generation with true roots, stems, and leaves; well developed vascular tissue of xylem, phloem, and other specialized tissues. They can all be grouped together in this one large Division, however this makes such a huge grouping that some prefer to divide it into a series of smaller Divisions. Others terms which are used in relation to the Tracheophyta are Cormophyta, Vascular cryptogams, and Phanerogams.

Cormophyta is a term used to group all plants with true roots, stems, and leaves together and thus includes the Pteridophyta, Gymnosperms, and Angiosperms.

Vascular cryptogams are those Tracheophyta with 'hidden' or inconspicuous reproductive organs, these are the Pteridophyta which have microscopic reproductive organs carried on a small gametophyte, whereas the conspicuous plant is the sporophyte which produces asexual spores.

Phanerogams are plants with conspicuous reproductive structures in cones or flowers, and which produce seeds; namely the Spermatophyta (Angiosperms and Gymnosperms).

DIVISION PTERIDOPHYTA

The 'club-mosses', the horse-tails, and the true ferns, and many extinct groups (especially in the Carboniferous). Well-developed heteromorphic alternation of generations; gametophyte typically a small short-lived thallus; zoidogamous fertilization; sporophyte vascular tissue only contains xylem tracheids; leaves bearing spore-producing sporangia are known as sporophylls; most are homosporous, although some are heterosporous with separate male and female gametophytes.

CLASS LYCOPODIATAE (LYCOPSIDA)

The 'club-mosses'. Extinct tree-forms were the dominant forms in the Carboniferous flora and some had developed the seed habit; present-day types have herbaceous creeping sporophytes with dichotomously branched stems and roots, and simple unstalked (sessile) leaves; sporophylls aggregated into spike-like cones or strobili.

Order Lycopodiales
Herbaceous sporophyte with creeping stem; only one main genus

Fig 14.4

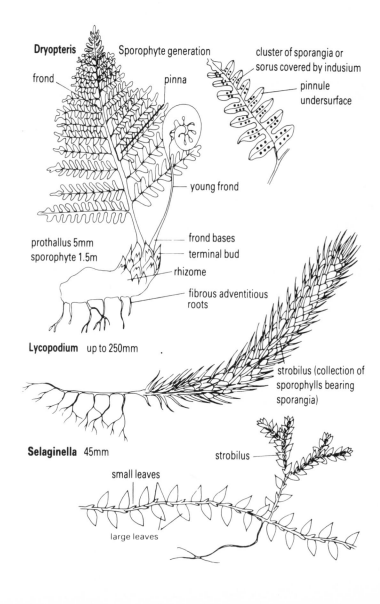

Lycopodium, e.g. *Lycopodium clavatum* [*commonest European species*] (Fig 14.4).

Order Selaginellales

Only one living (extant) genus, *Selaginella*; mainly tropical; herbaceous usually prostrate stem; small scale-like leaves usually in four rows; heterosporous with very reduced separate male and female gametophytes; e.g. *Selaginella* (Fig 14.4).

CLASS EQUISETATAE (SPHENOPSIDA)

The 'horse-tails'. Deep perennial underground rhizome produces erect annual stems with whorls of branches arising in the axils of scale leaves; distinct sporophylls in strobili born on distinctive sporangiophores with whorls of sheathing scale leaves; homosporous; only one extant genus, *Equisetum*.

CLASS FILICATAE

The ferns. Large, stalked leaves known as fronds bear many sporangia usually in clusters or sori on under-surface; generally homosporous but some are heterosporous; e.g. *Pteridium aquilinum* (bracken), *Dryopteris filix-mas* (male fern) (Fig 14.4).

DIVISION SPERMATOPHYTA

The seed-bearing plants. The dominant terrestrial plants since the upper Permian in the Mesophytic period; some are secondarily aquatic; the sporophyte has the highest degree of vascular differentiation; secondary thickening is common; heteromorphic alternation of generations with gametophyte much reduced and totally dependent on the sporophyte, being retained within the specialized reproductive structures known as cones and flowers; microspores containing the very reduced male gametophytes are released to be carried by wind or insects to the female parts, in the process of pollination; fertilization is via a pollen tube (siphonogamous), and therefore no longer dependent upon the presence of water; after fertilization seeds are formed.

SUB-DIVISION GYMNOSPERMAE

Trees and shrubs. Sporophylls aggregated into cones; seeds exposed on surface of megasporophylls; no fruits (hence naked seeds), xylem elements only tracheids; phloem has no companion cells.

CLASS CONIFERAE

The conifers. Mainly found in the northern hemisphere where they reach the northernmost limits and highest altitudes of all trees; have many xeromorphic features; e.g. *Pinus* (pine) (Fig 14.5), *Araucaria* (monkey puzzle), *Picea* (spruce), *Larix* (larch, deciduous conifers).

Fig 14.5. Pinus sylvestris
(Scot's Pine)

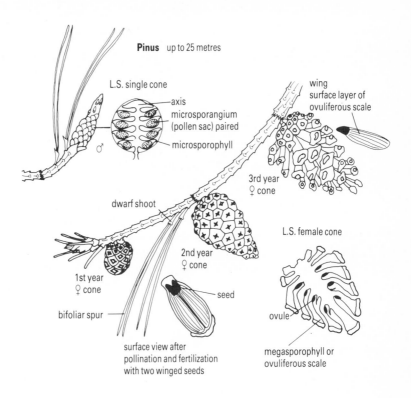

SUB-DIVISION ANGIOSPERMAE

The flowering plants. The dominant group of land plants with close to 25 000 known species; diverse forms adapted to every conceivable terrestrial habitat, with some secondarily aquatic, but only a few species marine (e.g. *Zostera* or eel grass); have the highest degree of cell and tissue differentiation with true vessels in the xylem, and sieve tubes with companion cells in the phloem; microsporophylls (stamens) and megasporophylls (carpels) aggregated into true flowers, flowers contain both sterile and fertile parts; gametophytes extremely reduced and develop entirely within the spore walls; fertilization always siphonogamous, characteristic double fertilization results in diploid zygote which gives rise to the embryo and triploid triple-fusion-nucleus which gives rise to the endosperm; carpels enclose ovules in ovaries; after fertilization ovary walls develop into fruits containing seeds.

Includes two classes, the Dicotyledonae and the Monocotyledonae. Major trends that are thought to have occurred in the evolution of the flowering plants are the reduction in the number of flowering parts, the fusion of floral parts, and the separation of the sexes into either separate male and female flowers on the same plants, or separate male and female flowers on different plants.

CLASS DICOTYLEDONAE

The larger of the two classes; seeds have two cotyledons or seed-leaves which act as the seed's food store; leaves have net venation; vascular tissue of stem occurs in ring of vascular bundles with cambium, therefore secondary thickening is common and many are woody perennials; flower parts arranged in twos, fours, or usually fives, or multiples of these numbers; root system typically a large primary tap root with lateral branches.

CLASS MONOCOTYLEDONAE

The smaller of the two classes. Seeds have only one seed leaf or cotyledon which frequently acts to transfer nutrients from the endo-sperm to the embryo; leaves have parallel venation; vascular tissue of stem occurs as scattered vascular bundles without cambium, there-fore secondary thickening lacking and are never woody perennials, except for a few palms which attain the tree habit via a diffuse mass of cambium; flower parts usually in threes or multiples of threes; root system typically fibrous, without large tap root; considered to have developed from the dicotyledons.

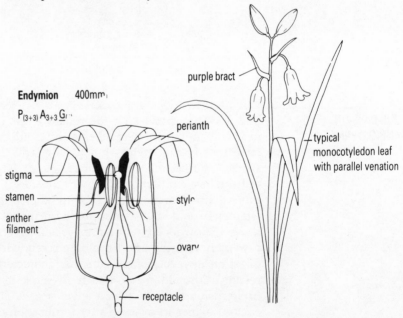

Fig 14.6. (When the calyx of sepals (K) and the corolla of petals (C) are indistinguishable they are collectively called the perianth (P).)
Endymion (bluebell), perennation by bulb, member of family Liliaceae.

ANIMAL KINGDOM

PHYLUM PROTOZOA   Unicellular; microscopic; about 50 000 species described.

CLASS RHIZOPODA (SARCODINA)

Amoeboid; moving and feeding by ever-changing cytoplasmic extrusions known as pseudopodia, e.g. *Amoeba* (Fig 14.7). Freshwater; feeding by phagocytosis, i.e. engulfing bacteria, diatoms, etc., with pseudopodia; contractile vacuole for expulsion of excess water that enters by osmosis; reproduction by binary fission.

CLASS FLAGELLATA (MASTIGOPHORA)

Flagellate, moving by one or more flagella; reproduction only by asexual longitudinal binary fission. Includes *Euglena*, *Trypanosoma* (blood parasite of vertebrates, including man, causing sleeping sickness).

Euglena
Found in pools and ditches rich in nitrogen. Cell membrane is a firm pellicle; chlorophyll in chloroplastids, therefore photosynthetic; positively phototropic with eye spot; can be saprozoic in dark.

CLASS CILIATA (CILIOPHORA)

Ciliated during at least one stage of the life cycle, moving and feeding by means of cilia; usually binucleate with mega- and micro-nucleus; unique form of sexual reproduction known as conjugation; e.g. *Paramecium*, *Zoothamnium* (stalked colonies), *Carchesium* (stalked colonies on the legs of shrimp).

Paramecium (Fig 14.7)
Freshwater. Slipper-shaped; firm pellicle with cilia; mega- and micro-nucleus; strong beating cilia known as the 'undulating membrane' of the oral groove draw in bacteria, etc., which are engulfed in food vacuoles and which then undergo a figure-of-eight passage through the cytoplasm known as cyclosis, undergoing first acid then alkaline digestion; spiralling and gyrating locomotion by metachronal beating of the cilia; reproduction by asexual fission, and sexual conjugation.

CLASS SPOROZOA

All parasitic; adults non-motile; usually complex life cycle, and reproduction by means of large numbers of spores; e.g. *Monocystis* (parasitic in the seminal vesicles of earthworm); *Plasmodium* (blood parasite of man causing malaria).

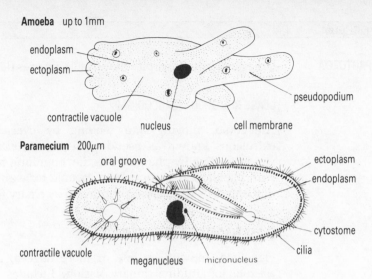

Fig 14.7

PHYLUM PORIFERA

The sponges. Freshwater and marine. Single body cavity connected to exterior by pores, cavity lined with flagellated choanocytes which create water currents; skeleton of calcareous, siliceous spicules, or horny fibres of spongin; no nervous cells, little integration between cells, body acts more as a colony of single cells; asexual reproduction by budding; e.g. *Euspongia* (the bath sponge).

SUB-KINGDOM METAZOA

Truly multicellular; division of labour between groups of cells constituting tissues and organs.

PHYLUM COELENTERATA

Are at the **tissue grade** of organization with muscular tissue and nervous tissue giving coordination of reactions and of locomotion; single sac-like body cavity (the enteron) opening to the exterior by a single opening: the mouth; **Diploblastic**, i.e. body wall of two layers of cells, the outer ectoderm and the inner endoderm, separated by a non-cellular mesogloea; sexual reproduction produces a characteristic ciliated planula larva, asexual reproduction by budding; can exist in two forms: the hydroid polyp and free-swimming sexually reproducing medusa; tentacles bear characteristic poisonous stinging cells known as nematoblasts or nematocysts (seventeen types); characteristic undifferentiated interstitial cells which can differentiate in to all types of cell (not however in *Obelia*).

CLASS HYDROZOA

Typically marine and colonial, with polyp colony budding off free-swimming medusae which carry the gonads and produce new polyp colonies as a result of sexual reproduction, e.g. *Obelia* (Fig 14.8) (found in coastal waters to a depth of 100 m), *Physalia* (Portuguese man-of-war), *Hydra* (atypical solitary freshwater form).

Hydra (Fig 14.8)

Atypical, freshwater; solitary polyp, no medusa. Feeding by trapping prey with nematocysts and passing food, such as *Daphnia*, to the mouth using tentacles in coordinated manner; can extend by contracting radial muscles in body wall, and contract to a blob using longitudinal muscles; symbiotic green algae (*H. viridis*) or brown algae (*H. fusca*) in endodermal cells.

CLASS SCYPHOZOA

Marine. The jelly-fish. Adults medusae; polyp form can be absent, when present it buds off medusae; e.g. *Aurelia* (Fig 14.8 overleaf).

CLASS ANTHOZOA

Marine. Polyp form only, solitary or colonial; enteron divided by vertical septa; endodermal gonads; e.g. *Actinia* (sea anemone) (Fig 14.8), *Tubipora* (organ-pipe coral).

Fig 14.8

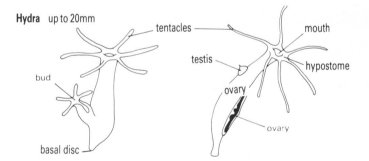

Hydra up to 20mm

tentacles — mouth
testis — hypostome
bud
ovary
ovary
basal disc

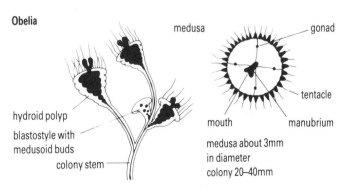

Obelia

medusa — gonad
hydroid polyp
blastostyle with medusoid buds
colony stem
mouth — manubrium — tentacle
medusa about 3mm in diameter
colony 20–40mm

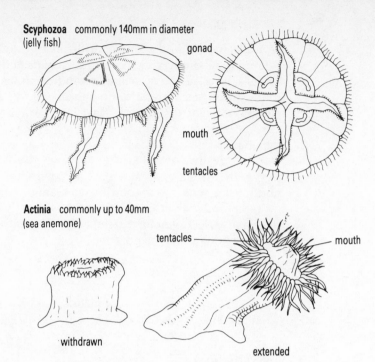

Scyphozoa   commonly 140mm in diameter
(jelly fish)

gonad

mouth

tentacles

Actinia   commonly up to 40mm
(sea anemone)

tentacles   mouth

withdrawn

extended

THE TRIPLOBLASTICA

Three-layered body wall, ectoderm, mesoderm, endoderm; general increase in size and complexity.

PHYLUM PLATYHELMINTHES

The 'flat worms'. Single opening to gut; excretion and osmoregulation by characteristic flame cells; usually hermaphrodite.

CLASS TURBELLARIA

Aquatic; ciliated ectoderm; fairly well developed sense organs; carnivorous scavengers; e.g. *Planaria* (freshwater) (Fig 14.9).

CLASS TREMATODA

The 'flukes'. All parasitic. No cilia; epidermis secretes a cuticle; suckers for attachment to host; strong powers of reproduction, larval stages and complex life cycle involving a secondary host; e.g. *Fasciola hepatica* (liver fluke of sheep), *Schistosoma* (in veins of man causing schistosomiasis or bilharzia).

CLASS CESTODA

The 'tapeworms'. All parasitic in the gut of vertebrates. No cilia; no gut; reduced sensitivity and powers of locomotion; hooks and/or suckers for attachment; prolific reproduction involving strobilization and budding-off of mature proglottids full of fertilized eggs; larval stages and complex life cycle involving a secondary host; e.g. *Taenia saginata* (beef tapeworm), *T. solium* (pork tapeworm), *T. serrata* (dog tapeworm), *Diplidium caninum* (dog tapeworm), *Echinococcus granulosus* (dog tapeworm).

Fig 14.9

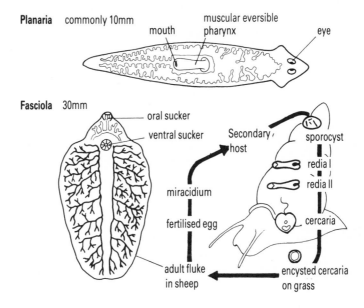

PHYLUM NEMATODA (ASCHELMINTHES)

The 'round worms'. No cilia; alimentary canal a straight tube with mouth and anus; usually separate sexes, free-living and parasitic e.g. *Ascaris* (common gut roundworm), *Proleptus* (dogfish gut worm), *Ancylostoma* (hookworm), *Toxacara* (dog and cat roundworm), *Trichinella spiralis* (man, rat, pig), *Aphelechus* (leaf parasite), *Heterodera* (plant root parasites).

COELOMATA

Possess a fluid-filled cavity in the mesoderm known as the **coelom.** The coelom is always lined with coelomic epithelium which secretes the coelomic fluid. All animals above the Nematoda are coelomate. Coelomate animals show an increase in complexity, and usually size, over the Acoelomates. The coelom allows for the separation of the gut wall from the body wall; the gut can therefore contract independently and there is a corresponding increase in efficiency of nutrition.

Indeed, the gut usually fills the greater part of the coelom. The coelomic fluid provides turgidity for the support, protection, and sometimes the locomotion of the animal, and ducts connect to the outside.

With the general increase in size and decrease in surface area to volume ratio, a blood vascular system with pumping heart carries out internal transport, for which simple diffusion alone is insufficient. The circulation of the blood supplies the complex organ systems.

The overall increase in complexity is reflected in the greater development of the coordinating nervous and hormonal systems seen in coelomates.

Metameric segmentation

All coelomate animals are also metamerically segmented, that is their bodies are divided into a linear series of segments from the earliest stages of embryological development, so that the body consists of a constant number of segments which are all of the same age (this contrasts with strobilization seen in the tapeworms). As the coelomates increase in complexity, the basic pattern of metameric segmentation becomes increasingly obscured by cephalization (fusion) and specialization, as for example in the head of vertebrates.

PHYLUM ANNELIDA

The segmented worms. Typically aquatic. Single, pre-oral segment – the prostomium; central nervous system with paired cerebral ganglia joined by circumoesophageal commissures to the ventral, solid, double nerve cord with segmental ganglia; excretion via characteristic segmental nephridia; thin chitinous cuticle; body wall bears characteristic bristle-like chaetae.

CLASS POLYCHAETA

Marine. Many chaetae borne on lateral extensions of the body wall known as parapodia, sexes usually separate; planktonic trochosphere larva; e.g. *Nereis* (ragworm) (Fig 14.10), *Arenicola* (lugworm), *Sabella* (fanworm).

CLASS OLIGOCHAETA

Terrestrial (the earthworms), some freshwater. Few chaetae per segment; no parapodia; reduced head region; hermaphrodite, but cross fertilization during copulation; eggs deposited in cocoon formed by a clitellum; direct development, no larval stage; e.g. *Lumbricus terrestris* (garden worm) (Fig 14.10). *Allobophora longa* (long worm), *Eisenia foetida* (brandling), *Octolasion cyaneum* (blue worm).

CLASS HIRUDINEA

Freshwater. No chaetae or parapodia; shortened body with thirty-two segments but many more ring markings on ectoderm; usually ecto-parasites – blood suckers, typically have anterior and posterior suckers, some feed as carnivores, hermaphrodite with clitellum producing a cocoon; e.g. *Hirudo* (medicinal leech).

Fig 14.10

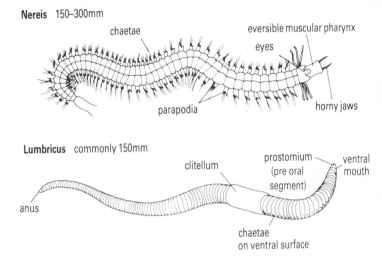

Nereis   150–300mm

chaetae · eversible muscular pharynx · eyes · parapodia · horny jaws

Lumbricus   commonly 150mm

clitellum · prostomium (pre oral segment) · ventral mouth · anus · chaetae on ventral surface

---

PHYLUM MOLLUSCA

Body divided into head, visceral mass, and muscular foot; skin covering visceral mass extends to form a mantle which encloses a mantle cavity, the mantle also secretes an external shell in most cases; open blood system with haemocoel; metameric segmentation much reduced and modified; aquatic forms have a trochophore larva.

CLASS GASTROPODA

Visceral mass undergoes torsion during development bringing the anus over the head, also shell coiled; large muscular foot; distinct head with eyes on tentacles, feed using radula; e.g. *Planorbis* (freshwater snail), *Patella* (limpet), *Buccinium* (whelk), *Helix* (common garden snail) (Fig 14.11), *Limax* (slug).

CLASS LAMELLIBRANCHIATA

Freshwater and marine. Body compressed laterally; head reduced; bivalved shells; reduced foot; layered sheets or lamellae of ciliated gills; e.g. *Anodonta* (freshwater mussel), *Mytilis* (marine mussel) (Fig 14.11).

CLASS CEPHALOPODA

Marine. Well developed head region with most complex invertebrate

Fig 14.11. Mussel and Snail.

Lamellibranch mollusc: marine mussel 50–60mm long

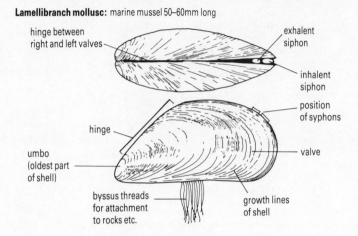

hinge between right and left valves

exhalent siphon

inhalent siphon

position of syphons

hinge

umbo (oldest part of shell)

valve

byssus threads for attachment to rocks etc.

growth lines of shell

Garden snail 60mm

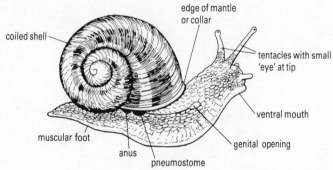

coiled shell

edge of mantle or collar

tentacles with small 'eye' at tip

ventral mouth

genital opening

muscular foot

anus

pneumostome

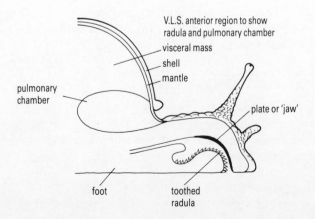

V.L.S. anterior region to show radula and pulmonary chamber

visceral mass

shell

mantle

pulmonary chamber

plate or 'jaw'

foot

toothed radula

brain and eyes; foot modified to form tentacles with suckers; muscular siphon; shell usually reduced and internal; e.g. *Architeuthis* (giant squid), *Loligo* (squid), *Sepia* ('cuttle fish' squid), *Octopus* (octopus), *Nautilus* (very distinct and ancient survivor, chambered shell, links with extinct Ammonites).

PHYLUM ARTHROPODA

Contain about 80% of all animal species. Chitin cuticle thickened to form strong exoskeleton, flexible at intervals to allow for jointing; paired jointed appendages; modified as mouthparts, limbs, respiratory and reproductive structures; exoskeleton shed during ecdysis to allow for growth; coelom much reduced, main body cavity is a blood-filled haemocoel which is part of the open circulatory system, contractile dorsal tubular heart; cerebral ganglia and ventral solid nerve cord with typical paired segmental ganglia; no cilia. (Such a large and complex phylum that only some typical sub-groupings are included.)

CLASS CRUSTACEA

Freshwater, marine, very few partially terrestrial. Two pairs of antennae, three pairs of head appendages, frequently some thoracic ones act as mouthparts; breathe by gills; usually heavy calcareous exoskeleton with dorsal shield carapace.

SUB-CLASS BRANCHIOPODA

Large number of appendages, with trunk limbs involved in breathing and feeding.

Compressed carapace covering trunk and limbs; compound eyes fused into one; large antennae used for swimming.

4–6 pairs of trunk limbs form compact and efficient feeding apparatus; e.g. *Daphnia* (water flea).

SUB-CLASS MALACOSTRACA

The 'highest' crustacea; wide diversity and large numbers of species; compound eyes, usually stalked; carapace covering cephalo-thorax of eight segments.

Order Eucarida
Carapace fused to all thoracic segments.

Sub-order Decapoda
Last four pairs of thoracic limbs adapted for locomotion; e.g. *Carcinus* (common shore crab) (Fig 14.12).

Order Peracarida
Carapace does not fuse with more than four thoracic segments.

Sub-order Isopoda

No carapace, dorso-ventrally flattened; e.g. *Armadillium* (pill-bug woodlouse, rolls into a ball), *Oniscus* (woodlouse) (Fig 14.12).

Fig 14.12

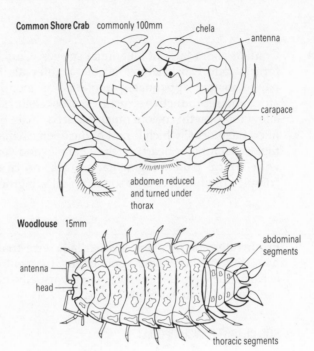

Common Shore Crab commonly 100mm

chela

antenna

carapace

abdomen reduced and turned under thorax

Woodlouse 15mm

antenna

head

abdominal segments

thoracic segments

CLASS INSECTA

1 Body divided into head, thorax and abdomen.
2 Three pairs of walking legs on the three thoracic segments.
3 Typically two pairs of wings arising from thorax.
4 Respiration via a system of air tubes or tracheae.
5 Excretion by Malpighian tubules.

COMMENT ▶

Typically terrestrial, some secondarily aquatic in fresh water. More than half the known species of animals are insects, with over one million having been described and thousands being added every year. They are thought to have evolved at about the same time as the Angiosperms in the Cretaceous period 125 million years ago.

The story of the insects is one of fantastic success. Their waterproof covering to the exoskeleton, efficient tracheal respiration, powers of flight, variation, and adaptability, have enabled them to colonize every conceivable terrestrial niche. Their prolific reproduction and astronomic numbers bring them into competition with man for his food supply, and many act as vectors of diseases of man, his crops, and his animals.

SUB CLASS PTERYGOTA (METABOLA)

Winged or secondarily wingless. Either gradual metamorphosis from nymph resembling adult form, and wings developing from external buds (Hemimetabola, Exopterygota); or marked metamorphosis from larval form not resembling adult form, with wings developing from internal buds (Holometabola, Endopterygota).

HEMIMETABOLA: EXOPTERYGOTA

Order Odonata

Damselflies, dragonflies (Fig 14.14). Aquatic nymphs, adults predaceous with biting mouthparts; large eyes.

Order Dictyoptera

Mantids and cockroaches. Most ancient group of winged insects still in existence.

Order Orthoptera

Locusts (Fig 14.13), grasshoppers, and crickets. Hind limbs adapted for jumping, stridulating (noise) organs.

Order Homoptera

Aphids and cicadas.

HOLOMETABOLA; ENDOPTERYGOTA

Order Coleoptera

Beetles. Fore wings modified as wing-covers or elytra.

Order Lepidoptera

Butterflies and moths. Mouthparts as coiled sucking proboscis; membranous wings with scales held vertically at rest in butterflies and flat in moths (Fig 14.13).

Order Diptera

Flies, gnats, and mosquitoes. One pair of wings, posterior pair of wings modified as balancing organs or halteres (Fig 14.13).

Order Hymenoptera

Ants, bees, and wasps. Polymorphic; first abdominal segment fused to thorax; four membranous wings, anterior wings linked by hooks to posterior wings; female has ovipositor (modified to sting in worker female bees and wasps) (Fig 14.14).

Fig 14.13. Fruit Fly.

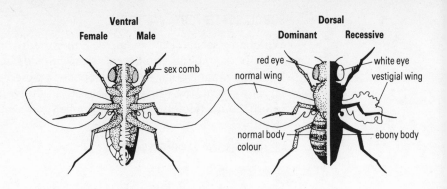

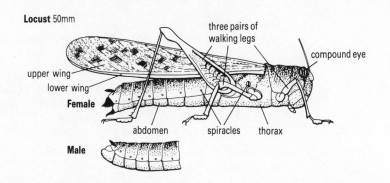

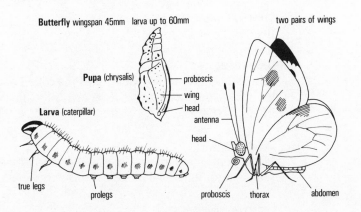

Fig 14.14

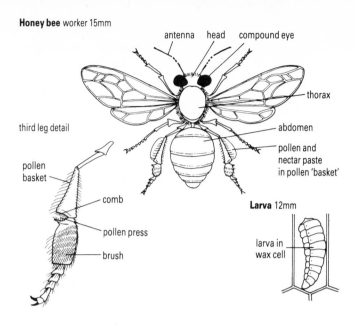

Honey bee worker 15mm

antenna head compound eye

thorax

abdomen

pollen and
nectar paste
in pollen 'basket'

third leg detail

pollen
basket

comb

pollen press

brush

Larva 12mm

larva in
wax cell

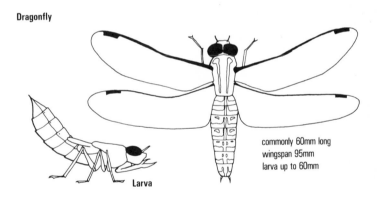

Dragonfly

commonly 60mm long
wingspan 95mm
larva up to 60mm

Larva

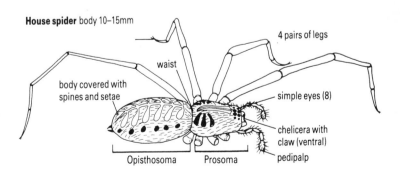

House spider body 10–15mm

4 pairs of legs

waist

body covered with
spines and setae

simple eyes (8)

chelicera with
claw (ventral)

pedipalp

Opisthosoma Prosoma

CLASS ARACHNIDA

Typically terrestrial, some aquatic. Body divided into two: the anterior prosoma, and posterior opisthosoma; four pairs of walking legs; no antennae; many simple eyes.

Order Araneida

Spiders. Prosoma and opisthosoma separated by narrow waist; spinning glands, which about half of the species use for building traps; e.g. *Tegenaria* (common house spider), *Araneus* (garden spider) (Fig 14.14), *Erigone* (money spider).

PHYLUM ECHINODERMATA

Marine. Larvae usually bilaterally symmetrical and segmented, adult radially symmetrical usually with five radii and unsegmented; unique water-vascular system involved in movement of characteristic tube feet; no excretory or circulatory system; gut always a simple coiled tube; mesodermal skeleton of calcareous plates.

The body plan of the adult shows no affinities with any other groups, but the larvae show affinities with those of some of the primitive Protochordates.

CLASS ASTEROIDEA

Star-shaped with five arms; have suckers on tube feet; mouth ventral, anus and external opening of water-vascular system (madreporite) dorsal; e.g. *Asterias* (the starfish) (Fig 14.15).

Fig 14.15

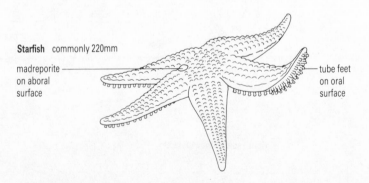

Starfish commonly 220mm

madreporite on aboral surface

tube feet on oral surface

CLASS ECHINOIDEA

Globular, cushion, or disc-shaped; no arms; large spines; larvae show affinities to Protochordate larvae; e.g. *Echinus* (the sea urchin).

PHYLUM CHORDATA

Possess a dorsal skeletal notochord, at some stage in their life history, running the length of the body just below a tubular nerve cord. Pharyngeal or visceral clefts at some stage in life history. Closed blood circulatory system with blood flowing forward ventrally and backwards dorsally. Post-anal metamerically segmented tail.

SUB-PHYLUM PROTOCHORDATA (ACRANIA)

No true cranium, brain, heart, or kidneys.

CLASS CEPHALOCHORDATA

Well-developed notochord in adult extending length of the body, fish-like appearance; e.g. *Amphioxus*.

SUB-PHYLUM VERTEBRATA (CRANIATA)

'The vertebrates.' Notochord is replaced in the adult by the vertebral column, associated with this is a well-developed head region with a well-developed brain protected by the cranium; organs of special sense are well-developed and usually closely associated with the brain; the visceral clefts are generally lost in the adult except in the fish where they persist and are modified as gills; a true muscular heart develops ventrally; true kidneys are formed which utilize the blood pressure produced by the pumping heart; one or more portal systems in the circulation; a well-developed endocrine system; usually two pairs of limbs. All have jaws except members of Class Cyclostomata. The jawed vertebrates are referred to as the **Gnathostomata,** and the jawless ones as the **Agnatha.**

CLASS PISCES

The fish. Paired pectoral and pelvic fins; respire by gills; single circulation with blood passing through the heart only once on each complete circulation of the body; lateral line sense organ; possess scales on the skin; no external or middle ear.

SUB-CLASS CHONDRICHTHYES (ELASMOBRANCHII)

Order Selachii
Entirely marine. The 'cartilagenous' fish with a cartilagenous endoskeleton; placoid scales; spiracles; no operculum covering the gills, each of which has its own septum; no air-filled swim-bladder, therefore 'heavier' than water and depth in water regulated by fleshy pectoral fins and typical heterocercal tail; spiral valve in the intestine; blood contains high concentration of urea; pelvic fins modified to claspers in male; fertilization internal, and few large-yolked eggs laid in special egg cases known as 'mermaid's purses'; overall tendency to

dorso-ventral flattening and bottom-living flat forms lie on their ventral surface; e.g. *Scyliorhinus* (the dogfish) (Fig 14.16), *Raja* (the skate).

SUB-CLASS OSTEICHTHYES

Freshwater and marine. The bony fish, with a bony endoskeleton, bony scales, and an air-filled bladder or sac derived as a diverticulum or branch of the gut.

Order Teleostei

The main group of living bony fish with some 25 000 living species. Bony scales reduced to thin cycloid scales; air sac or swim bladder operated as a hydrostatic organ, by controlling the volume of gas they can adjust their depth in the water; homocercal tail; operculum covering the gills; fins a series of rays supporting a thin membranous skin and with any basal elements retained inside the body; overall tendency to lateral flattening, and bottom living flat forms lie on their side e.g. trout (Fig 14.16).

Fig 14.16

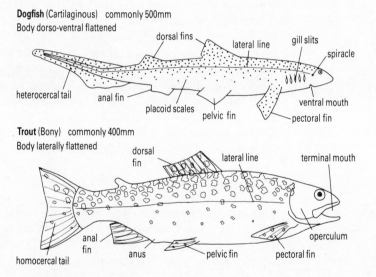

Dogfish (Cartilaginous)   commonly 500mm
Body dorso-ventral flattened
dorsal fins — lateral line — gill slits — spiracle — heterocercal tail — anal fin — placoid scales — pelvic fin — ventral mouth — pectoral fin

Trout (Bony)   commonly 400mm
Body laterally flattened
dorsal fin — lateral line — terminal mouth — anal fin — anus — pelvic fin — pectoral fin — operculum — homocercal tail

TETRAPODS

All the remaining groups of the vertebrates have two pairs of limbs based on the pentadactyl plan.

CLASS AMPHIBIA

Most members are only partially adapted to a terrestrial existence and are therefore restricted to damp habitats; eggs are not adapted to terrestrial conditions, therefore the adults return to the water to breed (although there are exceptions); the larval forms, known as tadpoles, are aquatic with gills; metamorphosis into the adult results in the loss of the gills and the development of simple sac-like lungs, although in the adult the main respiratory surface is the soft, permeable, well-vascularized skin; three-chambered heart; no external ear; and a single auditory ossicle in the middle ear.

Order Urodela

Tail persists in the adult and there is a long vertebral column; gills can persist into the adult stage of aquatic types and if they do the lungs atrophy; limbs are short. Contain about 900 species ranging from terrestrial forms to completely aquatic types; e.g. *Triton* (the newt), *Salamandra* (the salamander), *Amblystoma* (the axolotl, which attains sexual maturity in the larval form).

Order Anura

Distinct metamorphosis into tail-less adult, with no gills and long muscular hind limbs adapted for jumping and swimming. Includes the frogs and the more terrestrial toads; e.g. *Rana* (the frog), *Bufo* (the toad), *Xenopus* (the African clawed toad, completely aquatic).

CLASS REPTILIA

The first group of vertebrates completely adapted to a terrestrial environment. Waterproof keratinized scaly skin; true lungs are the only respiratory surface; heart almost completely divided into two halves to give a double circulation with blood passing through the heart twice on each circulation of the body; large, heavily-yolked 'cleidoic' egg with protective shell, and waterproof shell membranes allowing it to be laid on land.

COMMENT ▶

These features enabled the reptiles to exploit the vast, untapped food resources of the land masses and they underwent a wide adaptive radiation, culminating in the great Age of Reptiles in the Mesozoic period. Modern forms are but a relic of this once-dominant terrestrial group of vertebrates.

Order Squamata
The lizards and snakes.

Sub-order Lacertilia
The lizards.

CLASS AVES

Similar in many ways to the Reptilia, and considered to be descendants from the Dinosaurs of the Mesozoic period. Feathers, scales on legs; toothless jaws enclosed in a horny beak; many adaptations to flight, anterior limbs form wings, sternum explanded into 'keel' for attachment of powerful pectoral flight muscles, hollow bones with air sacs from lungs, air sacs also in abdomen, no rectum or bladder; well-developed cleidoic egg with rigid calcareous shell, complex mating, nesting and rearing behaviour.

CLASS MAMMALIA

The mammals. Mammary glands secrete milk to nourish the young; skin has sweat or sudorific glands, sebaceous glands, and hair; external ear and three auditory ossicles in middle ear; true diaphragm completely separates thoracic cavity from abdomen; lower jaw consists of a single bone, the dentary on either side; only the left systemic arch present, forming the aorta leaving the heart.

SUB-CLASS MONOTREMATA

Show many 'reptilian' features, e.g. cloaca; lay large-yolked eggs; relatively low body temperature; a relatively simple brain; have no mammary glands but pour a milky secretion into a groove on the abdomen; the adults lack true teeth but this is a specialization; e.g. *Echidna* (the spiny ant eater), *Ornithorhyncus* (the duck-billed platypus).

SUB-CLASS METATHERIA

The 'marsupials'. More mammal-like than the monotremes but still not considered as 'true' mammals. Viviparous, but the placenta is rarely allantoic, the young are born alive but are poorly developed at birth except for powerful fore-limbs which enable them to reach the pouch in which they complete their development. They are found only in South America and Australia, and are only abundant in the latter; e.g. *Macropus* (the kangaroo).

SUB-CLASS EUTHERIA

The 'true' mammals. Completely viviparous with a true allantoic placenta; true mammary glands developed from modified sebaceous glands; roof of forebrain, the neo-pallium, forms the bulk of the extremely well-developed cerebral hemispheres, both cerebellum and cerebrum convoluted, active, intelligent and high degree of parental care; diphyodont (not the rat), i.e. milk and permanent dentition, heterodont with different specialized types of teeth, e.g. incisors, canines, premolars, and molars.

Order Insectivora

Small nocturnal forms; many primitive characters; full mammalian dentition usually preserved $\frac{3}{3} \frac{1}{1} \frac{4}{4} \frac{3}{3}$; brain has large olfactory lobes, small cerebral hemispheres; some retain the cloaca; e.g. *Talpa europaea* (mole).

Order Chiroptera

More than 800 species, about 14% of all mammal species. The only mammals with flapping flight, the wing is a skin fold which involves all the digits except the first and extends along the body to include the legs but not the feet, great elongation of distal bones of the arms, sternum has a keel, also the clavicles are stout; hang upside down, when hanging metabolic rate drops; wide range of feeding habits within the group, e.g. insectivorous, licking nectar, sucking blood, eating fruit, catching fish; main sensory system is echolocation, high intensity and high frequency vibrations produced by large larynx, and reflection from objects, including prey, detected with great accuracy, echolocation and night flying enabled the bats to exploit the vast untapped food reserves of the night-flying insects; with absence of insects in winter in temperate climates bats must either hibernate or migrate.

Order Carnivora

Large brain with complicated behaviour for tracking prey; powerful jaws and dentition, with strong canines and some 'chewing' teeth modified as sharp carnassials; e.g. *Canis* (dog), *Felis* (cat).

The Ungulates

All have a herbivorous diet; usually large, elongated limbs for rapid locomotion, lateral digits reduced, movement of limbs in fore and aft direction only, formation of hooves; well-developed auditory and olfactory senses; teeth developed for dealing with large volumes of vegetation; alimentary canal with either stomach or caecum, or both, modified to harbour symbiotic cellulose-digesting bacteria.

Order Perissodactyla

The 'odd-toed' Ungulates. Main digit is III; e.g. *Equus* (horse), *Tapirus* (tapir).

Order Artiodactyla

The 'even-toed' Ungulates, with cloven hooves. Main digits are III and IV; elaboration of stomach into four chambers, the rumen, reticulum, omasum, and abomasum; food cropped and swallowed without chewing, acted on by symbiotic bacteria, regurgitated when softened and chewed ('chewing the cud'); the 'ruminants'; e.g *Bos* (cattle), *Capra* (goat), *Ovis* (sheep), *Camelus* (camel), *Capreolus* (roe deer).

Order Primates

Most features are associated with tree-climbing adaptations; ventral elements of pectoral girdle reduced but clavicles act as struts for the mobile arms, development of grasping; good vision with fovea centralis in retina; general reduction of the olfactory sense; typically omnivorous; claws become nails; have four grasping 'hands' (except for man).

Sub-order Anthropoidea

Infra-order Platyrrhina
New World forms. All forest-dwellers, some with prehensile tails.

Infra-order Catarrhina
Old World forms.

Family Cercopithicidae
Old World monkeys; e.g. baboons, macaques.

Family Simiidae
Great apes, e.g. gorilla, chimpanzee.

Family Hominidae
E.g. *Homo sapiens* (man).

THE 'FIVE KINGDOM' SYSTEM

One alternative classificatory system which is gaining wider usage is the 'Five Kingdom' System proposed by Whittaker (Whittaker, R. H., 'New concepts of Kingdoms of organisms', *Science*, 1969, 150–60). It is based both on levels of organization and on types of organization in relation to three main means of nutrition: photosynthesis, absorption, and ingestion.

1 KINGDOM MONERA

Eukaryotic, lacking nuclear membranes, mitochondria and plastids, e.g. bacteria and blue-green algae (Cyanophyta).

2 KINGDOM PROTISTA (PROTOCTISTA)

Mainly unicellular eukaryotic types, e.g. Protozoa (including *Euglena*).

3 KINGDOM PLANTAE

Photosynthetic plants.

4 KINGDOM FUNGI

Non-photosynthetic plants.

5 KINGDOM ANIMALIA

THE USE OF KEYS IN THE IDENTIFICATION OF LIVING ORGANISMS

A key is essentially a list of questions about observable features of living organisms that enable them to be sorted out from each other and eventually identified. At each stage, two or more alternative statements are presented, only one of which should apply to the particular specimen being examined. This will lead to the next set of alternatives, and so on until the organism is identified. The simplest type offers only two alternatives at each stage and is known as a **dichotomous key**. It is difficult to construct good keys, especially when attempting to differentiate between species, and at this level a key can only act as a guide.

Fig 14.17. Dichotomous key.

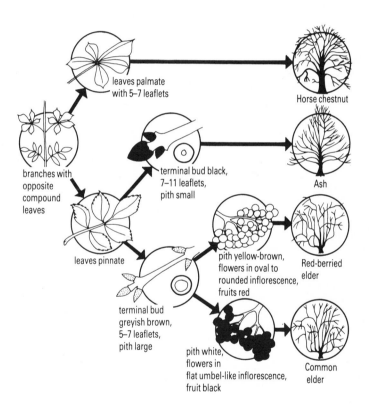

branches with opposite compound leaves

leaves palmate with 5–7 leaflets

Horse chestnut

terminal bud black, 7–11 leaflets, pith small

Ash

leaves pinnate

terminal bud greyish brown, 5–7 leaflets, pith large

pith yellow-brown, flowers in oval to rounded inflorescence, fruits red

Red-berried elder

pith white, flowers in flat umbel-like inflorescence, fruit black

Common elder

BACTERIA AND VIRUSES

BACTERIA

Bacteria are a mixed group of micro-organisms that are difficult to classify.

They are unicellular or colonial, lack a true nucleus (prokaryotic, or akaryotic) having only an ill-defined nuclear area containing genetic material.

They lack mitochondria, although most can carry out aerobic respiration; if a photosynthetic pigment (bacteriochlorophyll) is present, it is not enclosed in a special organelle such as the chloroplastid.

They have a polysaccharide cell wall which differs in nature from that found in plants; and which is surrounded by a mucilaginous capsule.

Some have flagella and are motile at some stage in their life history.

They can be named according to their shape, for example the rod-shaped bacilli (up to 20 micrometres long), the comma-shaped vibrios, the spiral-shaped spirilla, and the spherical-shaped cocci. (See Fig 14.1.)

NUTRITION

Some bacteria are autotrophic and some are heterotrophic.

Autotrophic bacteria

These are able to synthesize complex organic compounds from simple inorganic substances, either using light energy in a process known as photosynthesis, or chemical energy in a process of chemosynthesis.

Photosynthetic bacteria

These contain the photosynthetic pigment bacteriochlorophyll, which differs from the chlorophyll of higher plants. Also, unlike higher plants, they do not use water as the source of hydrogen for the reduction processes involved in the synthesis of complex organic compounds from carbon dioxide.

Photosynthesis in a green plant

$$H_2O + CO_2 \longrightarrow (CH_2O) + O_2$$

Photosynthesis in a green bacterium

$$2H_2S + CO_2 \longrightarrow (CH_2O) + 2S + H_2O$$

Chemosynthetic bacteria

These lack photosynthetic pigments, but can synthesize organic compounds from simple inorganic ones by using energy from inorganic chemical reactions. Some of these bacteria have key roles in the nitrogen cycle, for example *Nitrosomonas* and *Nitrobacter*.

Nitrosomonas

$$\underset{\text{ammonia}}{NH_3} + 3O \longrightarrow \underset{\text{nitrite}}{HNO_2} + H_2O + \text{energy}$$

Nitrobacter

$$\underset{\text{nitrite}}{HNO_2} + O \longrightarrow \underset{\text{nitrate}}{HNO_3} + \text{energy}$$

Heterotrophic bacteria

These cannot synthesize organic compounds from simple inorganic ones, and they therefore require a supply of organic material as food.

If they live and feed on dead organic matter, they are termed **saprophytic.** Such saprophytic bacteria are important **decomposers,** breaking down dead organic matter and rendering materials available again for recycling through the ecosystem. However they can also cause spoilage of stored products, such as food, and other materials used by man.

If they live and feed on living organisms, they are termed **parasitic.** Such parasitic bacteria are disease-producing or **pathogenic,** for example those causing tuberculosis and tetanus in humans; and leaf wilt disease in plants.

RESPIRATION

Bacteria can be either aerobic, that is respiring utilizing oxygen in the air, or anaerobic, that is respiring in the absence of oxygen (some are obligate anaerobes, that is they can only survive in anaerobic conditions).

Anaerobic respiration results in the production of fermentation products such as ethanol (ethyl alcohol) and acetic acid (vinegar).

REPRODUCTION

This is mainly by asexual binary fission, whereby a bacterium divides into two. Under optimum conditions this can occur every 20 minutes, resulting in a very rapid increase in population. Such populations of bacteria often form characteristic colonies visible to the naked eye, by which the particular type of bacteria may be identified. Also certain of the rod-shaped bacteria (bacilli) can form highly resistant spores which can withstand adverse conditions for long periods of time.

Sexual reproduction, by which members of different strains fuse in a form of conjugation, is found in some bacteria.

APPLIED ASPECTS OF BACTERIAL ACTIVITY

Role	Comments
(a) Silage	Silage production is a method of animal food preservation. Plant material is cut and packed into a 'silo', in which bacterial fermentation of the carbohydrates occurs. After about a month, the plant material has been changed into a nutritive mass which will keep for years.
(b) Sewage disposal	Aerobic saprophytic bacteria are important in percolating filters and activated sludge, and in breaking down organic wastes. Anaerobic bacteria digest sludge and are also active in cesspools and septic tanks.

Role	Comments
(c) Butter	A 'starter' bacterial culture (e.g. *Streptococcus lactis*) is added to pasteurized cream. The bacteria curdle and coagulate the cream, and yield products that impart flavour and aroma. The product is then churned to butter
(d) Cheese	Milk is coagulated either by rennet or bacteria-produced lactic acid. Bacteria are involved in the ripening of the cheese.
(e) Yoghurts	*Lactobacilli* bacteria and others are used to produce fermented milk beverages.
(f) Vinegar	Bacteria of the genus *Acetobacter* oxidize alcohol to acetic acid. Vinegar contains about 4% acetic acid; traces of other fermentation products give odour and taste.
(g) Leather	Bacteria are used in several stages of the preparation of leather from hides. The removal of the hair can be by carefully-controlled bacterial decomposition, bating (the placing of hides in weak fermenting infusions of dog or bird dung or bran mash) involves a complex of unknown bacterial action, as does the final process of tanning.
(h)	A variety of commercially important organic compounds can be made by bacterial action, e.g. lactic acid, acetone, and propionic acid.
(i) Enzymes	Several bacteria can be used for the commercial production of amylase and protease.
(j) Vitamin assay	The specific nutritional requirements of some bacteria for certain vitamins can be used as a means of determining the presence of these vitamins in food.

VIRUSES

Viruses consist of a protein coat surrounding a strand of nucleic acid (DNA in most animal viruses and RNA in most plant viruses).

They are so small that they can only be seen under the electron microscope: they range in size from 6–400 nm, and may be smaller than some protein molecules.

They do not have any of the normal cell organelles, and whether they can be considered as living organisms is questionable.

All viruses are obligate parasitic pathogens, unable to multiply outside the host cell.

They infect the host cells by attaching the protein coat to the host cell membrane and injecting the nucleic acid into the cell, leaving the protein coat as a 'ghost' outside the cell. Once inside the host cell the viral nucleic acid directs the host cell cytoplasm to construct new viruses, which are liberated by the rupture of the host cell. There is a group of viruses that specifically attack bacteria, known as bacterio-phages.

Viruses cause many diseases of economic and social importance to man. Plant viruses mainly infect Angiosperms. They are transmitted by plant-sucking insects such as Aphids and soil Nematodes, and some are transmitted from generation to generation in the plant's seeds. Examples of plant viruses include the Tobacco Mosaic Virus (TMV), and Potato Leaf Roll Virus. Animal viruses are spread by biting and sucking insects, by contact, and by droplets emitted from the respiratory tracts of mammals including man. Examples of virus diseases of man include influenza, poliomyelitis and the common cold.

Viruses are unaffected by antibiotics.

QUESTION ▶

Q.   What advantages are there in classifying organisms? (4) How would you classify
    (i) Bacteria (8)
    (ii) Viruses? (8)

COMMENT ▶

This question might appear to be rather general in nature, but it in fact still requires specific points to be made.

OUTLINE ▶ ANSWER

Advantages in classification. (4)
Introduces order into what would otherwise be an unmanage-able variety of organisms;
binomial system of genus and species allows internationally accepted identification;
hierarchial system of increasing complexity of structure suggests evolutionary relationships;
reduces length of descriptions as all members of a group share common features.
    (i) Bacteria (8)
Cell wall, but not of cellulose;
some possess bacteriochlorophyll but pigment is not enclosed within a membrane bound chloroplast;
oxygen is not evolved as a result of photosynthesis;
no true nucleus (prokaryotic or akaryotic);
no chromosomes, circular strand of DNA;
no membrane bound organelles e.g. mitochondria;
therefore although some are more plant like than animal like, their classification presents difficulties;
and some classify them in a separate Kingdom of prokaryotic organisms.
    (ii) Viruses (8)
Lack any of the normal cell organelles;

consist of a protein coat around DNA or RNA;

unlike other organisms, they never contain DNA and RNA together;

obligate parasites incapable of reproducing outside a host cell;

can be obtained in crystalline form and retain their powers of infection;

unlike any other living organisms and cannot be classified into any group;

can be considered as non-living.

QUESTIONS

1 With reference to named examples, give an account of the difficulties encountered in the classification of living organisms. Discuss how these difficulties may be overcome. (O)

2 (a) Place the following list of taxonomic categories in their correct sequence beginning with the largest unit of classification and ending with the smallest: genus; phylum; family; species; order; class.

(b) Name a *genus* of flowering plant or conifer.

(c) What does the term *genus* mean? (O)

3 In taxonomy, the closest grouping of related species is

A an order.

B a class.

C a genus.

D a phylum. (JMB)

4 Using specific examples, discuss the problems in classifying certain unicellular organisms as either animals or plants.

Why are such difficulties of classification, both in this area and elsewhere, inevitable if the theory of organic evolution is to be believed? (O&C)

5 Which of the following is found in both the Annelida and the Arthropoda?

A hollow dorsal nerve cord

B forward flow of blood in ventral vessel, backward flow in dorsal vessel

C solid ventral nerve cord

D haemocoel as the main body cavity (CAM)

6 Give a general account of arthropods, indicating

(a) the range of form,

(b) their occurrence,

(c) their biological importance. (LOND)

7 Platyhelminthes, Annelida and Arthropoda are triploblastic metazoans.

(a) Explain what is meant by
(i) triploblastic organism,
(ii) metazoan organism.

(b)   Give **one** example of animals belonging to each of the following groups:
        (i) Annelida
        (ii) Platyhelminthes
        (iii) Arthropoda
        (iv) Chordata.

(c)   Name **two** structural features which separate the Platyhelminthes from the Annelida.

(d)   Name **two** structural features of Arthropoda which separate them from Annelida.

(e)   Explain what is meant by 'analogous structures'.

(f)   List **three** structures of insects and vertebrates that can be described as analogous.   (W)

8   The diagrams below are of two invertebrates. Examine the diagrams carefully and complete the following table.

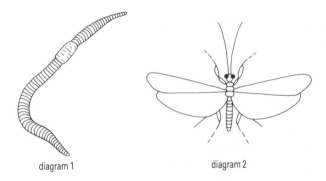

diagram 1   diagram 2

	Diagram 1	**Diagram 2**
Name the phylum to which each organism belongs		
For each phylum give *three* characteristic features not present in the other phylum. At least *three* of the *six* features must be evident on the diagrams.	1 2 3	1 2 3

(AEB)

9   Give a general account of *either* insects *or* fungi.   (LOND)

10 Explain, with the aid of diagrams, why:
    (a)   a sea anemone is classified as a coelenterate.
    (b)   an earthworm is classified as an annelid.
    (c)   a mushroom is classified as a fungus.
    (d)   a snail is classified as a mollusc.   (LOND)

11   (*a*)   What are the distinguishing features of chordate animals?
    (*b*)   Using a *named* example of (i) a fish, (ii) an amphibian and (iii) a bird, describe the ways in which their *external* features show adaptation to their environments.   (LOND)

12   The diagram below shows part of a culture of a species of *Mucor* growing on nutrient agar.

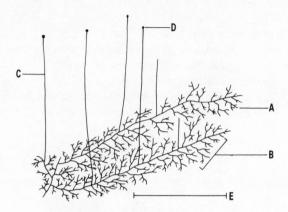

  (*a*)   Label the structures **A–D,**
and give the appropriate value for the scale **E** by circling one of the following:
1 mm   5 mm   10 mm   20 mm.
  (*b*)   (i) Name **one** feature of *Mucor* that suggests that it is a member of the plant kingdom.
         (ii) Name **one** feature of *Mucor* that contrasts with the general characteristics of plants.
  (*c*)   In view of your answers to (*b*) why are fungi usually considered to be members of the plant kingdom?
  (*d*)   Explain what is meant by the terms
         (i) heterothallism
         (ii) homothallism
  (*e*)   By means of fully annotated diagrams give an account of sexual reproduction.   (W)

13   Gymnosperms and angiosperms are classified as subdivisions of the same major group of plants.
What are the features which allow these two groups to be classified:
  (*a*)   in the same major group,
  (*b*)   as separate sub-groups?

14   By reference to an herbaceous flowering plant of your choice, indicate the features, in order of importance, which you would take into account in classifyiog it.   (SU)

GLOSSARY

CONTENTS

The contents of this glossary have been restricted mainly to the more general terminology of the subject, and concentrate on terms the meaning of which is often implied or assumed in the description of other phenomena.

acid Substances with a tendency to furnish a proton (hydrogen ion) in chemical reactions. They turn litmus red and have a pH less than 7.

acoelomate Without a coelom, e.g. Coelenterates, Platyhelminthes, and Nematoda.

action spectrum Rate of activity in relation to wavelength of light, e.g. photosynthesis most active in blue and red parts of the visible spectrum.

active transport Transport of a substance against its prevailing diffusion gradient, utilizing energy from respiration.

adaptive radiation The assumed development or evolution of a variety of descendent species adapted to different ways of life, from a single ancestral species.

adenosine triphosphate (ATP) The so-called 'energy carrier' molecule which is the immediate source of energy in the cell. It is continually regenerated from various energy-reserve compounds.

adhesion Force of attraction between molecules of different substances.

aerobic Organisms or processes requiring the presence of free oxygen.

afferent Carrying towards. Used for nerves and blood vessels, e.g. afferent arteriole carrying blood towards the glomerulus of the kidney.

anabolism Synthetic reactions of metabolism.

anaerobic Organisms or processes not requiring the presence of free oxygen. Obligate anaerobes cannot function in the presence of oxygen, facultative anaerobes can function with or without oxygen.

analogous Of similar function, but different embryological origin and structure, e.g. wing of insect and wing of bird.

antheridium Male sex organ of Fungi, Algae, Bryophyta (liverworts and mosses) and Pteridophyta (ferns, etc).

antibiotic Substance secreted by many micro-organisms (particularly fungi) which is toxic to other species. Viruses are unaffected by antibiotics.

apical At or near the tip.

archegonium Female sex organ of Bryophyta, Pteridophyta and most Gymnosperms. Multicellular, with neck and venter (base), containing egg cell.

artefact Artificially produced effect; a product of the preparation technique; e.g. as in the preparation of cells for examination under the electron microscope.

assimilation The incorporation of materials into the body.

atom Smallest particle of an element that can enter into combination with other elements.

auto Prefix meaning 'self', e.g. autotrophic, 'self-feeding'.

autonomic 'Self-controlling'.

autotrophic 'Self-feeding'. Able to synthesize organic compounds from simple inorganic substances (photosynthetic or chemosynthetic).

bacteriophage Virus that infects bacteria.

base Substance with a tendency to accept a proton in chemical reactions. Bases turn litmus blue, and have a pH greater than 7.

bioassay Quantitative measurement of the strength of a biologically active substance by means of its effect on a living organism.

biomass Total mass of living organisms in a particular population.

biome A particular community characterized by the climate and vegetation on a world scale, e.g. tropical rain forests, grasslands.

biosphere Region of the land, water and air in which living organisms are found.

buffer Buffer solutions have the property of being able to resist a change of pH on the addition of relatively small amounts of acids or alkalis.

The ability to resist changes in pH is essential for organisms, as changes in pH can drastically affect enzyme activity, and many other processes of cells. A relatively constant pH maintained within narrow limits is a major feature of homeostasis in organisms.

Amino acids and the proteins they form act as buffers in all living systems. Each amino acid has a specific pH at which it exists as a neutral zwitterion e.g. alanine (2-amino propanoic acid)

$$\underset{H}{\overset{H}{>}}N-\underset{\underset{COOH}{|}}{\overset{\overset{CH_3}{|}}{C}}-H \rightleftharpoons \underset{H}{\overset{H}{>}}N^+-\underset{\underset{COO^-}{|}}{\overset{\overset{CH_3}{|}}{C}}-H$$

zwitterion

They possess both acidic and basic properties, that is they are amphoteric. Like the amino acids of which they are composed, proteins are zwitterions, are amphoteric and act as buffers.

The proteins of the blood of mammals act as buffers, and maintain the pH of the blood within limits of 7.35–7.40 in the face of all the varying demands and activities of the body.

Examples include haemoglobin, plasma albumins (about 50% of the total plasma protein) and plasma globulins or immunoglobulins (anti-bodies).

Also the sodium and potassium hydrogencarbonate in the plasma has a buffering effect.

cambium Layer of meristematic cells that produces secondary tissues.

capillarity Force that draws fluids up narrow spaces.

carcinogen Cancer-inducing substance.

catabolism Breakdown reactions of metabolism in which complex molecules are broken down into simpler ones.

catalyst Substance that speeds up the rate of reaction without being used up in the process, so that relatively small amounts can catalyse relatively large amounts of reactants.

centrifugation Suspensions e.g. cell homogenates are spun at high speed to separate a sediment below a supernatant liquid. With cell homogenates the order of separation is nuclei, mitochondria, lysosomes, ribosomes and membranes.

cephalo Prefix meaning 'pertaining to the head', e.g. cephalothorax.

chemical formula When two or more atoms combine to form a molecule, the chemical formula tells one which atoms, and how many, are involved. For example the formula for carbon dioxide is CO_2, this means that there is one carbon atom and two oxygen atoms present.

chemical equation These describe chemical reactions in a short-hand way, for example:

$$\underset{\text{glucose}}{C_6H_{12}O_6} + \underset{\text{oxygen}}{6O_2} \longrightarrow \underset{\substack{\text{carbon} \\ \text{dioxide}}}{6CO_2} + \underset{\text{water}}{6H_2O}$$

The numbers in front of some of the molecules are necessary to balance the numbers of atoms on either side of the equation.

chemosynthetic (chemoautotrophic) Autotrophic, utilizing energy from inorganic reactions.

chrome Prefix or suffix meaning colour or pigment, e.g. cytochrome (cell pigment), chromosome (coloured body).

circadian Occurring approximately once a day.

cline Continuous gradation of variation shown by the members of a species from one end of their geographical range to another.

cloaca Common chamber into which gut, urinary and reproductive ducts open; in birds, reptiles, amphibia, and many fish.

clone Asexually produced descendants of a single cell or organism (all genetically identical).

coelom Cavity in the mesoderm of coelomate animals, lined with coelomic epithelium and filled with coelomic fluid.

coenocyte Multinucleate mass of cytoplasm in many fungi and some green algae.

co-enzyme Organic molecule that has an accessory role in enzyme catalysed reactions, e.g. NAD, NADP, FAD.

cohesion Force of attraction between like molecules, e.g. the cohesion of water molecules.

colloid A suspension of large molecules or aggregates of smaller molecules from 1 nm to 100 nm in size.

commensalism An association between members of different species in which one benefits, but which has no effect upon the other.

community Group of organisms living and interacting together in the same environment.

compensation point The point at which respiration and photosynthesis in a plant are proceeding at the same rate, and each process uses up the products of the other.

compound Substances consisting of two or more elements combined together chemically in definite proportions by weight.

condensation reaction Synthesis of complex substances from simple ones with the elimination of the elements of water.

conjugated protein Protein (e.g. globin) combined with a non-protein group (e.g. iron containing haem groups) forms a conjugated protein.

conjugation Type of sexual reproduction in which genetic material is exchanged during the temporary union of two cells, as in *Spirogyra*.

consumers Organisms (animals) that eat (consume) other organisms (as opposed to photosynthetic plants which are producers).

convergence The development (evolution) of superficially similar traits in unrelated organisms that live in a similar environment.

cortex Outer part of a structure.

cyclosis Circulation of protoplasm within a cell.

cytology Study of the cell.

cytoplasm The contents of a cell, not including the nucleus.

decomposers Organisms that convert dead organic material into simpler forms that can be used as plant nutrients (bacteria and fungi).

denaturation Rendering inactive (of an enzyme), for example by boiling or extremes of pH.

dialysis Separation of solute molecules in solution by means of their different rate of diffusion through a differentially-permeable membrane.

differentiation Development of an unspecialized cell into a specialized one.

diffusion Movement of substances (usually gases or substances in solution) down their diffusion gradient, from a region of higher concentration to a region of lower concentration. The smaller the particles, the higher the temperature and the greater the concentration difference, the faster is the rate of diffusion.

dikaryotic Cells with paired nuclei, derived from different parents but which do not fuse. Found in fungi (Ascomycetes and Basidiomycetes).

dioecious Plants having separate male and female individuals.

diploid Having two sets of chromosomes.

dissociation Separation of ions from a molecule, e.g. $H_2CO_3 \rightarrow H^+ + HCO_3^-$.

distal Close to the free end of an attached structure (opposite of proximal).

ecto Prefix meaning 'outside', e.g. ectoderm, ectoplasm.

effector Structures which perform actions, e.g. muscles and glands.

efferent Carrying away from. Used for nerves and blood vessels, e.g. efferent arteriole carries blood away from the glomerulus of the kidney.

egestion Elimination of undigested materials from the gut.

electron Negatively charged particle outside the nucleus of an atom.

electronmicrograph Photograph of image produced by electron microscope.

electrophoresis This is a method of separating substances e.g. proteins from a mixture based, not on their relative solubilities as in chromatography, but on their relative electropositivity and electronegativity.
   A concentrated spot of the mixture is put in the centre of a strip of paper soaked in a suitable electrolyte, and a potential difference is applied across it. The positively charged cations move towards the negative cathode, and the negatively charged anions to the positive anode.

encystment Formation of a resistant dormant stage (cyst) in a life cycle (particularly bacteria and protozoa).

endergonic Energy requiring (reaction).

endo Prefix meaning 'within', e.g. endoderm, endoplasm.

epi Prefix meaning 'on' or 'over', e.g. epidermis.

epiphyte Plant that grows on another plant but which is not parasitic.

equilibrium State of balance between opposing forces.

eukaryotic Having a true, membrane-bound nucleus.

evaporation The change from a liquid to a gaseous state. This requires energy – the latent heat of evaporation. Evaporation increases with increase in temperature.

excretion Elimination of toxic waste products produced by metabolism.

exergonic Energy yielding (reaction).

fauna Animal life of an environment.

fermentation Anaerobic decomposition of organic substances by organisms, especially bacteria and yeasts.

fission Asexual reproduction by division of body into two (binary fission) or more equal parts.

flora Plant life of an environment.

gamete Reproductive cell usually haploid, which fuses with another in the process of fertilization.

gene pool All the genes in a particular population of a species.

gonad Reproductive organ producing gametes.

haploid Having a single set of chromosomes (monoploid).

herbaceous Non-woody.

hermaphrodite Having both male and female organs in the same individual.

hertz (Hz) Cycles per second.

hetero Prefix meaning 'other' or 'different', opposite of homo, e.g. heterotrophic; feeding on other organisms.

heterogamy Unlike gametes, usually larger female and smaller male gamete.

heterotrophic Requiring a supply of organic compounds (food).

histology Study of tissues.

holophytic Typical plant nutrition. Photosynthesizes (in which complex organic compounds are synthesized from simple inorganic substances) utilizing energy from sunlight.

holozoic Typical animal nutrition.

homeostasis Steady state. Maintenance of the constancy of the internal environment in the face of fluctuating demands and a changing environment.

homogenates Cells are broken down mechanically to form a homogenous suspension.

homologous Structures in different species having basically similar embryonic development and structure (in genetics – similar chromosomes).

hybrid Organism produced from genetically dissimilar parents; extreme examples occur with hybridization between species.

hydrolysis Breakdown of complex compounds by the addition of the elements of water, e.g. digestion is achieved by hydrolysis.

hydrophytes Plants adapted to life in water and wet places, characteristic aerenchyma with large intercellular spaces.

hyper Prefix meaning 'above' or 'over', e.g. hypertonic.

hypo Prefix meaning 'under' or 'less', e.g. hypotonic.

ingestion Taking in of food and water into the body.

inter Prefix meaning 'between', e.g. intercellular.

intra Prefix meaning 'within', e.g. intracellular.

in vitro Literally 'in glass', experiment or observation done in isolation from the whole organism.

in vivo Literally 'in life'. Within the living organism.

ion Atom or group of atoms with an electrical charge resulting from the loss or gain of electrons.

iso Prefix meaning 'equal', e.g. isotonic.

isogamy Having identical gametes.

isomer Molecules with the same molecular formula as one another, but with different structural configurations, e.g. glucose and fructose.

isotope Atom that differs in atomic weight (mass number) from other atoms of the same element because of a different number of neutrons in its nucleus. Some are unstable and radioactive, e.g. ^{14}C (as opposed to ^{12}C).

karyotype Description of the chromosome complement of a cell.

larva Sexually immature stage of many animals that differs in appearance from the adult, and must undergo some form of metamorphosis to become an adult.

latent period Interval between a stimulus and a response.

latent heat Heat energy needed to change the state of a substance, e.g. the latent heat of evaporation is needed to change a liquid to a vapour.

leaching Washing out of substances by the flow of water.

limiting factor That factor controlling (limiting) the rate of a reaction, or the size of a population.

littoral Sea floor down to about 200 m depth.

lumen Cavity of a tube or hollow organ.

macro (mega) Large, opposite of micro.

matrix 'Background substance', usually intercellular material in which animal cells are embedded.

medulla Inner part of a structure.

meristem A plant tissue that is capable of repeated division, by mitosis, to produce new cells.

mesoderm Layer of tissue in triploblastic animal embryos, between the ectoderm and the endoderm.

mesophytes Plants adapted to average conditions of water supply.

metabolism All the chemical reactions of the body.

metamorphosis Process of change from larval to adult form.

micro-organism Microscopic organism, e.g. Bacteria, Protozoa and many algae.

mixture Composed of two or more substances, each of which retains its characteristic properties. Its composition can be variable. A solution is a particular type of mixture.

molar solution One mole per litre of solution.

mole The quantity of a compound (the mass in grams) equal to its molecular weight. For example, the molecular weight of water is 18, therefore one mole of water weighs 18 g.

molecular weight (mass) Sum of the atomic weights of the atoms in a molecule.

molecule Smallest particle of an element or a compound that can have a separate existence, usually a combination of two or more atoms, e.g. H_2 (hydrogen), O_2 (oxygen), CO_2 (carbon dioxide).

monoecious Having both male and female flowers or cones on the same plant.

morpho Prefix (or suffix -morph) meaning shape or form, e.g. morphology.

morphogenesis Development of shape and form.

morphology Study of form and structure.

mutagen Agent that increases the mutation rate.

mutualism Association between organisms of different species that is to their mutual advantage, i.e. both derive benefit. (*See also* symbiosis.)

nicotinamide adenine dinucleotide (NAD) (Formerly DPN and CO-ENZYME I) Co-enzyme that acts as a hydrogen acceptor (transfers electrons).

nucleotide Compound consisting of a nitrogenous base, pentose sugar and phosphate group, e.g. ATP, co-enzymes e.g. NAD, and as poly-nucleotides e.g. the nucleic acids DNA and RNA.

oogamy Fertilization of a large non-motile egg, by a small motile male gamete.

oogonium In botany: female sex organs of some algae, containing one or more oospheres.

oosphere Spherical, non-motile female gamete formed within an organism.

oospore Resting spore with thick walls formed from a fertilized oosphere.

organ Collection of tissues coordinated to a specific function.

organelle Part of a cell specialized for a specific function, e.g. mitochondria and respiration.

organic Compounds containing carbon (except some such as the metal carbonates (e.g. Na_2CO_3, etc.) and the oxides and sulphides of carbon).

organism Living being.

osmosis Passage of water from a dilute (hypotonic) solution, to a concentrated (hypertonic) solution, through a differentially permeable membrane.

osmotic pressure The pressure required to prevent water entering a solution by osmosis. Proportional to the concentration difference of the two solutions involved.

oviparous Young are born alive, as a result of the retention of the developing egg within the female, but the embryo is always separated from the maternal tissues by the egg membrane.

ovule Reproductive structure in the Gymnosperms and Angiosperms containing an egg-cell. Develops into seed after the egg cell has been fertilized.

ovum Egg cell.

oxidation The addition of oxygen or the removal of hydrogen from a substance. More strictly, the removal of electrons from a substance for example the change from a ferrous ion, FE^{++}, to a ferric ion, Fe^{+++}.

palaeontology Study of fossils.

parasite Organism living on or in another organism of a different species (the host), to the benefit of itself and the detriment of the host.

parthenogenesis Development of a female gamete into a new individual without fertilization.

pathogen Disease-causing organism (or virus).

peri Prefix meaning 'around', e.g. periderm.

pH Measure of acidity (pH<7) or alkalinity (pH>7); neutral pH = 7.

phagocytosis Engulfing of solid particles by a cell.

phenotype Appearance of an organism, the product of its genotype and the effect of its environment on its development: genotype+ environment = phenotype.

physiology Study of the functioning of living organisms.

plankton Microscopic plants (phytoplankton) and animals (zooplankton) found floating near the surface of the sea or lakes.

plasmolysis Withdrawal of cytoplasm away from the plant cell wall due to the loss of water by osmosis in a hypertonic solution.

poly Prefix meaning 'many', e.g. polysaccharide.

polymorphism The occurrence in a freely interbreeding population of two or more distinctly different types, in such proportions that the rarest of them cannot be maintained at the observed frequency by continuing mutation, e.g. the queen, drone and worker of the bee.

polyploidy Having three or more sets of chromosomes.

precursor Substance from which another is formed.

pressure (and volume) The volume of a gas is affected by temperature and pressure. If the temperature increases the gas expands (i.e. its volume increases), and vice versa. If the temperature is kept constant, and the pressure is increased, the volume decreases proportionately.

producer Autotrophic plants (photosynthetic) and bacteria (photosynthetic and chemosynthetic) which 'produce' organic substances from inorganic ones. The basis of all food chains.

prokaryote Organism without a membrane-bound nucleus (nor other membrane organelles, e.g. mitochondria, chloroplastids). Bacteria and blue-green algae.

proximal Nearer to the origin or place of attachment of a free-ending structure (opposite of distal).

pseudo Prefix meaning 'false'.

reduction The removal of oxygen or the addition of hydrogen to a substance. More strictly the addition of electrons to a substance.

saprophyte Heterotrophic plants (fungi and bacteria) living on dead organic matter, performing external digestion and absorbing the soluble end-product of digestion by diffusion.

saprozoic Animals living on dead organic matter, performing external digestion and absorbing the soluble end-products of digestion by diffusion.

secretion Production of useful substances by cells and glands.

sessile Animal attached to the substratum. Plant structures lacking a stalk.

solute Substance dissolved in a solvent.

solution Mixture of solute and liquid solvent.

solvent Dissolving medium of a solution.

somatic To do with the body.

speciation Formation of species.

substrate Substance that is acted on by an enzyme. Substance that an organism is found living on.

succession Sequential change in the plant population of an area.

suspension Mixture containing solid particles that will ultimately settle out under gravity.

symbiosis Broad sense – any association between organisms of different species i.e. mutualism, commensalism, parasitism. Narrow sense – association between organisms of different species to their mutual advantage (i.e. = mutualism).

syncitium Mass of cytoplasm in animals containing many nuclei as in striated muscle fibres.

synthesis Formation of complex substances from simpler ones. Requires energy.

terresphere Terrestrial part of the biosphere.

thallus Plant body without root, stem or leaves.

tissue Collection of similar cells performing a particular function.

tropho Prefix (or suffix-troph) meaning 'feeding', e.g. autotrophic: 'self-feeding'.

turgor Distension with water, particularly of plant cells.

vascular Vessels that transport fluids.

vaso Prefix meaning 'to do with vessels', e.g. vasodilation, the dilation of blood vessels.

vector Animal that actively transmits parasites from one host to another.

ventilation Movement of air or water over a respiratory surface for the purposes of physiological exchange.

vesicle Intracellular membrane-bound sac.

vestigial Reduced and simplified structure which is assumed to have become reduced in importance during evolution.

viable Capable of living. Of seeds and spores – capable of developing.

viscera Organs in the body cavity.

viviparous Young born alive after developing on nutrients obtained from the mother rather than from egg yolk. Not separated from the maternal tissues by the egg membrane.

water potential A special case of 'chemical potential'. All substances diffuse from regions of high concentration or high chemical potential to regions of low concentration or low chemical potential. With respect to water, pure water has the highest chemical or water potential, and the presence of solutes lowers the water potential of a solution. Thus in osmosis water diffuses from regions of high water potential to regions of low water potential.

wild type Phenotype (appearance) characteristic of the majority of a species in a natural environment.

xerophytes Plants adapted to dry habitats.

zoospores Flagellate, motile spores found in some fungi and algae.

zygospore Thick-walled resistant resting spore produced by sexual reproduction in some fungi; for example *Mucor*, and in some algae; for example *Spirogyra*.

zygote Cell (typically diploid) formed by the fusion of two gametes (each typically haploid).

A NOTE ABOUT ENERGY

Energy: the joule (J) This was formally defined as the ability to do work, that is the force × distance moved in the direction of the force. The SI unit of energy is the joule (J) which can be defined in a variety of equivalent ways. The simplest defines it as that work done when a force of 1 newton moves its point of application through 1 metre. The joule is rapidly replacing the former unit, the calorie, but the calorie is still a useful unit of heat energy. The calorie was defined as the amount of heat required to raise 1 g of water through 1°C, strictly from 14.5 to 15.5°C (1 calorie is equal to 4.18 J).

First Law of Thermodynamics (Law of conservation of energy) Energy may be transformed from one form into another but is neither created nor destroyed.

Second Law of Thermodynamics Processes involving energy transformations will not occur spontaneously unless there is a degradation of energy from a non-random to a random form.

SYNONYMS

CONTENTS

INTRODUCTION Many biological terms have synonyms, that is an alternative word with the same meaning. Frequently the alternative forms of a particular term consist of the technical word (based on Greek, Latin, or sometimes a mixture of both), and the common English word; which sometimes is more easily understood.

However, in other cases synonymous technical terms exist, so that neither term is any more easily understood than the other. The list presented here includes most of the more commonly used examples, and is intended to aid the understanding of the vocabulary of the subject.

abscisic acid, abscisin, dormin
accommodation, focusing
adapted, specialized
adrenal gland, suprarenal gland
adrenaline, epinephrine
afferent nerve, sensory nerve
air bladder, swim bladder
alimentary canal, gut, digestive tract
allelomorphic, pair of alleles
amylase, diastase
anterior vena cava, superior vena cava
atrium, auricle
atrophy, degeneration
binocular vision, stereoscopic vision, 3-dimensional vision
bisexual, hermaphrodite, monoecious
breathing, external respiration
caudal, tail
cell division, cytokinesis
cellular respiration, internal respiration, tissue respiration
chemosynthetic, chemoautotrophic
chrysalis, pupa
circadian rhythm, diurnal rhythm
circulatory system, vascular system, blood vascular system
cleavage, division
codominance, incomplete dominance
cork, phellem
cork cambium, phellogen
diffusion pressure deficit (DPD), suction pressure (SP), water potential

ear bone, ear ossicle, auditory ossicle
ecdysis, moulting
endocrine gland, ductless gland
erythrocyte, red blood corpuscle, red blood cell
fructose, laevulose
gamete, germ-cell, sex cell
haploid, monoploid
glucose, dextrose
glycogen, animal starch
Golgi body, Golgi apparatus, dictyosome
gonad, sex organ
hereditary, inherited (or inheritance)
holophytic, photosynthetic
hybrid vigour, heterosis
imago, adult
inferior vena cava, posterior vena cava
inner ear, membranous labyrinth
integument, skin
intestinal juice, succus entericus
invertase, sucrase
involuntary muscle, smooth muscle, unstriated muscle, unstriped
    muscle
keratinization, cornification
Krebs' cycle, citric acid cycle
lamella, layer
leucocyte, white blood cell, white blood corpuscle
mastication, chewing
medullated nerve, myelinated nerve
meiosis, reduction division
metameric segmentation, metamerism
micrometre, micron
motor nerve, efferent nerve
nerve cell, neurone, neuron
nephron, uriniferous tubule, kidney tubule
oviduct, fallopian tube, uterine tube
ovum, egg cell
uterus, womb
pith, medulla
plasmalemma, plasma-membrane, cell membrane
ptyalin, salivary amylase
receptor, sense organ
semi-permeable, selectively permeable, differentially permeable
smell, olfaction
symbiotic, mutualism
taste, gustation
tonoplast, vacuole membrane (in plants)
tympanic membrane, tympanum, ear drum
unicellular, accelular
unisexual, dioecious

vascular cambium, fascicular cambium, intra-fascicular cambium
vegetative reproduction, propagation
vertebral column, backbone, spine
voluntary muscle, skeletal muscle, striated muscle, striped muscle
wood, secondary xylem

HISTOGRAMS AND GRAPHS

CONTENTS

HISTOGRAMS

If results are listed in the order in which they are obtained, it is often difficult to gain much information from the figures. For example, consider the set of measurements of stem length in a population of plants. If the results are listed as given below in the order in which they were obtained, then little information can be derived from the figures.

LENGTH OF STEM IN MM

30, 41, 53, 42, 36, 50, 61, 56, 35, 46, 58, 61, 37, 66, 76, 28, 40, 20, 48, 60, 52, 22, 57, 70, 43, 57, 62, 63, 73, 31, 49, 52, 47, 37, 53, 63, 56, 71, 23, 63, 24, 58, 39, 44, 56, 36, 64, 74, 55, 66, 75, 29, 48, 26, 46, 61, 53, 26, 59, 72, 45, 25, 68, 51, 66, 21, 75, 30, 47, 54, 46, 31, 59, 62, 51, 34, 46, 54, 69, 37, 69, 75, 46, 53, 45, 62, 57, 68, 53, 79, 47, 53, 63, 81, 82, 79, 37, 48, 56, 43, 33, 58, 69, 52, 31, 48, 52, 61, 31, 83, 43, 56, 42, 68, 51, 63, 54, 78, 49, 51, 68, 84, 85, 76, 38, 42, 57, 41, 32, 51, 62, 53, 33, 40, 50, 78, 33, 86, 78, 41, 58, 44, 69, 52, 64, 78, 76, 45, 51, 79, 71, 87, 77, 88, 59, 69, 68, 89, 89.

However, if they are grouped into classes then it becomes easier to notice any trends or patterns.

The range of frequencies in each class interval is purely a matter of choice, for example each length could constitute a class of its own, or all the measurements could be placed in one large class. The choice of these extreme examples would obliterate any emergent patterns in the results, and therefore a happy medium must be sought so that the class intervals are large enough to reduce the effects of chance variations in frequency, but not so large as to obscure any patterns.

The results above can be classified as follows:

From		Up to		Number in class
20	–	30	=	10
30	–	40	=	20
40	–	50	=	30
50	–	60	=	40
60	–	70	=	30
70	–	80	=	20
80	–	90	=	10
Total				160

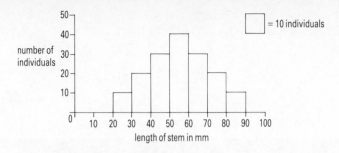

A diagrammatic representation of these groupings in the form of a histogram makes them even clearer.

A histogram is essentially a frequency distribution diagram in which, for example, the number or frequency of individuals within a certain range of measurements is represented by a rectangle of a certain area. The area of each rectangle is proportional to the frequency, and if the rectangles are of equal width then their heights are also proportional to the frequency.

Such a distribution that builds up gradually from a low number at the two extremes to a maximum in the middle is known as a **normal distribution.**

GRAPHS

A graph shows the relationship between two quantities in a way that is easily understood. Every graph should be self-explanatory, and should therefore be correctly titled, should have the axes fully labelled, and the scales used fully explained. Standard graph paper is divided by thick lines into centimetre squares or two centimetre squares, and by finer lines into millimetre squares. On such graph paper equal increments on the scale must represent equal numerical values.

Generally, values such as frequency or rate, in other words values which 'fluctuate' during an experiment, are represented on the vertical scale (y-axis); and the other values, usually those that are changed in a regular manner, such as time, are represented on the horizontal scale (x-axis).

The scale representing frequency should always start with zero. If the range of figures is very wide then the scale should still start at zero, but a break may be made across the range of figures that are not used.

The points of the graph should be plotted as accurately as possible, using either a cross ($\times$) or a circled dot ($\odot$).

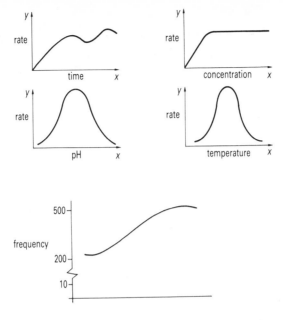

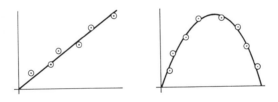

There are no hard and fast rules about drawing the line of a graph. Generally if there is a theoretical expected shape to the curve then the line may be drawn to this shape, even if it does not actually pass through all the points. For example, the line may be either straightened up by drawing the 'best straight line' between the points, or rounded off to a shape.

LOG SCALES

The use of log scales shortens the scale required for a certain set of values, and also confers other advantages. Log scales are mainly used in biology in relation to population growth curves. Under certain conditions populations can grow exponentially, thus giving typical exponential growth curves when plotted on normal graph paper.

For example, consider a population which grows with a doubling every day:

Time in days	0	1	2	3	4	5	6	7	8	9	10
Number in population	1	2	4	8	16	32	64	128	256	512	1024

When plotted on normal graph paper the following exponential curve is obtained.

However, when these figures are plotted on log/linear graph paper, a straight line is obtained.

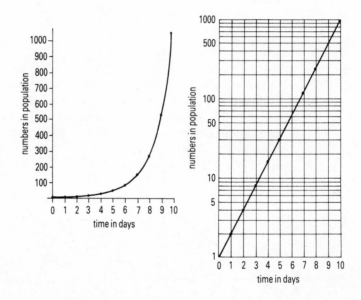

STATISTICS

CONTENTS

STATISTICAL TESTING OF RESULTS

When a set of results has been obtained, for example in a breeding experiment, it is necessary to decide whether they are acceptable on the basis of the theory or hypothesis behind the experiment. In a breeding experiment with garden peas, Mendel obtained 787 tall plants and 277 dwarf plants in the F2 generation. These results represent a 2.84:1 ratio, and it must be decided whether this is close enough to the expected 3:1 ratio to be acceptable, or not. Common sense would tend to indicate that 2.84:1 is close enough to 3:1 to be acceptable, but this judgement is essentially arbitrary, and there are no natural limits to the extent of the deviation from the expected results which could be accepted.

A method of statistical analysis known as the **chi-squared χ^2 test** tests the 'goodness of fit' between observed and expected results. However, although it is a reliable test, it is not infallible, and the decision as to what is acceptable is still essentially arbitrary. The chi-squared test helps to decide whether the difference, or **deviation**, of the actual results from the expected results is just due to pure chance; or whether the deviation is significantly different from the predicted ratio, that is, due to some reason (including the possibility of some mistake in the prediction.) The chi-squared test gives the probability of a particular deviation occurring by chance. In other words the proportion or percentage of times a particular deviation would be expected to occur by chance. For example, if (after making the calculations for a certain deviation) the chi-squared test indicates a probability value of 50 per cent, this means that the deviation obtained would be expected to occur by chance in half the results produced by a particular cross. It is generally accepted that, a probability above 5 per cent that of chance alone producing the observed deviation, means that the results of the cross do not differ significantly from the expected ratio. The results show that the deviation is not significant. It can be assumed that the observed deviations are due to chance alone.

However if the probability is less than 5 per cent, then the deviation is considered significant, that is not due to chance alone.

THE CHI-SQUARED TEST

1   Calculate the deviation of the observed from the expected results for each class (in a genetic breeding experiment a class would be one

particular phenotype, for example, tall pea plants).

deviation = observed − expected.

2   Then square the deviation and divide it by the expected:

$$\frac{(\text{deviation})^2}{\text{expected}}$$

3   This is done for each class of results, which are then added together to give a value for χ^2.

$$\chi^2 = \sum \frac{(\text{deviation})^2}{\text{expected}}$$

(Σ is the symbol for the 'sum of')

For example consider Mendel's results with pea plants of 787 tall and 277 dwarf out of a total of 1064 plants. For an exact 3:1 ratio we would expect 798 tall and 266 dwarf.

	Class	
	Tall	**Dwarf**
observed	787	277
expected	798	266
deviation	−11	+11
deviation²	121	121
$\dfrac{\text{deviation}^2}{e}$	$\dfrac{121}{798}$	$\dfrac{121}{266}$

$$\chi^2 = \frac{121}{798} + \frac{121}{266}$$

$$= 0.1516 + 0.4548$$

$$= \underline{0.6064}$$

Now there are two classes of phenotypes, tall and dwarf, and therefore only one degree of freedom (do not worry about what this means, it is mentioned just for completeness sake as it is part of χ^3 tables, in general the number of degrees of freedom is one less than the number of classes).

Refer to the χ^2 table below and look along the row for two classes and one degree of freedom until a number greater than 0.6064 is found.

No. of classes	Degrees of freedom	0.90 (90%)	0.80 (80%)	0.70 (70%)	0.50 (50%)	0.30 (30%)	0.20 (20%)	0.10 (10%)	0.05 (5%)	0.02 (2%)	0.01 (1%)
2	1	0.16	0.064	0.148	0.455	1.074	1.642	2.706	3.841	5.412	6.635
					Acceptable					Suspect	

Therefore the probability that chance alone could produce these deviations from the expected lies between 50 per cent and 30 per cent, which is well over the generally accepted limit of 5 per cent. Therefore the ratio does not differ significantly from the predicted 3:1.

Consider another example using Mendel's results of an experiment on dihybrid inheritance in the garden pea, where self-fertilization of the F_2 generation gave 315 smooth yellow seeds, 108 smooth green seeds, 101 wrinkled yellow seeds, and 32 wrinkled green seeds.

	Smooth yellow	Smooth green	Wrinkled yellow	Wrinkled green
observed	315	108	101	32
expected	313	104	104	35
deviation	2	4	3	3
deviation^2	4	16	9	9
$\dfrac{\text{deviation}^2}{\text{expected}}$	$\dfrac{4}{313}$	$\dfrac{16}{104}$	$\dfrac{9}{104}$	$\dfrac{9}{35}$

$$\chi^2 = \frac{4}{313} + \frac{16}{104} + \frac{9}{104} + \frac{9}{35}$$

$$= 0.013 + 0.154 + 0.087 + 0.257$$

$$= \underline{0.511}$$

Here there are four classes of phenotype (smooth yellow, smooth green, wrinkled yellow and wrinkled green) and therefore three degrees of freedom. Refer to the χ^2 table and look along the line for four classes and three degrees of freedom until a number greater than 0.511 is found.

Therefore the probability that chance alone could produce this deviation from the expected is above 90 per cent which is well over the generally accepted limit of 5 per cent.

Probability that change alone could produce the deviation

No. of classes	Degrees of freedom	0.90 (90%)	0.80 (80%)	0.70 (70%)	0.50 (50%)	0.30 (30%)	0.20 (20%)	0.10 (10%)	0.05 (5%)	0.02 (2%)	0.01 (1%)
2	1	.016	.064	.148	.455	1.074	1.642	2.706	3.841	5.412	6.635
3	2	.211	.446	.713	1.386	2.408	3.219	4.605	5.991	7.824	9.210
4	3	.584	1.005	1.424	2.366	3.665	4.642	6.251	7.815	9.837	11.341
5	4	1.064	1.649	2.195	3.357	4.878	5.989	7.779	9.488	11.668	13.277
						Acceptable				Suspect	

Table of χ^2 (based on Fisher and Yates)

χ^2 can only be used for numerical frequencies not for ratios or percentages.

χ^2 cannot be used if the frequency of any one class is less than 5.

STANDARD DEVIATION

This is a measure of the distribution of a series of numbers or measurements about their mean value. It is defined as the square root of the average value of the squares of the deviation from their mean value. A relatively small standard deviation means that there is a relatively narrow distribution of the figures about their mean, and vice versa.

CHAPTER 2

2.2 A:5, B:3, C:1, D:2, E:4; **2.4** 4; **2.6** (*b*).

CHAPTER 3

3.1 (*e*); **3.2** (*c*); **3.3** 1:C, 2:D, 3:A, 4:E, 5:B; **3.4** (*b*); **3.5** (*b*); **3.6** (*b*).

CHAPTER 5

5.2 (*c*); **5.3** (*b*); **5.5** (*a*); **5.6** (*b*).

CHAPTER 7

7.2 (*b*); **7.4** (*c*).

CHAPTER 9

9.1 A:3, B:5, C:4, D:1, E:2, F:6; **9.4** 1:D, 2:B, 3:C, 4:A, 5:E.

CHAPTER 10

10.1 (*b*); **10.2** (*c*).

CHAPTER 11

11.1 (*i*): (*a*) (*c*) (*d*); (*ii*): (*b*); **11.2** (*c*); **11.3** (*b*).

CHAPTER 12

12.1 (*c*); **12.2** (*c*), **12.5** (*c*).

CHAPTER 13

13.1 (*d*); **13.2** (*c*); **13.3** (*b*); **13.4** (*a*); **13.5** (C), (B), (A); **13.6** (*b*).

CHAPTER 14

14.1 D, A, B, C, G, E, F.

INDEX

More advanced level exam help from Pan

BRODIE'S NOTES
on English Literature texts

This popular and respected series provides reliable guidance on texts commonly set for literature exams in the UK and the Republic of Ireland.

Brodie's Notes on texts set for A level, Highers and Leaving Certificate reflect the deeper critical appreciation and analysis required for study at such levels.

Some selected Brodie's Notes for advanced level are:

William Shakespeare
ANTONY AND CLEOPATRA
CORIOLANUS
HAMLET
KING LEAR
OTHELLO
THE TEMPEST

Geoffrey Chaucer
THE MILLER'S TALE†
THE NUN'S PRIEST'S
 TALE†
THE PARDONER'S TALE†
THE WIFE OF BATH'S TALE†
(With parallel texts)

Jane Austen	EMMA
	MANSFIELD PARK
	SENSE AND SENSIBILITY
Emily Brontë	WUTHERING HEIGHTS
Joseph Conrad	HEART OF DARKNESS
T. S. Eliot	MURDER IN THE CATHEDRAL
Thomas Hardy	RETURN OF THE NATIVE
	TESS OF THE D'URBERVILLES
James Joyce	DUBLINERS
Christopher Marlowe	DR FAUSTUS
Thomas Middleton & William Rowley	THE CHANGELING
John Milton	COMUS/SAMSON AGONISTES
Tom Stoppard	ROSENCRANTZ AND GUILDENSTERN ARE DEAD
Jonathan Swift	GULLIVER'S TRAVELS
John Webster	THE DUCHESS OF MALFI
	THE WHITE DEVIL
William Wordsworth	THE PRELUDE Books 1 and 2
William Wycherley	THE COUNTRY WIFE
Various	THE METAPHYSICAL POETS

*Written by experienced teachers and examiners who can give you effective advice

*Designed to increase your understanding, appreciation and enjoyment of a set work or author

*With textual notes, commentaries, critical analysis, background information and revision questions

£1.25 each except for †£1.75. On sale in bookshops.

For information write to:

Pan Study Aids & Brodie's Notes
Pan Books Ltd
18–21 Cavaye Place
London SW10 9PG

For business courses at school or college

BREAKTHROUGH BUSINESS BOOKS

This series covers a wide range of subjects for students following business and professional training syllabuses. The Breakthrough books make ideal texts for BTEC, SCOTVEC, LCCI and RSA exams.

Many business teachers and lecturers have praised the books for their *excellent value, clear presentation, practical, down-to-earth style* and *modern approach to learning*.

'An excellent range of texts at a price students can afford.'
'The self-study presentation and style make these ideal college books.'

The range of 30 includes the following major titles:

BACKGROUND TO BUSINESS	£3.50
BUSINESS ADMINISTRATION	
A fresh approach	£3.95
THE BUSINESS OF COMMUNICATING	£3.95
WHAT DO YOU MEAN 'COMMUNICATION'	£3.95
THE ECONOMICS OF BUSINESS	£2.95
EFFECTIVE ADVERTISING AND PR	£2.95
MANAGEMENT	
A fresh approach	£3.95
MARKETING	
A fresh approach	£3.50
PRACTICAL COST AND MANAGEMENT ACCOUNTING	£3.50
UNDERSTANDING COMPANY ACCOUNTS	£2.95
PRACTICAL BUSINESS LAW	£3.95

On sale in bookshops.

For information write to:

Business Books
Pan Books Ltd
18–21 Cavaye Place
London SW10 9PG